Open the door to the fascinating world of physics

Physics, the most fundamental of all natural sciences, will reveal to you the basic principles of the Universe. And while physics can seem challenging, its true beauty lies in the sheer simplicity of fundamental physical theories—theories and concepts that can alter and expand your view of the world around you. Other courses that follow will use the same principles, so it is important that you understand and are able to apply the various concepts and theories discussed in the text. **Physics for Scientists and Engineers, Sixth Edition** is your guide to this fascinating science.

THOMSON

BROOKS/COLE

Serway / Jewett
6th Edition

W9-CDL-564

Your quick start for studying smart

Achieve success in your physics course by making the most of what **Physics for Scientists and Engineers, Sixth Edition** has to offer you. From a host of in-text features to a range of Web resources, you'll have everything you need to understand the natural forces and principles of physics:

▶ **Dynamic built-in study aids.** Throughout every chapter the authors have built in a wide range of examples, exercises, and illustrations that will help you understand and appreciate the laws of physics. *See pages 2 and 3 for more information.*

▶ **A powerful Web-based learning system**. The text is fully integrated with **PhysicsNow**, an interactive learning system that tailors  itself to your needs in the course. It's like having a personal tutor available whenever you need it! *See pages 4–7 to explore* **PhysicsNow**.

Your *Quick Start for Studying Smart* begins with this special tour through the book. On the following pages you'll discover how **Physics for Scientists and Engineers, Sixth Edition** and **PhysicsNow** not only enhance your experience in this course, but help you to succeed!

Quick Start for Studying Smart!

Take charge of your success

Everything you need to succeed in your course is available to you in **Physics for Scientists and Engineers, Sixth Edition.** Authors Serway and Jewett have filled their text with learning tools and study aids that will clarify concepts and help you build a solid base of knowledge. The end result: confidence in the classroom, in your study sessions, and in your exams.

THE RIGHT APPROACH

Start out right! Early on in the text the authors outline a general problem-solving strategy that will enable you to increase your accuracy in solving problems, enhance your understanding of physical concepts, eliminate initial worry or lack of direction in approaching a problem, and organize your work. The problem-solving strategy is integrated into the *Coached Problems* found on **PhysicsNow** to reinforce this key skill. (See pages 4–7 for more information about the **PhysicsNow** Web-based and student-centered learning system.)

PROBLEM-SOLVING HINTS

Problem-Solving Hints help you approach homework assignments with greater confidence. General strategies and suggestions are included for solving the types of problems featured in the worked examples, end-of-chapter problems, and **PhysicsNow**. This feature helps you identify the essential steps in solving problems and increases your skills as a problem solver.

WORKED EXAMPLES

Reinforce your understanding of essential problem-solving techniques using a large number of realistic *Worked Examples.* In many cases, these examples serve as models for solving the end-of-chapter problems. Numerous *Worked Examples* include specific references to the general problem-solving strategy to illustrate the underlying concepts and methodology used in arriving at a correct solution. This will help you understand the logic behind the solution and the advantage of using a particular approach to solve the problem. **PhysicsNow** also features a number of worked examples to further enhance your understanding of problem solving and to give you even more practice solving problems.

GENERAL PROBLEM-SOLVING STRATEGY

Conceptualize

- The first thing to do when approaching a problem is to *think about* and *understand* the situation. Study carefully any diagrams, graphs, tables, or photographs that accompany the problem. Imagine a movie, running in your mind, of what happens in the problem.

- If a diagram is not provided, you should almost always make a quick drawing of the situation. Indicate any known values, perhaps in a table or directly on your sketch.

- Now focus on what algebraic or numerical information is given in the problem. Carefully read the problem statement, looking for key phrases such as "starts from rest" ($v_i = 0$), "stops" ($v_f = 0$), or "freely falls" ($a_y = -g = -9.80 \text{ m/s}^2$).

- Now focus on the expected result of solving the problem. Exactly what is the question asking? Will the final result be numerical or algebraic? Do you know what units to expect?

- Don't forget to incorporate information from your own experiences and common sense. What should a reasonable answer look like? You wouldn't expect to calculate the speed of an automobile to be

Analyze

- Now you must analyze the problem and strive for a mathematical solution. Because you have already categorized the problem, it should not be too difficult to select relevant equations that apply to the type of situation in the problem. For example, if the problem involves a particle moving under constant acceleration, Equations 2.9 to 2.13 are relevant.

- Use algebra (and calculus, if necessary) to solve symbolically for the unknown variable in terms of what is given. Substitute in the appropriate numbers, calculate the result, and round it to the proper number of significant figures.

Finalize

- This is the most important part. Examine your numerical answer. Does it have the correct units? Does it meet your expectations from your conceptualization of the problem? What about the algebraic form of the result — before you substituted numerical values? Does it make sense? Examine the variables in the problem to see whether the answer would change in a physically meaningful way if they were drastically increased or decreased or even became zero. Looking at limiting cases to see whether they yield expected values is a very useful way to make sure that you are obtaining reasonable results.

  Think about how this problem compares with others you have done. How was it similar? In what critical ways did it differ? Why was this problem assigned? You should have learned something by doing it. Can you figure out what? If it is a new category of problem, be sure you understand it so that you can use it as a model for solving future problems in the same category.

When solving complex problems, you may need to identify a series of sub-problems and apply the problem-solv-

---

PROBLEM-SOLVING HINTS

Applying Newton's Laws

The following procedure is recommended when dealing with problems involving Newton's laws:

- Draw a simple, neat diagram of the system to help *conceptualize* the problem.

- *Categorize* the problem: if any acceleration component is zero, the particle is in equilibrium in this direction and $\Sigma F = 0$. If not, the particle is undergoing an acceleration, the problem is one of nonequilibrium in this direction, and $\Sigma F = ma$.

- *Analyze* the problem by isolating the object whose motion is being analyzed. Draw a free-body diagram for this object. For systems containing more than one object, draw *separate* free-body diagrams for each object. *Do not* include in the free-body diagram forces exerted by the object on its surroundings.

- Establish convenient coordinate axes for each object and find the components of the forces along these axes. Apply Newton's second law, $\Sigma F = ma$, in component form. Check your dimensions to make sure that all terms have units of force.

- Solve the comp... have as many in... complete soluti...

- *Finalize* by maki... Also check the ... variables. By do...

Example 4.3 The Long Jump

A long-jumper (Fig. 4.12) leaves the ground at an angle of 20.0° above the horizontal and at a speed of 11.0 m/s.

(A) How far does he jump in the horizontal direction? (Assume his motion is equivalent to that of a particle.)

Solution We *conceptualize* the motion of the long-jumper as equivalent to that of a simple projectile such as the ball in Example 4.2, and *categorize* this problem as a projectile motion problem. Because the initial speed and launch angle are given, and because the final height is the same as the initial height, we further categorize this problem as satisfying the conditions for which Equations 4.13 and 4.14 can be used. This is the most direct way to *analyze* this problem... describ... the gen...

provides a graphical representation of the flight of the long-jumper. As before, we set our origin of coordinates at the takeoff point and label the peak as Ⓐ and the landing point as Ⓑ. The horizontal motion is described by Equation 4.11:

$$x_f = x_B = (v_i \cos \theta_i)t_B = (11.0 \text{ m/s})(\cos 20.0°)t_B$$

The value of x_B can be found if the time of landing t_B is known. We can find t_B by remembering that $a_y = -g$ and by using the y part of Equation 4.8a. We also note that at the top of the jump the vertical component of velocity v_{yA} is zero:

$$v_{yf} = v_{yA} = v_i \sin \theta_i - gt_A$$

This is the time at which the long-jumper is at the *top* of the jump. Because of the symmetry of the vertical motion, another 0.384 s passes before the jumper returns to the ground. Therefore, the time at which the jumper lands is $t_B = 2t_A = 0.768$ s. Substituting this value into the above expression for x_f gives

$$x_f = x_B = (11.0 \text{ m/s})(\cos 20.0°)(0.768 \text{ s}) = \boxed{7.94 \text{ m}}$$

This is a reasonable distance for a world-class athlete.

(B) What is the maximum height reached?

Solution We find the maximum height reached by using Equation 4.12:

$$y_{max} = y_A = (v_i \sin \theta_i)t_A - \tfrac{1}{2}gt_A^2$$
$$= (11.0 \text{ m/s})(\sin 20.0°)(0.384 \text{ s})$$
$$-\tfrac{1}{2}(9.80 \text{ m/s}^2)(0.384 \text{ s})^2 = \boxed{0.722 \text{ m}}$$

To *finalize* this problem, find the answers to parts (a) and (b) using Equations 4.13 and 4.14. The results should agree. Treating the long-jumper as a particle is an oversimplification. Nevertheless, the values obtained are consistent with experience in sports. We learn that we can model a complicated system such as a long-jumper as a particle and still obtain results that are reasonable.

Figure 4.12 (Example 4.3) Mike Powell, current holder of the world long jump record of 8.95 m.

where k is a dimensionless constant of proportionality. Knowing the dimensions of a, r, and v, we see that the dimensional equation must be

$$\frac{L}{T^2} = L^n \left(\frac{L}{T}\right)^m = \frac{L^{n+m}}{T^m}$$

$n = -1$, and we can write the acceleration expression as

$$a = kr^{-1}v^2 = k\,\frac{v^2}{r}$$

When we discuss uniform circular motion later, we shall see that $k = 1$ if a consistent set of units is used. The constant k would not equal 1 if, for example, v were in km/h and you wanted a in m/s^2.

1.5 Conversion of Units

Sometimes it is necessary to convert units from one measurement system to another, or to convert within a system, for example, from kilometers to meters. Equalities between SI and U.S. customary units of length are as follows:

$$1 \text{ mile} = 1\,609 \text{ m} = 1.609 \text{ km} \qquad 1 \text{ ft} = 0.304\,8 \text{ m} = 30.48 \text{ cm}$$

$$1 \text{ m} = 39.37 \text{ in.} = 3.281 \text{ ft} \qquad 1 \text{ in.} = 0.025\,4 \text{ m} = 2.54 \text{ cm (exactly)}$$

A more complete list of conversion factors can be found in Appendix A.

Units can be treated as algebraic quantities that can cancel each other. For example, suppose we wish to convert 15.0 in. to centimeters. Because 1 in. is defined as exactly 2.54 cm, we find that

---

Example 4.5 That's Quite an Arm!

A stone is thrown from the top of a building upward at an angle of 30.0° to the horizontal with an initial speed of 20.0 m/s, as shown in Figure 4.14. If the height of the building is 45.0 m,

(A) how long before the stone hits the ground?

Solution We *conceptualize* the problem by studying Figure 4.14, in which we have indicated the various parameters. By now, it should be natural to *categorize* this as a projectile motion problem.

To *analyze* the problem, let us once again separate motion into two components. The initial x and y components of the stone's velocity are

$$v_{xi} = v_i \cos\theta_i = (20.0 \text{ m/s})\cos 30.0° = 17.3 \text{ m/s}$$

$$v_{yi} = v_i \sin\theta_i = (20.0 \text{ m/s})\sin 30.0° = 10.0 \text{ m/s}$$

To find t, we can use $y_f = y_i + v_{yi}t + \frac{1}{2}a_y t^2$ (Eq. 4.9a) with $y_i = 0$, $y_f = -45.0$ m, $a_y = -g$, and $v_{yi} = 10.0$ m/s (there is a negative sign on the numerical value of y_f because we have chosen the top of the building as the origin):

$$-45.0 \text{ m} = (10.0 \text{ m/s})t - \frac{1}{2}(9.80 \text{ m/s}^2)t^2$$

Solving the quadratic equation for t gives, for the positive root, $t = 4.22$ s . To *finalize* this part, think: Does the negative root have any physical meaning?

(B) What is the speed of the stone just before it strikes the ground?

Solution We can use Equation 4.8a, $v_{yf} = v_{yi} + a_y t$, with $t = 4.22$ s to obtain the y component of the velocity just before the stone strikes the ground:

$$v_{yf} = 10.0 \text{ m/s} - (9.80 \text{ m/s}^2)(4.22 \text{ s}) = -31.4 \text{ m/s}$$

Because $v_{xf} = v_{xi} = 17.3$ m/s, the required speed is

$$v_f = \sqrt{v_{xf}^2 + v_{yf}^2} = \sqrt{(17.3)^2 + (-31.4)^2} \text{ m/s} = 35.9 \text{ m/s}$$

What If? What if a horizontal wind is blowing in the same direction as the ball is thrown and it causes the ball to have a horizontal acceleration component $a_x = 0.500$ m/s^2. Which part of this example, (a) or (b), will have a different answer?

Answer Recall that the motions in the x and y directions are independent. Thus, the horizontal wind cannot affect the vertical motion. The vertical motion determines the time of the projectile in the air, so the answer to (a) does not change. The wind will cause the horizontal velocity component to increase with time, so that the final speed will change in part (b).

We can find the new final horizontal velocity component by using Equation 4.8a:

$$v_{xf} = v_{xi} + a_x t = 17.3 \text{ m/s} + (0.500 \text{ m/s}^2)(4.22 \text{ s})$$
$$= 19.4 \text{ m/s}$$

and the new final speed:

$$v_f = \sqrt{v_{xf}^2 + v_{yf}^2} = \sqrt{(19.4)^2 + (-31.4)^2} \text{ m/s} = 36.9 \text{ m/s}$$

Figure 4.14 (Example 4.5) A stone is thrown from the top of a building.

Explore this situation by logging into PhysicsNow at www.pse6.com and going to Interactive Example link at http://www.pse6.com.

Quick Quiz 5.2 An object experiences no acceleration. Which of the following *cannot* be true for the object? (a) A single force acts on the object. (b) No forces act on the object. (c) Forces act on the object, but the forces cancel.

Quick Quiz 5.3 An object experiences a net force and exhibits an acceleration in response. Which of the following statements is *always* true? (a) The object moves in the direction of the force. (b) The acceleration is in the same direction as the velocity. (c) The acceleration is in the same direction as the force. (d) The velocity of the object increases.

Quick Quiz 5.4 You push an object, initially at rest, across a frictionless floor with a constant force for a time interval Δt, resulting in a final speed of v for the object. You repeat the experiment, but with a force that is twice as large. What time interval is now required to reach the same final speed v? (a) $4\Delta t$ (b) $2\Delta t$ (c) Δt (d) $\Delta t/2$ (e) $\Delta t/4$.

Answers to Quick Quizzes

5.1 (d). Choice (a) is true. Newton's first law tells us that motion requires no force: an object in motion continues to move at constant velocity in the absence of external forces. Choice (b) is also true. A stationary object can have several forces acting on it, but if the vector sum of all these external forces is zero, there is no net force and the object remains stationary.

5.2 (a). If a single force acts, this force constitutes the net force and there is an acceleration according to Newton's second law.

5.3 (c). Newton's second law relates only the force and the acceleration. Direction of motion is part of an object's *velocity*, and force determines the direction of acceleration, not that of velocity.

5.4 (d). With twice the force, the object will experience twice the acceleration. Because the force is constant, the accel-

---

"*You do not know anything until you have practiced.*"

R. P. Feynman, Nobel Laureate in Physics

Quick Start for Studying Smart!

3

What do you need to learn now?

Take charge of your learning with **PhysicsNow**, a powerful, interactive study tool that will help you manage and maximize your study time. This collection of dynamic technology resources will assess your unique study needs, giving you an individualized learning plan that will enhance your conceptual and computational skills. Designed to maximize your time investment, **PhysicsNow** helps you succeed by focusing your study time on the concepts you need to master. And best of all, **PhysicsNow** is FREE with every new copy of this text!

INTERACTIVE LEARNING BEGINS WITH THIS BOOK

PhysicsNow directly links with **Physics for Scientists and Engineers, Sixth Edition**. **PhysicsNow** and this text were built in concert to enhance each other and provide you with a seamless, integrated learning system. As you work through the chapters you'll see notes that direct you to the media-enhanced activities on **PhysicsNow** (www.pse6.com). This precise page-by-page integration means you'll spend less time flipping through pages and navigating Web sites for useful exercises. It is far easier to understand physics if you see it in action, and **PhysicsNow** enables you to *become* a part of the action!

Quick Start for Studying Smart!

Take a practice test for this chapter by clicking on the Practice Test link at http://www.pse6.com.

SUMMARY

Scalar quantities are those that have only magnitude and no associated direction. **Vector quantities** have both magnitude and direction and obey the laws of vector addition. The magnitude of a vector is *always* a positive number.

When two or more vectors are added together, all of them must have the same units and all of them must be the same type of quantity. We can add two vectors **A** and **B** graphically. In this method (Fig. 3.6), the resultant vector $\mathbf{R} = \mathbf{A} + \mathbf{B}$ runs from the tail of **A** to the tip of **B**.

A second method of adding vectors involves **components** of the vectors. The x component A_x of the vector **A** is equal to the projection of **A** along the x axis of a coordinate system, as shown in Figure 3.13, where $A_x = A\cos\theta$. The y component A_y of **A** is the projection of **A** along the y axis, where $A_y = A\sin\theta$. Be sure you can determine which trigonometric functions you should use in all situations, especially when θ is defined as something other than the counterclockwise angle from the positive x axis.

If a vector **A** has an x component A_x and a y component A_y, the vector can be expressed in unit–vector form as $\mathbf{A} = A_x\hat{\mathbf{i}} + A_y\hat{\mathbf{j}}$. In this notation, $\hat{\mathbf{i}}$ is a unit vector pointing in the positive x direction, and $\hat{\mathbf{j}}$ is a unit vector pointing in the positive y direction. Because $\hat{\mathbf{i}}$ and $\hat{\mathbf{j}}$ are unit vectors, $|\hat{\mathbf{i}}| = |\hat{\mathbf{j}}| = 1$.

We can find the resultant of two or more vectors by resolving all vectors into their x and y components, adding their resultant x and y components, and then using the Pythagorean theorem to find the magnitude of the resultant vector. We can find the angle that the resultant vector makes with respect to the x axis by using a suitable trigonometric function.

QUESTIONS

1. Two vectors have unequal magnitudes. Can their sum be zero? Explain.

2. Can the magnitude of a particle's displacement be greater

4. Which of the following are vectors and which are not: force, temperature, the volume of water in a can, the ratings of a TV show, the height of a building, the velocity of ... the Universe?

... plane. For what orientations of **A** ... ents be negative? For what orienta-... s have opposite signs?

Example 4.5   That's Quite an Arm!

A stone is thrown from the top of a building upward at an angle of 30.0° to the horizontal with an initial speed of 20.0 m/s, as shown in Figure 4.14. If the height of the building is 45.0 m,

(A) how long before the stone hits the ground?

Solution We *conceptualize* the problem by studying Figure 4.14, in which we have indicated the various parameters. By now, it should be natural to *categorize* this as a projectile motion problem.

To *analyze* the problem, let us once again separate motion into two components. The initial x and y components of the stone's velocity are

$$v_{xi} = v_i\cos\theta_i = (20.0 \text{ m/s})\cos 30.0° = 17.3 \text{ m/s}$$

$$v_{yi} = v_i\sin\theta_i = (20.0 \text{ m/s})\sin 30.0° = 10.0 \text{ m/s}$$

To find t, we can use $y_f = y_i + v_{yi}t + \frac{1}{2}a_yt^2$ (Eq. 4.9a) with $y_i = 0$, $y_f = -45.0$ m, $a_y = -g$, and $v_{yi} = 10.0$ m/s (there is a negative sign on the numerical value of y_f because we have chosen the top of the building as the origin):

$$-45.0 \text{ m} = (10.0 \text{ m/s})t - \frac{1}{2}(9.80 \text{ m/s}^2)t^2$$

Solving the quadratic equation for t gives, for the positive root, $t = \boxed{4.22 \text{ s}}$. To *finalize* this part, think: Does the negative root have any physical meaning?

(B) What is the speed of the stone just before it strikes the ground?

Solution We can use Equation 4.8a, $v_{yf} = v_{yi} + a_yt$, with $t = 4.22$ s to obtain the y component of the velocity just before the stone strikes the ground:

$$v_{yf} = 10.0 \text{ m/s} - (9.80 \text{ m/s}^2)(4.22 \text{ s}) = -31.4 \text{ m/s}$$

Because $v_{xf} = v_{xi} = 17.3$ m/s, the required speed is

$$v_f = \sqrt{v_{xf}^2 + v_{yf}^2} = \sqrt{(17.3)^2 + (-31.4)^2} \text{ m/s} = \boxed{35.9 \text{ m/s}}$$

To *finalize* this part, is it reasonable that the y component of the final velocity is negative? Is it reasonable that the final speed is larger than the initial speed of 20.0 m/s?

What If? What if a horizontal wind is blowing in the same direction as the ball is thrown and it causes the ball to have a horizontal acceleration component $a_x = 0.500 \text{ m/s}^2$. Which part of this example, (a) or (b), will have a different answer?

Answer Recall that the motions in the x and y directions are independent. Thus, the horizontal wind cannot affect the vertical motion. The vertical motion determines the time of the projectile in the air, so the answer to (a) does not change. The wind will cause the horizontal velocity component to increase with time, so that the final speed will change in part (b).

We can find the new final horizontal velocity component by using Equation 4.8a:

$$v_{xf} = v_{xi} + a_xt = 17.3 \text{ m/s} + (0.500 \text{ m/s}^2)(4.22 \text{ s})$$
$$= 19.4 \text{ m/s}$$

and the new final speed:

$$v_f = \sqrt{v_{xf}^2 + v_{yf}^2} = \sqrt{(19.4)^2 + (-31.4)^2} \text{ m/s} = 36.9 \text{ m/s}$$

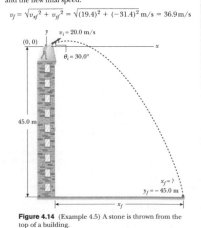

Figure 4.14 (Example 4.5) A stone is thrown from the top of a building.

Investigate this situation at the Interactive Worked Example link at http://www.pse6.com.

GO ONLINE AT www.pse6.com

Log on to **PhysicsNow** at **www.pse6.com** by using the free pincode packaged with this text.* You'll immediately notice the system's easy-to-use, browser-based format. Getting to where you need to go is as easy as a click of the mouse. The **PhysicsNow** system is made up of three interrelated parts:

► **How Much Do I Know?**

► **What Do I Need to Learn?**

► **What Have I Learned?**

These three interrelated elements work together, but are distinct enough to allow you the freedom to explore only those assets that meet your personal needs. You can use **PhysicsNow** like a traditional Web site, accessing all assets of a particular chapter and exploring on your own. The best way to maximize the system and *your* time is to start by taking the *Pre-Test*.

* Free PIN codes are only available with new copies of
Physics for Scientists and Engineers, Sixth Edition.

HOW MUCH DO I KNOW?

The Pre-Test is the first step in creating your *Personalized Learning Plan*. Each *Pre-Test* is based on the end-of-chapter homework problems and includes approximately 15 questions.

Once you've completed the *Pre-Test* you'll be presented with a detailed *Learning Plan* that outlines the elements you need to review to master the chapter's most essential concepts.

At each stage, the text is referenced to reinforce its value as a learning tool.

Turn the page to view problems from a sample *Personalized Learning Plan.*

WHAT DO I NEED TO LEARN?

Once you've completed the *Pre-Test* you're ready to work the problems in your *Personalized Learning Plan*—problems that will help you master concepts essential to your success in this course.

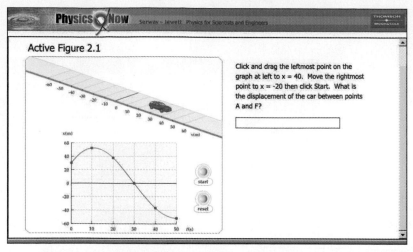

More than 200 *Active Figures* are taken from the text and animated to help you visualize physics in action. Each figure is paired with a question to help you focus on physics at work, and a brief quiz ensures that you understand the concept played out in the animations.

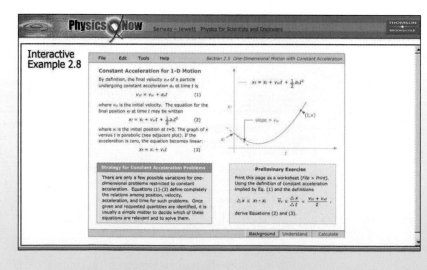

You'll continue to master the concepts though *Coached Problems.* These engaging problems reinforce the lessons in the text by taking a step-by-step approach to problem-solving methodology. Each *Coached Problem* gives you the option of working a question and receiving feedback, or seeing a solution worked for you. You'll find approximately five *Coached Problems* per chapter.

You'll strengthen your problem-solving and visualization skills by working through the *Interactive Examples.* Each step in the examples uses the authors' problem-solving methodology that is introduced in the text (see page 2 of this Visual Preface). You'll find *Interactive Examples* for each chapter of the text.

WHAT HAVE I LEARNED?

After working through the problems highlighted in your personal *Learning Plan* you'll move on to a *Chapter Quiz*. These multiple-choice quizzes present you with questions that are similar to those you might find in an exam. You can even e-mail your quiz results to your instructor.

Once you've completed the quiz you'll receive your results in the form of a percentage. If you need to improve your score, **PhysicsNow** will take you back through the system, beginning with *What Do I Know?*, and work with you as you continue to build your knowledge and skills and master concepts.

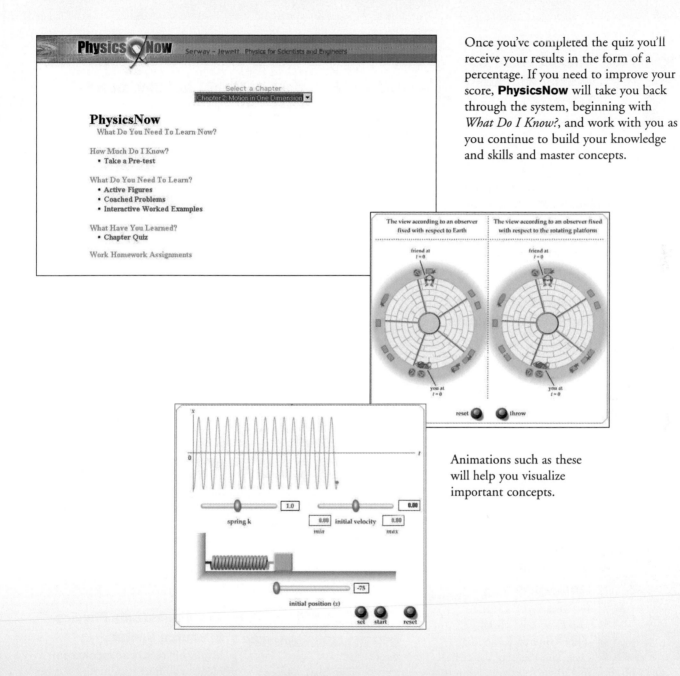

Animations such as these will help you visualize important concepts.

Chart your own course for success . . .

Log on to **www.pse6.com** to take advantage of **PhysicsNow!**

Make the most of the course and your time with these exclusive study tools

Enrich your experience outside of the classroom with a host of resources designed to help you excel in the course. To purchase any of these supplements, contact your campus bookstore or visit our online BookStore at www.brookscole.com.

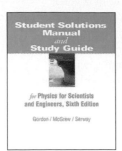

Student Solutions Manual with Study Guide

Volume I ISBN: 0-534-40855-9
Volume II ISBN: 0-534-40856-7

by John R. Gordon, Ralph McGrew, and Raymond Serway This two-volume manual features detailed solutions to 20% of the end-of-chapter problems from the text. The manual also features a list of important equations, concepts, and answers to selected end-of-chapter questions.

Essential Study Skills for Science Students

ISBN: 0-534-37595-2

by Daniel D. Chiras Written specifically for science students, this book discusses how to develop good study habits, sharpen memory, learn more quickly, get the most out of lectures, prepare for tests, produce excellent term papers, and improve critical-thinking skills.

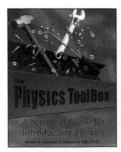

The Physics Toolbox: A Survival Guide for Introductory Physics

ISBN: 0-03-034652-5

by Kirsten A. Hubbard and Debora M. Katz This "paperback mentor" gives you the material critical for success in physics, including an introduction to the nature of physics and science, a look at what to expect and how to succeed, a verbal overview of the concepts you'll encounter, and an extensive review of the math you'll need to solve the problems.

WebTutor™ Advantage on WebCT and Blackboard

WebCT ISBN: 0-534-40859-1
Blackboard ISBN: 0-534-40950-4

WebTutor Advantage offers real-time access to a full array of study tools, including chapter outlines, summaries, learning objectives, glossary flashcards (with audio), practice quizzes, **InfoTrac® College Edition** exercises, and Web links. **WebTutor Advantage** also provides robust communication tools, such as a course calendar, asynchronous discussion, real-time chat, a whiteboard, and an integrated e-mail system. Also new to **WebTutor Advantage** is access to *NewsEdge,* an online news service that brings the latest news to the **WebTutor Advantage** site daily.

Contact your instructor for more information.

Additional Web resources . . .

available FREE to you with each new copy of this text:

InfoTrac® College Edition

When you purchase a new copy of **Physics for Scientists and Engineers, Sixth Edition**, you automatically receive a FREE four-month subscription to **InfoTrac College Edition!** Newly improved, this extensive online library opens the door to the full text (not just abstracts) of countless articles from thousands of publications including *American Scientist, Physical Review, Science, Science Weekly,* and more! Use the passcode included with the new copy of this text and log on to **www.infotrac-college.com** to explore the wealth of resources available to you—24 hours a day and seven days a week!

Available only to college and university students. Journals subject to change.

The Brooks/Cole Physics Resource Center

http://physics.brookscole.com
Here you'll find even more opportunities to hone your skills and expand your knowledge. **The Brooks/Cole Physics Resource Center** is filled with helpful content that will engage you while you master the material. You'll find additional online quizzes, Web links, animations, and *NewEdge*—an online news service that brings the latest news to this site daily.

*We dedicate this book to the courageous astronauts
who died on the space shuttle* Columbia *on February 1, 2003.
The women and men of the international team lost their lives
not in a contest between countries or a struggle for
necessities but in advancing one of humankind's noblest
creations—science.*

6th Edition

PHYSICS

for Scientists and Engineers

Chapters 35 – 39

Raymond A. Serway

John W. Jewett, Jr.

California State Polytechnic University–Pomona

THOMSON
————————
BROOKS/COLE

Australia • Canada • Mexico • Singapore • Spain
United Kingdom • United States

THOMSON

BROOKS/COLE

Editor-in-Chief: Michelle Julet
Publisher: David Harris
Physics Editor: Chris Hall
Development Editor: Susan Dust Pashos
Assistant Editor: Rebecca Heider, Alyssa White
Editorial Assistant: Seth Dobrin, Jessica Howard
Technology Project Manager: Sam Subity
Marketing Manager: Kelley McAllister
Marketing Assistant: Sandra Perin
Advertising Project Manager: Stacey Purviance
Project Manager, Editorial Production: Teri Hyde
Print/Media Buyer: Barbara Britton
Permissions Editor: Joohee Lee

Production Service: Sparkpoint Communications,
a division of J. B. Woolsey Associates
Text Designer: Lisa Devenish
Photo Researcher: Terri Wright
Copy Editor: Andrew Potter
Illustrator: Rolin Graphics
Cover Designer: Lisa Devenish
Cover Image: Water Displaced by Oil Tanker, © Stuart
Westmorland/CORBIS
Compositor: Progressive Information Technologies
Cover Printer: Quebecor World, Versailles
Printer: Quebecor World, Versailles

For more information about our products, contact us at:
Thomson Learning Academic Resource Center
1-800-423-0563

For permission to use material from this text, contact us by:
Phone: 1-800-730-2214
Fax: 1-800-730-2215
Web: http://www.thomsonrights.com

Library of Congress Control Number: 2003100126

PHYSICS FOR SCIENTISTS AND ENGINEERS, Sixth Edition
0-534-40848-6, Volume 1 (Chapters 1–14)
0-534-40849-4, Volume 2 (Chapters 15–22)
0-534-40850-8, Volume 3 (Chapters 23–34)
0-534-40853-2, Volume 4 (Chapters 35–39)

Brooks/Cole—Thomson Learning
10 Davis Drive
Belmont, CA 94002
USA

Asia
Thomson Learning
5 Shenton Way #01-01
UIC Building
Singapore 068808

Australia
Nelson Thomson Learning
102 Dodds Street
South Melbourne, Victoria 3205
Australia

Canada
Nelson Thomson Learning
1120 Birchmount Road
Toronto, Ontario M1K 5G4
Canada

Europe/Middle East/Africa
Thomson Learning
High Holborn House
50/51 Bedford Row
London WC1R 4LR
United Kingdom

Latin America
Thomson Learning
Seneca, 53
Colonia Polanco
11560 Mexico D.F.
Mexico

Spain
Paraninfo Thomson Learning
Calle/Magallanes, 25
28015 Madrid, Spain

Contents Overview

Steve Niedorf/Getty Images

v

Table of Contents

elektraVision/Index Stock Imagery

Courtesy Tourism Malaysia

PART 2   Oscillations and Mechanical Waves   451

Don Bonsey/Getty Images

PART 3   Thermodynamics   579

PART 4   Electricity and Magnetism   705

Richard Megna/Fundamental Photographs

About the Authors

Raymond A. Serway received his doctorate at Illinois Institute of Technology and is Professor Emeritus at James Madison University. Dr. Serway began his teaching career at Clarkson University, where he conducted research and taught from 1967 to 1980. His second academic appointment was at James Madison University as Professor of Physics and Head of the Physics Department from 1980 to 1986. He remained at James Madison University until his retirement in 1997. He was the recipient of the Madison Scholar Award at James Madison University in 1990, the Distinguished Teaching Award at Clarkson University in 1977, and the Alumni Achievement Award from Utica College in 1985. As Guest Scientist at the IBM Research Laboratory in Zurich, Switzerland, he worked with K. Alex Müller, 1987 Nobel Prize recipient. Dr. Serway also held research appointments at Rome Air Development Center from 1961 to 1963, at IIT Research Institute from 1963 to 1967, and as a visiting scientist at Argonne National Laboratory, where he collaborated with his mentor and friend, Sam Marshall. In addition to earlier editions of this textbook, Dr. Serway is the co-author of the high-school textbook *Physics* with Jerry Faughn, published by Holt, Rinehart, & Winston and co-author of the third edition of *Principles of Physics* with John Jewett, the sixth edition of *College Physics* with Jerry Faughn, and the second edition of *Modern Physics* with Clem Moses and Curt Moyer. In addition, Dr. Serway has published more than 40 research papers in the field of condensed matter physics and has given more than 70 presentations at professional meetings. Dr. Serway and his wife Elizabeth enjoy traveling, golfing, gardening, and spending quality time with their four children and five grandchildren.

John W. Jewett, Jr. earned his doctorate at Ohio State University, specializing in optical and magnetic properties of condensed matter. Dr. Jewett began his academic career at Richard Stockton College of New Jersey, where he taught from 1974 to 1984. He is currently Professor of Physics at California State Polytechnic University, Pomona. Throughout his teaching career, Dr. Jewett has been active in promoting science education. In addition to receiving four National Science Foundation grants, he helped found and direct the Southern California Area Modern Physics Institute (SCAMPI). He also directed Science IMPACT (Institute for Modern Pedagogy and Creative Teaching), which works with teachers and schools to develop effective science curricula. Dr. Jewett's honors include the Stockton Merit Award at Richard Stockton College, the Outstanding Professor Award at California State Polytechnic University for 1991–1992, and the Excellence in Undergraduate Physics Teaching Award from the American Association of Physics Teachers (AAPT) in 1998. He has given over 80 presentations at professional meetings, including presentations at international conferences in China and Japan. In addition to his work on this textbook, he is co-author of the third edition of *Principles of Physics* with Ray Serway and author of *The World of Physics . . . Mysteries, Magic, and Myth*. Dr. Jewett enjoys playing piano, traveling, and collecting antiques that can be used as demonstration apparatus in physics lectures, as well as spending time with his wife Lisa and their children and grandchildren.

Preface

In writing this sixth edition of *Physics for Scientists and Engineers,* we continue our ongoing efforts to improve the clarity of presentation and we again include new pedagogical features that help support the learning and teaching processes. Drawing on positive feedback from users of the fifth edition and reviewers' suggestions, we have refined the text in order to better meet the needs of students and teachers. We have for the first time integrated a powerful collection of media resources into many of the illustrations, examples, and end-of-chapter problems in the text. These resources compose the Web-based learning system *PhysicsNow* and are flagged by the media icon . Further details are described below.

This textbook is intended for a course in introductory physics for students majoring in science or engineering. The entire contents of the text in its extended version could be covered in a three-semester course, but it is possible to use the material in shorter sequences with the omission of selected chapters and sections. The mathematical background of the student taking this course should ideally include one semester of calculus. If that is not possible, the student should be enrolled in a concurrent course in introductory calculus.

Objectives

This introductory physics textbook has two main objectives: to provide the student with a clear and logical presentation of the basic concepts and principles of physics, and to strengthen an understanding of the concepts and principles through a broad range of interesting applications to the real world. To meet these objectives, we have placed emphasis on sound physical arguments and problem-solving methodology. At the same time, we have attempted to motivate the student through practical examples that demonstrate the role of physics in other disciplines, including engineering, chemistry, and medicine.

Changes in the Sixth Edition

A large number of changes and improvements have been made in preparing the sixth edition of this text. Some of the new features are based on our experiences and on current trends in science education. Other changes have been incorporated in response to comments and suggestions offered by users of the fifth edition and by reviewers of the manuscript. The following represent the major changes in the sixth edition:

Active Figures Many diagrams from the text have been animated to form **Active Figures,** part of the *PhysicsNow* integrated Web-based learning system. By visualizing phenomena and processes that cannot be fully represented on a static page, students greatly increase their conceptual understanding. **Active Figures** are identified with the media icon . An addition to the figure caption in blue type describes briefly the nature and contents of the animation.

Interactive Worked Examples Approximately 76 of the worked examples in the text have been identified as interactive, labeled with the media icon . As part of the *PhysicsNow* Web-based learning system, students can engage in an extension of the problem solved in the example. This often includes elements of both visualization and calculation, and may also involve prediction and intuition building. Often the interactivity is inspired by the **"What If?"** question we posed in the example text.

What If? Approximately one-third of the worked examples in the text contain this new feature. At the completion of the example solution, a **What If?** question offers a variation on the situation posed in the text of the example. For instance, this feature might explore the effects of changing the conditions of the situation, determine what happens when a quantity is taken to a particular limiting value, or question whether additional information can be determined about the problem situation. The answer to the question generally includes both a conceptual response and a mathematical response. This feature encourages students to think about the results of the example and assists in conceptual understanding of the principles. It also prepares students to encounter novel problems featured on exams. Some of the end-of-chapter problems also carry the **"What If?"** feature.

Quick Quizzes   The number of Quick Quiz questions in each chapter has been increased. Quick Quizzes provide students with opportunities to test their understanding of the physical concepts presented. The questions require students to make decisions on the basis of sound reasoning, and some of them have been written to help students overcome common misconceptions. Quick Quizzes have been cast in an objective format, including multiple choice, true–false, and ranking. Answers to all Quick Quiz questions are found at the end of each chapter. Additional Quick Quizzes that can be used in classroom teaching are available on the instructor's companion Web site. Many instructors choose to use such questions in a "peer instruction" teaching style, but they can be used in standard quiz format as well.

Pitfall Preventions   These new features are placed in the margins of the text and address common student misconceptions and situations in which students often follow unproductive paths. Over 200 Pitfall Preventions are provided to help students avoid common mistakes and misunderstandings.

General Problem-Solving Strategy   A general strategy to be followed by the student is outlined at the end of Chapter 2 and provides students with a structured process for solving problems. In Chapters 3 through 5, the strategy is employed explicitly in every example so that students learn how it is applied. In the remaining chapters, the strategy appears explicitly in one example per chapter so that students are encouraged throughout the course to follow the procedure.

Line-by-Line Revision   The entire text has been carefully edited to improve clarity of presentation and precision of language. We hope that the result is a book that is both accurate and enjoyable to read.

Problems   A substantial revision of the end-of-chapter problems was made in an effort to improve their variety and interest, while maintaining their clarity and quality. Approximately 17% of the problems (about 550) are new. All problems have been carefully edited. Solutions to approximately 20% of the end-of-chapter problems are included in the *Student Solutions Manual and Study Guide*. These problems are identified by boxes around their numbers. A smaller subset of solutions, identified by the media icon ⟨⟩, are available on the World Wide Web (**http://www.pse6.com**) as coached solutions with hints. Targeted feedback is provided for students whose instructors adopt *Physics for Scientists and Engineers,* sixth edition. See the next section for a complete description of other features of the problem set.

Content Changes   The content and organization of the textbook is essentially the same as that of the fifth edition. An exception is that Chapter 13 (Oscillatory Motion) in the fifth edition has been moved to the Chapter 15 position in the sixth edition, in order to form a cohesive four-chapter Part 2 on oscillations and waves. Many sections in various chapters have been streamlined, deleted, or combined with other sections to allow for a more balanced presentation. The chapters on Modern Physics, Chapters 39–46, have been extensively rewritten to provide more up-to-date material as well as modern applications. A more detailed list of content changes can be found on the instructor's companion Web site.

Content

The material in this book covers fundamental topics in classical physics and provides an introduction to modern physics. The book is divided into six parts. Part 1 (Chapters 1 to 14) deals with the fundamentals of Newtonian mechanics and the physics of fluids, Part 2 (Chapters 15 to 18) covers oscillations, mechanical waves, and sound, Part 3 (Chapters 19 to 22) addresses heat and thermodynamics, Part 4 (Chapters 23 to 34) treats electricity and magnetism, Part 5 (Chapters 35 to 38) covers light and optics, and Part 6 (Chapters 39 to 46) deals with relativity and modern physics. Each part opener includes an overview of the subject matter covered in that part, as well as some historical perspectives.

Text Features

Most instructors would agree that the textbook selected for a course should be the student's primary guide for understanding and learning the subject matter. Furthermore, the textbook should be easily accessible and should be styled and written to facilitate instruction and learning. With these points in mind, we have included many pedagogical features in the textbook that are intended to enhance its usefulness to both students and instructors. These features are as follows:

Style   To facilitate rapid comprehension, we have attempted to write the book in a style that is clear, logical, and engaging. We have chosen a writing style that is somewhat informal and relaxed so that students will find the text appealing and enjoyable to read. New terms are carefully defined, and we have avoided the use of jargon.

Previews   All chapters begin with a brief preview that includes a discussion of the chapter's objectives and content.

Important Statements and Equations   Most important statements and definitions are set in **boldface** type or are highlighted with a background screen for added emphasis and ease of review. Similarly, important equations are highlighted with a background screen to facilitate location.

Bruce Ayers/Getty Images

Problem-Solving Hints   In several chapters, we have included general strategies for solving the types of problems featured both in the examples and in the end-of-chapter problems. This feature helps students to identify necessary steps in problem solving and to eliminate any uncertainty they might have. Problem-solving strategies are highlighted with a light red background screen for emphasis and ease of location.

Marginal Notes   Comments and notes appearing in blue type in the margin can be used to locate important statements, equations, and concepts in the text.

Pedagogical Use of Color   Readers should consult the **pedagogical color chart** (second page inside the front cover) for a listing of the color-coded symbols used in the text diagrams, Web-based **Active Figures,** and diagrams within **Interactive Worked Examples.** This system is followed consistently whenever possible, with slight variations made necessary by the complexity of physical situations depicted in Part 4.

Mathematical Level   We have introduced calculus gradually, keeping in mind that students often take introductory courses in calculus and physics concurrently. Most steps are shown when basic equations are developed, and reference is often made to mathematical appendices at the end of the textbook. Vector products are introduced later in the text, where they are needed in physical applications. The dot product is introduced in Chapter 7, which addresses energy and energy transfer; the cross product is introduced in Chapter 11, which deals with angular momentum.

Worked Examples   A large number of worked examples of varying difficulty are presented to promote students' understanding of concepts. In many cases, the examples serve as models for solving the end-of-chapter problems. Because of the increased emphasis on understanding physical concepts, many examples are conceptual in nature and are labeled as such. The examples are set off in boxes, and the answers to examples with numerical solutions are highlighted with a background screen. We have already mentioned that a number of examples are designated as interactive and are part of the *PhysicsNow* Web-based learning system.

Questions Questions of a conceptual nature requiring verbal or written responses are provided at the end of each chapter. Over 1 000 questions are included in this edition. Some questions provide the student with a means of self-testing the concepts presented in the chapter. Others could serve as a basis for initiating classroom discussions. Answers to selected questions are included in the *Student Solutions Manual and Study Guide,* and answers to all questions are found in the *Instructor's Solutions Manual.*

Significant Figures Significant figures in both worked examples and end-of-chapter problems have been handled with care. Most numerical examples are worked out to either two or three significant figures, depending on the precision of the data provided. End-of-chapter problems regularly state data and answers to three-digit precision.

Problems An extensive set of problems is included at the end of each chapter; in all, over 3 000 problems are given throughout the text. Answers to odd-numbered problems are provided at the end of the book in a section whose pages have colored edges for ease of location. For the convenience of both the student and the instructor, about two thirds of the problems are keyed to specific sections of the chapter. The remaining problems, labeled "Additional Problems," are not keyed to specific sections.

Usually, the problems within a given section are presented so that the straightforward problems (those with black problem numbers) appear first. For ease of identification, the numbers of intermediate-level problems are printed in blue, and those of challenging problems are printed in magenta.

- **Review Problems** Many chapters include review problems requiring the student to combine concepts covered in the chapter with those discussed in previous chapters. These problems reflect the cohesive nature of the principles in the text and verify that physics is not a scattered set of ideas. When facing real-world issues such as global warming or nuclear weapons, it may be necessary to call on ideas in physics from several parts of a textbook such as this one.

- **Paired Problems** To allow focused practice in solving problems stated in symbolic terms, some end-of-chapter numerical problems are paired with the same problems in symbolic form. Paired problems are identified by a common light red background screen.

- **Computer- and Calculator-Based Problems** Many chapters include one or more problems whose solution requires the use of a computer or graphing calculator. Computer modeling of physical phenomena enables students to obtain graphical representations of variables and to perform numerical analyses.

- **Coached Problems with Hints** These have been described above as part of the *PhysicsNow* Web-based learning system. These problems are identified by the media icon www and targeted feedback is provided to students of instructors adopting the sixth edition.

Units The international system of units (SI) is used throughout the text. The U.S. customary system of units is used only to a limited extent in the chapters on mechanics, heat, and thermodynamics.

Summaries Each chapter contains a summary that reviews the important concepts and equations discussed in that chapter. A marginal note in blue type next to each chapter summary directs students to a practice test (Post-Test) for the chapter.

Appendices and Endpapers Several appendices are provided at the end of the textbook. Most of the appendix material represents a review of mathematical concepts and techniques used in the text, including scientific notation, algebra, geometry, trigonometry, differential calculus, and integral calculus. Reference to these appendices is made

Courtesy NASA

throughout the text. Most mathematical review sections in the appendices include worked examples and exercises with answers. In addition to the mathematical reviews, the appendices contain tables of physical data, conversion factors, atomic masses, and the SI units of physical quantities, as well as a periodic table of the elements. Other useful information, including fundamental constants and physical data, planetary data, a list of standard prefixes, mathematical symbols, the Greek alphabet, and standard abbreviations of units of measure, appears on the endpapers.

Student Ancillaries

Student Solutions Manual and Study Guide by John R. Gordon, Ralph McGrew, and Raymond Serway. This two-volume manual features detailed solutions to 20% of the end-of-chapter problems from the text. The manual also features a list of important equations, concepts, and notes from key sections of the text, in addition to answers to selected end-of-chapter questions. Volume 1 contains Chapters 1 through 22 and Volume 2 contains Chapters 23 through 46.

WebTutor™ on WebCT and Blackboard **WebTutor** offers students real-time access to a full array of study tools, including chapter outlines, summaries, learning objectives, glossary flashcards (with audio), practice quizzes, **InfoTrac® College Edition** exercises, and Web links.

InfoTrac® College Edition Adopters and their students automatically receive a four-month subscription to **InfoTrac® College Edition** with every new copy of this book. Newly improved, this extensive online library opens the door to the full text (not just abstracts) of countless articles from thousands of publications including *American Scientist, Physical Review, Science, Science Weekly,* and more! Available only to college and university students. Journals subject to change.

The Brooks/Cole Physics Resource Center You will find additional online quizzes, Web links and animations at **http://physics.brookscole.com.**

Ancillaries for Instructors

The first four ancillaries below are available to qualified adopters. Please consult your local sales representative for details.

Instructor's Solutions Manual by Ralph McGrew and James A. Currie. This two-volume manual contains complete worked solutions to all of the end-of-chapter problems in the textbook as well as answers to even-numbered problems. The solutions to problems new to the sixth edition are marked for easy identification by the instructor. New to this edition are complete answers to the conceptual questions in the main text. Volume 1 contains Chapters 1 through 22 and Volume 2 contains Chapters 23 through 46.

Printed Test Bank by Edward Adelson. This two-volume test bank contains approximately 2 300 multiple-choice questions. These questions are also available in electronic format with complete answers and solutions in the Brooks/Cole Assessment test program. Volume 1 contains Chapters 1 through 22 and Volume 2 contains Chapters 23 through 46.

Multimedia Manager This easy-to-use multimedia lecture tool allows you to quickly assemble art and database files with notes to create fluid lectures. The CD-ROM set (Volume 1, Chapters 1–22; Volume 2, Chapters 23–46) includes a database of animations, video clips, and digital art from the text as well as electronic files of the *Instructor's Solutions Manual and Test Bank.* The simple interface makes it easy for you to incorporate graphics, digital video, animations, and audio clips into your lectures.

Transparency Acetates Each volume contains approximately 100 acetates featuring art from the text. Volume 1 contains Chapters 1 through 22 and Volume 2 contains Chapters 23 through 46.

Brooks/Cole Assessment With a balance of efficiency, high performance, simplicity and versatility, **Brooks/Cole Assessment (BCA)** gives you the power to transform the learning and teaching experience. **BCA** is fully integrated testing, tutorial, and course management software accessible by instructors and students anytime, anywhere. Delivered for FREE in a browser-based format without the need for any proprietary software or plug-ins, **BCA** uses correct scientific notation to provide the drill of basic skills that students need, enabling the instructor to focus more time in higher-level learning activities (i.e., concepts and applications). Students can have unlimited practice in questions and problems, building their own confidence and skills. Results flow automatically to a grade book for tracking so that instructors will be better able to assess student understanding of the material, even prior to class or an actual test.

George Sample

WebTutor™ on WebCT and Blackboard With **WebTutor's** text-specific, preformatted content and total flexibility, instructors can easily create and manage their own personal Web site. **WebTutor's** course management tool gives instructors the ability to provide virtual office hours, post syllabi, set up threaded discussions, track student progress with the quizzing material, and much more. **WebTutor** also provides robust communication tools, such as a course calendar, asynchronous discussion, real-time chat, a whiteboard, and an integrated e-mail system.

Additional Options for Online Homework For detailed information and demonstrations, contact your Thomson•Brooks/Cole representative or visit the following:

- WebAssign: A Web-based Homework System
  http://www.webassign.net or contact WebAssign at *webassign@ncsu.edu*
- Homework Service
  http://hw.ph.utexas.edu/hw.html or contact *moore@physics.utexas.edu*
- CAPA: A Computer-Assisted Personalized Approach
  http://capa4.lite.msu.edu/homepage/

Instructor's Companion Web Site Consult the instructor's site at *http://www.pse6.com* for additional Quick Quiz questions, a detailed list of content changes since the fifth edition, a problem correlation guide, images from the text, and sample PowerPoint lectures. Instructors adopting the sixth edition of *Physics for Scientists and Engineers* may download these materials after securing the appropriate password from their local Thomson•Brooks/Cole sales representative.

Teaching Options

The topics in this textbook are presented in the following sequence: classical mechanics, oscillations and mechanical waves, and heat and thermodynamics followed by electricity and magnetism, electromagnetic waves, optics, relativity, and modern physics. This presentation represents a traditional sequence, with the subject of mechanical waves being presented before electricity and magnetism. Some instructors may prefer to cover this material after completing electricity and magnetism (i.e., after Chapter 34). The chapter on relativity is placed near the end of the text because this topic often is treated as an introduction to the era of "modern physics." If time permits, instructors may choose to cover Chapter 39 after completing Chapter 13, as it concludes the material on Newtonian mechanics.

For those instructors teaching a two-semester sequence, some sections and chapters could be deleted without any loss of continuity. The following sections can be considered optional for this purpose:

2.7	Kinematic Equations Derived from Calculus	6.4	Motion in the Presence of Resistive Forces
4.6	Relative Velocity and Relative Acceleration	6.5	Numerical Modeling in Particle Dynamics
6.3	Motion in Accelerated Frames	7.9	Energy and the Automobile

Topham Picturepoint/The Image Works

Acknowledgments

The sixth edition of this textbook was prepared with the guidance and assistance of many professors who reviewed selections of the manuscript, the pre-revision text, or both. We wish to acknowledge the following scholars and express our sincere appreciation for their suggestions, criticisms, and encouragement:

Edward Adelson, *Ohio State University*

Michael R. Cohen, *Shippensburg University*

Jerry D. Cook, *Eastern Kentucky University*

J. William Dawicke, *Milwaukee School of Engineering*

N. John DiNardo, *Drexel University*

Andrew Duffy, *Boston University*

Robert J. Endorf, *University of Cincinnati*

F. Paul Esposito, *University of Cincinnati*

Joe L. Ferguson, *Mississippi State University*

Perry Ganas, *California State University, Los Angeles*

John C. Hardy, *Texas A&M University*

Michael Hayes, *University of Pretoria (South Africa)*

John T. Ho, *The State University of New York, Buffalo*

Joseph W. Howard, *Salisbury University*

Robert Hunt, *Johnson County Community College*

Walter S. Jaronski, *Radford University*

Sangyong Jeon, *McGill University, Quebec*

Stan Jones, *University of Alabama*

L. R. Jordan, *Palm Beach Community College*

Teruki Kamon, *Texas A & M University*

Louis E. Keiner, *Coastal Carolina University*

Mario Klarič, *Midlands Technical College*

Laird Kramer, *Florida International University*

Edwin H. Lo, *American University*

James G. McLean, *The State University of New York, Geneseo*

Richard E. Miers, *Indiana University–Purdue University, Fort Wayne*

Oscar Romulo Ochoa, *The College of New Jersey*

Frank Oberle/Getty Images

Paul S. Ormsby, *Moraine Valley Community College*

Didarul I. Qadir, *Central Michigan University*

Judith D. Redling, *New Jersey Institute of Technology*

Richard W. Robinett, *Pennsylvania State University*

Om P. Rustgi, *SUNY College at Buffalo*

Mesgun Sebhatu, *Winthrop University*

Natalia Semushkina, *Shippensburg University*

Daniel Stump, *Michigan State University*

Uwe C. Täuber, *Virginia Polytechnic Institute*

Perry A. Tompkins, *Samford University*

Doug Welch, *McMaster University, Ontario*

Augden Windelborn, *Northern Illinois University*

Jerzy M. Wrobel, *University of Missouri, Kansas City*

Jianshi Wu, *Fayetteville State University*

Michael Zincani, *University of Dallas*

This title was carefully checked for accuracy by Michael Kotlarchyk *(Rochester Institute of Technology)*, Chris Vuille *(Embry-Riddle Aeronautical University)*, Laurencin Dunbar *(St. Louis Community College)*, William Dawicke *(Milwaukee School of Engineering)*, Ioan Kosztin *(University of Missouri)*, Tom Barrett *(Ohio State University)*, Z. M. Stadnik *(University of Ottawa)*, Ronald E. Jodoin *(Rochester Institute of Technology)*, Brian A. Raue *(Florida International University)*, Peter Moeck *(Portland State University)*, and Grant Hart *(Brigham Young University)*. We thank them for their diligent efforts under schedule pressure!

We are grateful to Ralph McGrew for organizing the end-of-chapter problems, writing many new problems, and his excellent suggestions for improving the content of the textbook. Problems new to this edition were written by Edward Adelson, Ronald Bieniek, Michael Browne, Andrew Duffy, Robert Forsythe, Perry Ganas, Michael Hones, John Jewett, Boris Korsunsky, Edwin Lo, Ralph McGrew, Raymond Serway, and Jerzy Wrobel, with the help of Bennett Simpson and JoAnne Maniago. Students Alexander Coto, Karl Payne, and Eric Peterman made corrections to problems taken from previous editions, as did teachers David Aspnes, Robert Beichner, Joseph Biegen, Tom Devlin, Vasili Haralambous, Frank Hayes, Erika Hermon, Ken Menningen, Henry Nebel, and Charles Teague. We are grateful to authors John R. Gordon and Ralph McGrew and compositor Michael Rudmin for preparing the *Student Solutions Manual and Study Guide*. Authors Ralph McGrew and James Currie and compositor Mary Toscano have prepared an excellent *Instructor's Solutions Manual,* and we thank them. Edward Adelson has carefully edited and improved the Test Bank for the sixth edition. Kurt Vandervoort prepared extra Quick Quiz questions for the instructor's companion Web site.

Special thanks and recognition go to the professional staff at the Brooks/Cole Publishing Company—in particular Susan Pashos, Rebecca Heider and Alyssa White (who managed the ancillary program and so much more), Jessica Howard, Seth Dobrin, Peter McGahey, Teri Hyde, Michelle Julet, David Harris, and Chris Hall—for their fine work during the development and production of this textbook. We are most appreciative of Sam Subity's masterful management of the *PhysicsNow* media program. Kelley McAllister is our energetic Marketing Manager, and Stacey Purviance coordinates our marketing communications. We recognize the skilled production service provided by the staff at Sparkpoint Communications, the excellent artwork produced by Rolin Graphics, and the dedicated photo research efforts of Terri Wright.

Finally, we are deeply indebted to our wives and children for their love, support, and long-term sacrifices.

Raymond A. Serway
Leesburg, Virginia

John W. Jewett, Jr.
Pomona, California

To the Student

t is appropriate to offer some words of advice that should be of benefit to you, the student. Before doing so, we assume that you have read the Preface, which describes the various features of the text that will help you through the course.

How to Study

Very often instructors are asked, "How should I study physics and prepare for examinations?" There is no simple answer to this question, but we would like to offer some suggestions that are based on our own experiences in learning and teaching over the years.

First and foremost, maintain a positive attitude toward the subject matter, keeping in mind that physics is the most fundamental of all natural sciences. Other science courses that follow will use the same physical principles, so it is important that you understand and are able to apply the various concepts and theories discussed in the text.

Concepts and Principles

It is essential that you understand the basic concepts and principles before attempting to solve assigned problems. You can best accomplish this goal by carefully reading the textbook before you attend your lecture on the covered material. When reading the text, you should jot down those points that are not clear to you. We've purposely left wide margins in the text to give you space for making notes. Also be sure to make a diligent attempt at answering the questions in the Quick Quizzes as you come to them in your reading. We have worked hard to prepare questions that help you judge for yourself how well you understand the material. Study carefully the **What If?** features that appear with many of the worked examples. These will help you to extend your understanding beyond the simple act of arriving at a numerical result. The Pitfall Preventions will also help guide you away from common misunderstandings about physics. During class, take careful notes and ask questions about those ideas that are unclear to you. Keep in mind that few people are able to absorb the full meaning of scientific material after only one reading. Several readings of the text and your notes may be necessary. Your lectures and laboratory work supplement reading of the textbook and should clarify some of the more difficult material. You should minimize your memorization of material. Successful memorization of passages from the text, equations, and derivations does not necessarily indicate that you understand the material. Your understanding of the material will be enhanced through a combination of efficient study habits, discussions with other students and with instructors, and your ability to solve the problems presented in the textbook. Ask questions whenever you feel clarification of a concept is necessary.

Study Schedule

It is important that you set up a regular study schedule, preferably a daily one. Make sure that you read the syllabus for the course and adhere to the schedule set by your instructor. The lectures will make much more sense if you read the corresponding text material before attending them. As a general rule, you should devote about two hours of study time for every hour you are in class. If you are having trouble with the course, seek the advice of the instructor or other students who have taken the course. You may find it necessary to seek further instruction from experienced students. Very often, instructors offer review sessions in addition to regular class periods. It is important that you avoid the practice of delaying study until a day or two before an exam. More often than not, this approach has disastrous results. Rather than undertake an all-night study session, briefly review the basic concepts and equations, and get a good night's rest. If you feel you need additional help in understanding the concepts, in preparing for exams, or in problem solving, we suggest that you acquire a copy of the *Student Solutions Manual and Study Guide* that accompanies this textbook; this manual should be available at your college bookstore.

Use the Features

George Sample

You should make full use of the various features of the text discussed in the Preface. For example, marginal notes are useful for locating and describing important equations and concepts, and **boldfaced** type indicates important statements and definitions. Many useful tables are contained in the Appendices, but most are incorporated in the text where they are most often referenced. Appendix B is a convenient review of mathematical techniques.

Answers to odd-numbered problems are given at the end of the textbook, answers to Quick Quizzes are located at the end of each chapter, and answers to selected end-of-chapter questions are provided in the *Student Solutions Manual and Study Guide.* Problem-Solving Strategies and Hints are included in selected chapters throughout the text and give you additional information about how you should solve problems. The Table of Contents provides an overview of the entire text, while the Index enables you to locate specific material quickly. Footnotes sometimes are used to supplement the text or to cite other references on the subject discussed.

After reading a chapter, you should be able to define any new quantities introduced in that chapter and to discuss the principles and assumptions that were used to arrive at certain key relations. The chapter summaries and the review sections of the *Student Solutions Manual and Study Guide* should help you in this regard. In some cases, it may be necessary for you to refer to the index of the text to locate certain topics. You should be able to associate with each physical quantity the correct symbol used to represent that quantity and the unit in which the quantity is specified. Furthermore, you should be able to express each important equation in a concise and accurate prose statement.

Problem Solving

R. P. Feynman, Nobel laureate in physics, once said, "You do not know anything until you have practiced." In keeping with this statement, we strongly advise that you develop the skills necessary to solve a wide range of problems. Your ability to solve problems will be one of the main tests of your knowledge of physics, and therefore you should try to solve as many problems as possible. It is essential that you understand basic concepts and principles before attempting to solve problems. It is good practice to try to find alternate solutions to the same problem. For example, you can solve problems in mechanics using Newton's laws, but very often an alternative method that draws on energy considerations is more direct. You should not deceive yourself into thinking that you understand a problem merely because you have seen it solved in class. You must be able to solve the problem and similar problems on your own.

The approach to solving problems should be carefully planned. A systematic plan is especially important when a problem involves several concepts. First, read the problem several times until you are confident you understand what is being asked. Look for any key words that will help you interpret the problem and perhaps allow you to make certain assumptions. Your ability to interpret a question properly is an integral part of problem solving. Second, you should acquire the habit of writing down the information given in a problem and those quantities that need to be found; for example, you might construct a table listing both the quantities given and the quantities to be found. This procedure is sometimes used in the worked examples of the textbook. Finally, after you have decided on the method you feel is appropriate for a given problem, proceed with your solution. Specific problem-solving strategies (Hints) of this type are included in the text and are highlighted with a light red screen. We have also developed a General Problem-Solving Strategy to help guide you through complex problems. If you follow the steps of this procedure (*Conceptualize, Categorize, Analyze, Finalize*), you will not only find it easier to come up with a solution, but you will also gain more from your efforts. This Strategy is located at the end of Chapter 2 (page 47) and is used in all worked examples in Chapters 3 through 5 so that you can learn how to apply it. In the remaining chapters, the Strategy is used in one example per chapter as a reminder of its usefulness.

Often, students fail to recognize the limitations of certain equations or physical laws in a particular situation. It is very important that you understand and remember the assumptions that underlie a particular theory or formalism. For example, certain equations in kinematics apply only to a particle moving with constant acceleration. These equations are not valid for describing motion whose acceleration is not constant, such as the motion of an object connected to a spring or the motion of an object through a fluid.

Experiments

Physics is a science based on experimental observations. In view of this fact, we recommend that you try to supplement the text by performing various types of "hands-on" experiments, either at home or in the laboratory. These can be used to test ideas and models discussed in class or in the textbook. For example, the common Slinky™ toy is excellent for studying traveling waves; a ball swinging on the end of a long string can be used to investigate pendulum motion; various masses attached to the end of a vertical spring or rubber band can be used to determine their elastic nature; an old pair of Polaroid sunglasses and some discarded lenses and a magnifying glass are the components of various experiments in optics; and an approximate measure of the free-fall acceleration can be determined simply by measuring with a stopwatch the time it takes for a ball to drop from a known height. The list of such experiments is endless. When physical models are not available, be imaginative and try to develop models of your own.

© Phil Degginger/Stone/Getty

New Media

We strongly encourage you to use the **PhysicsNow** Web-based learning system that accompanies this textbook. It is far easier to understand physics if you see it in action, and these new materials will enable you to become a part of that action. **PhysicsNow** media described in the Preface are accessed at the URL *http://www.pse6.com,* and feature a three-step learning process consisting of a Pre-Test, a personalized learning plan, and a Post-Test.

In addition to other elements, **PhysicsNow** includes the following Active Figures and Interactive Worked Examples:

Chapter 2
Active Figures 2.1, 2.3, 2.9, 2.10, 2.11, and 2.13
Examples 2.8 and 2.12

Chapter 3
Active Figures 3.2, 3.3, 3.6, and 3.16
Example 3.5

Chapter 4
Active Figures 4.5, 4.7, and 4.11
Examples 4.4, 4.5, and 4.18

Chapter 5
Active Figure 5.16
Examples 5.9, 5.10, 5.12, and 5.14

Chapter 6
Active Figures 6.2, 6.8, 6.12, and 6.15
Examples 6.4, 6.5, and 6.7

Chapter 7
Active Figure 7.10
Examples 7.9 and 7.11

Chapter 8
Active Figures 8.3, 8.4, and 8.16
Examples 8.2 and 8.4

Chapter 9
Active Figures 9.8, 9.9, 9.13, 9.16, and 9.17
Examples 9.1, 9.5, and 9.8

Chapter 10
Active Figures 10.4, 10.14, and 10.30
Examples 10.12, 10.13, and 10.14

Chapter 11
Active Figures 11.1, 11.3, and 11.4
Examples 11.6 and 11.10

An Invitation to Physics

It is our sincere hope that you too will find physics an exciting and enjoyable experience and that you will profit from this experience, regardless of your chosen profession. Welcome to the exciting world of physics!

The scientist does not study nature because it is useful; he studies it because he delights in it, and he delights in it because it is beautiful. If nature were not beautiful, it would not be worth knowing, and if nature were not worth knowing, life would not be worth living.

—Henri Poincaré

Light and Optics

Light is basic to almost all life on the Earth. Plants convert the energy transferred by sunlight to chemical energy through photosynthesis. In addition, light is the principal means by which we are able to transmit and receive information to and from objects around us and throughout the Universe.

The nature and properties of light have been a subject of great interest and speculation since ancient times. The Greeks believed that light consisted of tiny particles (*corpuscles*) that were emitted by a light source and that these particles stimulated the perception of vision upon striking the observer's eye. Newton used this particle theory to explain the reflection and refraction (bending) of light. In 1678, one of Newton's contemporaries, the Dutch scientist Christian Huygens, was able to explain many other properties of light by proposing that light is a wave. In 1801, Thomas Young showed that light beams can interfere with one another, giving strong support to the wave theory. In 1865, Maxwell developed a brilliant theory that electromagnetic waves travel with the speed of light (see Chapter 34). By this time, the wave theory of light seemed to be firmly established.

However, at the beginning of the twentieth century, Max Planck returned to the particle theory of light to explain the radiation emitted by hot objects. Einstein then used the particle theory to explain how electrons are emitted by a metal exposed to light. Today, scientists view light as having a dual nature—that is, light exhibits characteristics of a wave in some situations and characteristics of a particle in other situations.

We shall discuss the particle nature of light in Part 6 of this text, which addresses modern physics. In Chapters 35 through 38, we concentrate on those aspects of light that are best understood through the wave model. First, we discuss the reflection of light at the boundary between two media and the refraction that occurs as light travels from one medium into another. Then, we use these ideas to study reflection and refraction as light forms images due to mirrors and lenses. Next, we describe how the lenses and mirrors used in such instruments as telescopes and microscopes help us view objects not clearly visible to the naked eye. Finally, we study the phenomena of diffraction, polarization, and interference as they apply to light. ■

◀ *The Grand Tetons in western Wyoming are reflected in a smooth lake at sunset. The optical principles that we study in this part of the book will explain the nature of the reflected image of the mountains and why the sky appears red. (David Muench/CORBIS)*

Chapter 35

The Nature of Light and the Laws of Geometric Optics

▲ *This photograph of a rainbow shows a distinct secondary rainbow with the colors reversed. The appearance of the rainbow depends on three optical phenomena discussed in this chapter—reflection, refraction, and dispersion. (Mark D. Phillips/Photo Researchers, Inc.)*

In this first chapter on optics, we begin by introducing two historical models for light and discussing early methods for measuring the speed of light. Next we study the fundamental phenomena of geometric optics—reflection of light from a surface and refraction as the light crosses the boundary between two media. We will also study the dispersion of light as it refracts into materials, resulting in visual displays such as the rainbow. Finally, we investigate the phenomenon of total internal reflection, which is the basis for the operation of optical fibers and the burgeoning technology of fiber optics.

35.1 The Nature of Light

Before the beginning of the nineteenth century, light was considered to be a stream of particles that either was emitted by the object being viewed or emanated from the eyes of the viewer. Newton, the chief architect of the particle theory of light, held that particles were emitted from a light source and that these particles stimulated the sense of sight upon entering the eye. Using this idea, he was able to explain reflection and refraction.

Most scientists accepted Newton's particle theory. During his lifetime, however, another theory was proposed—one that argued that light might be some sort of wave motion. In 1678, the Dutch physicist and astronomer Christian Huygens showed that a wave theory of light could also explain reflection and refraction.

In 1801, Thomas Young (1773–1829) provided the first clear demonstration of the wave nature of light. Young showed that, under appropriate conditions, light rays interfere with each other. Such behavior could not be explained at that time by a particle theory because there was no conceivable way in which two or more particles could come together and cancel one another. Additional developments during the nineteenth century led to the general acceptance of the wave theory of light, the most important resulting from the work of Maxwell, who in 1873 asserted that light was a form of high-frequency electromagnetic wave. As discussed in Chapter 34, Hertz provided experimental confirmation of Maxwell's theory in 1887 by producing and detecting electromagnetic waves.

Although the wave model and the classical theory of electricity and magnetism were able to explain most known properties of light, they could not explain some subsequent experiments. The most striking of these is the photoelectric effect, also discovered by Hertz: when light strikes a metal surface, electrons are sometimes ejected from the surface. As one example of the difficulties that arose, experiments showed that the kinetic energy of an ejected electron is independent of the light intensity. This finding contradicted the wave theory, which held that a more intense beam of light should add more energy to the electron. An explanation of the photoelectric effect was proposed by Einstein in 1905 in a theory that used the concept of quantization developed by Max Planck (1858–1947) in 1900. The quantization model assumes that the energy of a light wave is present in particles called *photons*; hence, the energy is said to be quantized. According to Einstein's theory, the energy of a photon is proportional to the frequency of the electromagnetic wave:

Energy of a photon

$$E = hf \tag{35.1}$$

where the constant of proportionality $h = 6.63 \times 10^{-34}$ J·s is Planck's constant (see Section 11.6). We will study this theory in Chapter 40.

In view of these developments, light must be regarded as having a dual nature: **Light exhibits the characteristics of a wave in some situations and the characteristics of a particle in other situations.** Light is light, to be sure. However, the question "Is light a wave or a particle?" is inappropriate. Sometimes light acts like a wave, and at other times it acts like a particle. In the next few chapters, we investigate the wave nature of light.

35.2   Measurements of the Speed of Light

Light travels at such a high speed ($c = 3.00 \times 10^8$ m/s) that early attempts to measure its speed were unsuccessful. Galileo attempted to measure the speed of light by positioning two observers in towers separated by approximately 10 km. Each observer carried a shuttered lantern. One observer would open his lantern first, and then the other would open his lantern at the moment he saw the light from the first lantern. Galileo reasoned that, knowing the transit time of the light beams from one lantern to the other, he could obtain the speed. His results were inconclusive. Today, we realize (as Galileo concluded) that it is impossible to measure the speed of light in this manner because the transit time is so much less than the reaction time of the observers.

Roemer's Method

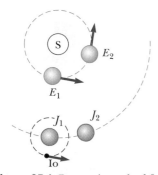

In 1675, the Danish astronomer Ole Roemer (1644–1710) made the first successful estimate of the speed of light. Roemer's technique involved astronomical observations of one of the moons of Jupiter, Io, which has a period of revolution around Jupiter of approximately 42.5 h. The period of revolution of Jupiter around the Sun is about 12 yr; thus, as the Earth moves through 90° around the Sun, Jupiter revolves through only $(1/12)90° = 7.5°$ (Fig. 35.1).

An observer using the orbital motion of Io as a clock would expect the orbit to have a constant period. However, Roemer, after collecting data for more than a year, observed a systematic variation in Io's period. He found that the periods were longer than average when the Earth was receding from Jupiter and shorter than average when the Earth was approaching Jupiter. If Io had a constant period, Roemer should have seen it become eclipsed by Jupiter at a particular instant and should have been able to predict the time of the next eclipse. However, when he checked the time of the second eclipse as the Earth receded from Jupiter, he found that the eclipse was late. If the interval between his observations was three months, then the delay was approximately 600 s. Roemer attributed this variation in period to the fact that the distance between the Earth and Jupiter changed from one observation to the next. In three months (one quarter of the period of revolution of the Earth around the Sun), the light from Jupiter must travel an additional distance equal to the radius of the Earth's orbit.

Using Roemer's data, Huygens estimated the lower limit for the speed of light to be approximately 2.3×10^8 m/s. This experiment is important historically because it demonstrated that light does have a finite speed and gave an estimate of this speed.

Figure 35.1 Roemer's method for measuring the speed of light. In the time interval during which the Earth travels 90° around the Sun (three months), Jupiter travels only about 7.5° (drawing not to scale).

Fizeau's Method

The first successful method for measuring the speed of light by means of purely terrestrial techniques was developed in 1849 by French physicist Armand H. L. Fizeau (1819–1896). Figure 35.2 represents a simplified diagram of Fizeau's apparatus. The basic procedure is to measure the total time interval during which light travels from some point to a distant mirror and back. If d is the distance between the light source (considered to be at the location of the wheel) and the mirror and if the time interval for one round trip is Δt, then the speed of light is $c = 2d/\Delta t$.

To measure the transit time, Fizeau used a rotating toothed wheel, which converts a continuous beam of light into a series of light pulses. The rotation of such a wheel controls what an observer at the light source sees. For example, if the pulse traveling toward the mirror and passing the opening at point A in Figure 35.2 should return to the wheel at the instant tooth B had rotated into position to cover the return path, the pulse would not reach the observer. At a greater rate of rotation, the opening at point C could move into position to allow the reflected pulse to reach the observer. Knowing the distance d, the number of teeth in the wheel, and the angular speed of the wheel, Fizeau arrived at a value of 3.1×10^8 m/s. Similar measurements made by subsequent investigators yielded more precise values for c, which led to the currently accepted value of 2.9979×10^8 m/s.

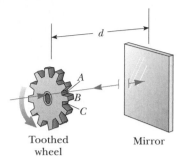

Figure 35.2 Fizeau's method for measuring the speed of light using a rotating toothed wheel. The light source is considered to be at the location of the wheel; thus, the distance d is known.

Example 35.1   Measuring the Speed of Light with Fizeau's Wheel

Assume that Fizeau's wheel has 360 teeth and is rotating at 27.5 rev/s when a pulse of light passing through opening A in Figure 35.2 is blocked by tooth B on its return. If the distance to the mirror is 7 500 m, what is the speed of light?

Solution The wheel has 360 teeth, and so it must have 360 openings. Therefore, because the light passes through opening A but is blocked by the tooth immediately adjacent to A, the wheel must rotate through an angular displacement of $(1/720)$ rev in the time interval during which the light pulse

makes its round trip. From the definition of angular speed, that time interval is

$$\Delta t = \frac{\Delta\theta}{\omega} = \frac{(1/720)\text{ rev}}{27.5\text{ rev/s}} = 5.05 \times 10^{-5}\text{ s}$$

Hence, the speed of light calculated from this data is

$$c = \frac{2d}{\Delta t} = \frac{2(7\,500\text{ m})}{5.05 \times 10^{-5}\text{ s}} = \boxed{2.97 \times 10^8\text{ m/s}}$$

35.3 The Ray Approximation in Geometric Optics

The field of **geometric optics** involves the study of the propagation of light, with the assumption that light travels in a fixed direction in a straight line as it passes through a uniform medium and changes its direction when it meets the surface of a different medium or if the optical properties of the medium are nonuniform in either space or time. As we study geometric optics here and in Chapter 36, we use what is called the **ray approximation.** To understand this approximation, first note that the rays of a given wave are straight lines perpendicular to the wave fronts as illustrated in Figure 35.3 for a plane wave. In the ray approximation, we assume that a wave moving through a medium travels in a straight line in the direction of its rays.

If the wave meets a barrier in which there is a circular opening whose diameter is much larger than the wavelength, as in Figure 35.4a, the wave emerging from the opening continues to move in a straight line (apart from some small edge effects); hence, the ray approximation is valid. If the diameter of the opening is on the order of the wavelength, as in Figure 35.4b, the waves spread out from the opening in all directions. This effect is called *diffraction* and will be studied in Chapter 37. Finally, if the opening is much smaller than the wavelength, the opening can be approximated as a point source of waves (Fig. 35.4c). Similar effects are seen when waves encounter an opaque object of dimension d. In this case, when $\lambda \ll d$, the object casts a sharp shadow.

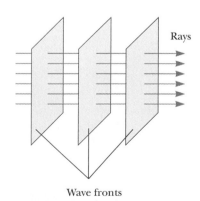

Figure 35.3 A plane wave propagating to the right. Note that the rays, which always point in the direction of the wave propagation, are straight lines perpendicular to the wave fronts.

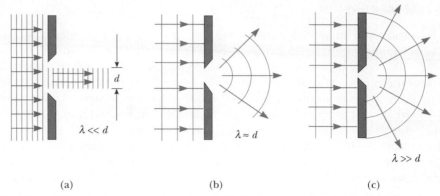

(a)   (b)   (c)

*At the Active Figures link
at* http://www.pse6.com, *you
can adjust the size of the
opening and observe the effect
on the waves passing through.*

Active Figure 35.4 A plane wave of wavelength λ is incident on a barrier in which there is an opening of diameter d. (a) When $\lambda \ll d$, the rays continue in a straight-line path, and the ray approximation remains valid. (b) When $\lambda \approx d$, the rays spread out after passing through the opening. (c) When $\lambda \gg d$, the opening behaves as a point source emitting spherical waves.

The ray approximation and the assumption that $\lambda \ll d$ are used in this chapter and in Chapter 36, both of which deal with geometric optics. This approximation is very good for the study of mirrors, lenses, prisms, and associated optical instruments, such as telescopes, cameras, and eyeglasses.

35.4 Reflection

When a light ray traveling in one medium encounters a boundary with another medium, part of the incident light is reflected. Figure 35.5a shows several rays of a beam of light incident on a smooth, mirror-like, reflecting surface. The reflected rays are parallel to each other, as indicated in the figure. The direction of a reflected ray is in the plane perpendicular to the reflecting surface that contains the

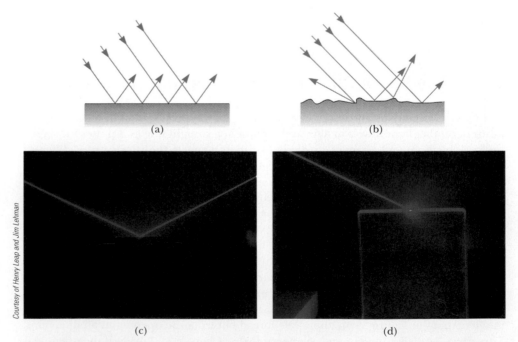

Courtesy of Henry Leap and Jim Lehman

Figure 35.5 Schematic representation of (a) specular reflection, where the reflected rays are all parallel to each other, and (b) diffuse reflection, where the reflected rays travel in random directions. (c) and (d) Photographs of specular and diffuse reflection using laser light.

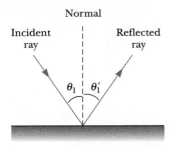

Active Figure 35.6 According to the law of reflection, $\theta_1' = \theta_1$. The incident ray, the reflected ray, and the normal all lie in the same plane.

At the Active Figures link at http://www.pse6.com, vary the incident angle and see the effect on the reflected ray.

incident ray. Reflection of light from such a smooth surface is called **specular reflection.** If the reflecting surface is rough, as shown in Figure 35.5b, the surface reflects the rays not as a parallel set but in various directions. Reflection from any rough surface is known as **diffuse reflection.** A surface behaves as a smooth surface as long as the surface variations are much smaller than the wavelength of the incident light.

The difference between these two kinds of reflection explains why it is more difficult to see while driving on a rainy night. If the road is wet, the smooth surface of the water specularly reflects most of your headlight beams away from your car (and perhaps into the eyes of oncoming drivers). When the road is dry, its rough surface diffusely reflects part of your headlight beam back toward you, allowing you to see the highway more clearly. In this book, we concern ourselves only with specular reflection and use the term *reflection* to mean specular reflection.

Consider a light ray traveling in air and incident at an angle on a flat, smooth surface, as shown in Figure 35.6. The incident and reflected rays make angles θ_1 and θ_1', respectively, where the angles are measured between the normal and the rays. (The normal is a line drawn perpendicular to the surface at the point where the incident ray strikes the surface.) Experiments and theory show that **the angle of reflection equals the angle of incidence:**

$$\theta_1' = \theta_1 \tag{35.2}$$

This relationship is called the **law of reflection.**

> ⚠️ **PITFALL PREVENTION**
>
> **35.1 Subscript Notation**
>
> We use the subscript 1 to refer to parameters for the light in the initial medium. When light travels from one medium to another, we use the subscript 2 for the parameters associated with the light in the new medium. In the current discussion, the light stays in the same medium, so we only have to use the subscript 1.

Law of reflection

Quick Quiz 35.1 In the movies, you sometimes see an actor looking in a mirror and you can see his face in the mirror. During the filming of this scene, what does the actor see in the mirror? (a) his face (b) your face (c) the director's face (d) the movie camera (e) impossible to determine

---

Example 35.2 The Double-Reflected Light Ray   Interactive

Two mirrors make an angle of 120° with each other, as illustrated in Figure 35.7a. A ray is incident on mirror M_1 at an angle of 65° to the normal. Find the direction of the ray after it is reflected from mirror M_2.

Solution Figure 35.7a helps conceptualize this situation. The incoming ray reflects from the first mirror, and the reflected ray is directed toward the second mirror. Thus, there is a second reflection from this latter mirror. Because the interactions with both mirrors are simple reflections, we categorize this problem as one that will require the law of reflection and some geometry. To analyze the problem, note that from the

law of reflection, we know that the first reflected ray makes an angle of 65° with the normal. Thus, this ray makes an angle of $90° - 65° = 25°$ with the horizontal.

From the triangle made by the first reflected ray and the two mirrors, we see that the first reflected ray makes an angle of 35° with M_2 (because the sum of the interior angles of any triangle is 180°). Therefore, this ray makes an angle of 55° with the normal to M_2. From the law of reflection, the second reflected ray makes an angle of 55° with the normal to M_2.

To finalize the problem, let us explore variations in the angle between the mirrors as follows.

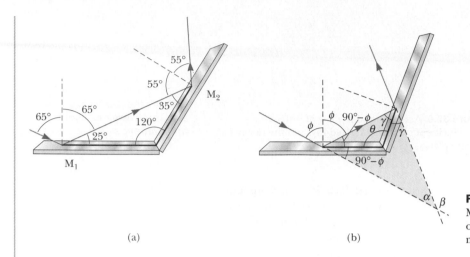

(a)   (b)

Figure 35.7 (Example 35.2) (a) Mirrors M_1 and M_2 make an angle of 120° with each other. (b) The geometry for an arbitrary mirror angle.

What If? If the incoming and outgoing rays in Figure 35.7a are extended behind the mirror, they cross at an angle of 60°, so that the overall change in direction of the light ray is 120°. This is the same as the angle between the mirrors. What if the angle between the mirrors is changed? Is the overall change in the direction of the light ray always equal to the angle between the mirrors?

Answer Making a general statement based on one data point is always a dangerous practice! Let us investigate the change in direction for a general situation. Figure 35.7b shows the mirrors at an arbitrary angle θ and the incoming light ray striking the mirror at an arbitrary angle ϕ with respect to the normal to the mirror surface. In accordance with the law of reflection and the sum of the interior angles of a triangle, the angle γ is $180° - (90° - \phi) - \theta = 90° + \phi - \theta$. Considering the triangle highlighted in blue

in Figure 35.7b, we see that

$$\alpha + 2\gamma + 2(90° - \phi) = 180°$$

$$\alpha = 2(\phi - \gamma)$$

The change in direction of the light ray is angle β, which is $180° - \alpha$:

$$\beta = 180° - \alpha = 180° - 2(\phi - \gamma)$$
$$= 180° - 2[\phi - (90° + \phi - \theta)]$$
$$= 360° - 2\theta$$

Notice that β is not equal to θ. For $\theta = 120°$, we obtain $\beta = 120°$, which happens to be the same as the mirror angle. But this is true only for this special angle between the mirrors. For example, if $\theta = 90°$, we obtain $\beta = 180°$. In this case, the light is reflected straight back to its origin.

Investigate this reflection situation for various mirror angles at the Interactive Worked Example link at **http://www.pse6.com.**

As discussed in the **What If?** section of the preceding example, if the angle between two mirrors is 90°, the reflected beam returns to the source parallel to its original path. This phenomenon, called *retroreflection*, has many practical applications. If a third mirror is placed perpendicular to the first two, so that the three form the corner of a cube, retroreflection works in three dimensions. In 1969, a panel of many small reflectors was placed on the Moon by the *Apollo 11* astronauts (Fig. 35.8a). A laser beam from the Earth is reflected directly back on itself and its transit time is measured. This information is used to determine the distance to the Moon with an uncertainty of 15 cm. (Imagine how difficult it would be to align a regular flat mirror so that the reflected laser beam would hit a particular location on the Earth!) A more everyday application is found in automobile taillights. Part of the plastic making up the taillight is formed into many tiny cube corners (Fig. 35.8b) so that headlight beams from cars approaching from the rear are reflected back to the drivers. Instead of cube corners, small spherical bumps are sometimes used (Fig. 35.8c). Tiny clear spheres are used in a coating material found on many road signs. Due to retroreflection from these spheres, the stop sign in Figure 35.8d appears much brighter than it would if it were simply a flat, shiny surface reflecting most of the light hitting it away from the highway.

Another practical application of the law of reflection is the digital projection of movies, television shows, and computer presentations. A digital projector makes use

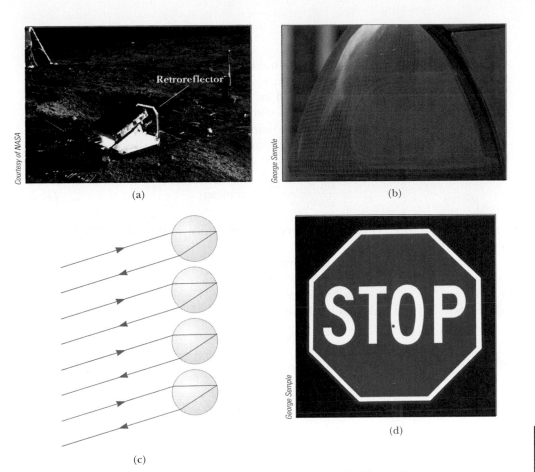

(a)

(b)

(c)

(d)

Figure 35.8 Applications of retroreflection. (a) This panel on the Moon reflects a laser beam directly back to its source on the Earth. (b) An automobile taillight has small retroreflectors that ensure that headlight beams are reflected back toward the car that sent them. (c) A light ray hitting a transparent sphere at the proper position is retroreflected. (d) This stop sign appears to glow in headlight beams because its surface is covered with a layer of many tiny retroreflecting spheres. What would you see if the sign had a mirror-like surface?

of an optical semiconductor chip called a *digital micromirror device.* This device contains an array of over one million tiny mirrors (Fig. 35.9a) that can be individually tilted by means of signals to an address electrode underneath the edge of the mirror. Each mirror corresponds to a pixel in the projected image. When the pixel corresponding to a given mirror is to be bright, the mirror is in the "on" position—oriented so as to reflect light from a source illuminating the array to the screen (Fig. 35.9b). When the pixel for this mirror is to be dark, the mirror is "off"—tilted so that the light is reflected away from the screen. The brightness of the pixel is determined by the total time interval during which the mirror is in the "on" position during the display of one image.

Digital movie projectors use three micromirror devices, one for each of the primary colors red, blue, and green, so that movies can be displayed with up to 35 trillion colors. Because information is stored as binary data, a digital movie does not degrade with time as does film. Furthermore, because the movie is entirely in the form of computer software, it can be delivered to theaters by means of satellites, optical discs, or optical fiber networks.

Several movies have been projected digitally to audiences and polls show that 85 percent of the viewers describe the image quality as "excellent." The first all-digital movie, from cinematography to post-production to projection, was *Star Wars Episode II: Attack of the Clones* in 2002.

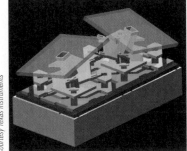

(a)

(b)

Figure 35.9 (a) An array of mirrors on the surface of a digital micromirror device. Each mirror has an area of about 16 μm^2. To provide a sense of scale, the leg of an ant appears in the photograph. (b) A close-up view of two single micromirrors. The mirror on the left is "on" and the one on the right is "off."

35.5   Refraction

When a ray of light traveling through a transparent medium encounters a boundary leading into another transparent medium, as shown in Figure 35.10, part of the energy is reflected and part enters the second medium. The ray that enters the second medium is bent at the boundary and is said to be **refracted.** The incident ray, the reflected ray, and the refracted ray all lie in the same plane. The **angle of refraction,** θ_2 in Figure 35.10a, depends on the properties of the two media and on the angle of incidence through the relationship

$$\frac{\sin \theta_2}{\sin \theta_1} = \frac{v_2}{v_1} = \text{constant} \tag{35.3}$$

where v_1 is the speed of light in the first medium and v_2 is the speed of light in the second medium.

The path of a light ray through a refracting surface is reversible. For example, the ray shown in Figure 35.10a travels from point A to point B. If the ray originated at B, it would travel to the left along line BA to reach point A, and the reflected part would point downward and to the left in the glass.

Quick Quiz 35.2   If beam ① is the incoming beam in Figure 35.10b, which of the other four red lines are reflected beams and which are refracted beams?

From Equation 35.3, we can infer that when light moves from a material in which its speed is high to a material in which its speed is lower, as shown in Figure 35.11a, the angle of refraction θ_2 is less than the angle of incidence θ_1, and the ray is bent *toward* the normal. If the ray moves from a material in which light moves slowly to a material in which it moves more rapidly, as illustrated in Figure 35.11b, θ_2 is greater than θ_1, and the ray is bent *away* from the normal.

The behavior of light as it passes from air into another substance and then re-emerges into air is often a source of confusion to students. When light travels in air,

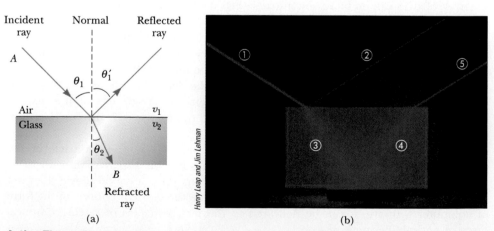

(a)   (b)

Active Figure 35.10 (a) A ray obliquely incident on an air–glass interface. The refracted ray is bent toward the normal because $v_2 < v_1$. All rays and the normal lie in the same plane. (b) Light incident on the Lucite block bends both when it enters the block and when it leaves the block.

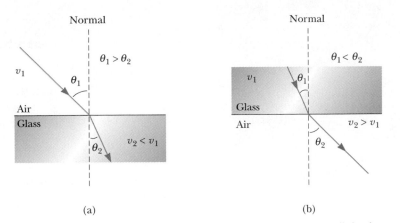

(a)   (b)

Active Figure 35.11 (a) When the light beam moves from air into glass, the light slows down on entering the glass and its path is bent toward the normal. (b) When the beam moves from glass into air, the light speeds up on entering the air and its path is bent away from the normal.

At the Active Figures link at http://www.pse6.com, *light passes through three layers of material. You can vary the incident angle and see the effect on the refracted rays for a variety of values of the index of refraction (page 1104) of the three materials.*

its speed is 3.00×10^8 m/s, but this speed is reduced to approximately 2×10^8 m/s when the light enters a block of glass. When the light re-emerges into air, its speed instantaneously increases to its original value of 3.00×10^8 m/s. This is far different from what happens, for example, when a bullet is fired through a block of wood. In this case, the speed of the bullet is reduced as it moves through the wood because some of its original energy is used to tear apart the wood fibers. When the bullet enters the air once again, it emerges at the speed it had just before leaving the block of wood.

To see why light behaves as it does, consider Figure 35.12, which represents a beam of light entering a piece of glass from the left. Once inside the glass, the light may encounter an electron bound to an atom, indicated as point A. Let us assume that light is absorbed by the atom; this causes the electron to oscillate (a detail represented by the double-headed vertical arrows). The oscillating electron then acts as an antenna and radiates the beam of light toward an atom at B, where the light is again absorbed. The details of these absorptions and radiations are best explained in terms of quantum mechanics (Chapter 42). For now, it is sufficient to think of light passing from one atom to another through the glass. Although light travels from one glass atom to another at 3.00×10^8 m/s, the absorption and radiation that take place cause the *average* light speed through the material to fall to about 2×10^8 m/s. Once the light emerges into the air, absorption and radiation cease and the speed of the light returns to the original value.

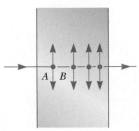

Figure 35.12 Light passing from one atom to another in a medium. The dots are electrons, and the vertical arrows represent their oscillations.

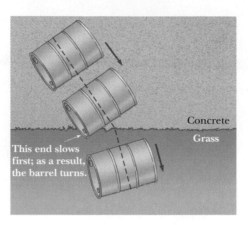

Figure 35.13 Overhead view of a barrel rolling from concrete onto grass.

▲ **PITFALL PREVENTION**

35.2 *n* Is Not an Integer Here

We have seen *n* used several times as an integer, such as in Chapter 18 to indicate the standing wave mode on a string or in an air column. The index of refraction *n* is *not* an integer.

Index of refraction

A mechanical analog of refraction is shown in Figure 35.13. When the left end of the rolling barrel reaches the grass, it slows down, while the right end remains on the concrete and moves at its original speed. This difference in speeds causes the barrel to pivot, and this changes the direction of travel.

Index of Refraction

In general, the speed of light in any material is *less* than its speed in vacuum. In fact, *light travels at its maximum speed in vacuum*. It is convenient to define the **index of refraction** *n* of a medium to be the ratio

$$n \equiv \frac{\text{speed of light in vacuum}}{\text{speed of light in a medium}} = \frac{c}{v} \tag{35.4}$$

From this definition, we see that the index of refraction is a dimensionless number greater than unity because v is always less than c. Furthermore, n is equal to unity for vacuum. The indices of refraction for various substances are listed in Table 35.1.

As light travels from one medium to another, its frequency does not change but its wavelength does. To see why this is so, consider Figure 35.14. Waves pass an observer at point A in medium 1 with a certain frequency and are

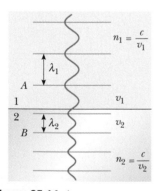

Figure 35.14 As a wave moves from medium 1 to medium 2, its wavelength changes but its frequency remains constant.

Table 35.1

Indices of Refraction[a]			
Substance	**Index of Refraction**	**Substance**	**Index of Refraction**
Solids at 20°C		*Liquids at 20°C*	
Cubic zirconia	2.20	Benzene	1.501
Diamond (C)	2.419	Carbon disulfide	1.628
Fluorite (CaF_2)	1.434	Carbon tetrachloride	1.461
Fused quartz (SiO_2)	1.458	Ethyl alcohol	1.361
Gallium phosphide	3.50	Glycerin	1.473
Glass, crown	1.52	Water	1.333
Glass, flint	1.66		
Ice (H_2O)	1.309	*Gases at 0°C, 1 atm*	
Polystyrene	1.49	Air	1.000 293
Sodium chloride (NaCl)	1.544	Carbon dioxide	1.000 45

[a] All values are for light having a wavelength of 589 nm in vacuum.

incident on the boundary between medium 1 and medium 2. The frequency with which the waves pass an observer at point B in medium 2 must equal the frequency at which they pass point A. If this were not the case, then energy would be piling up at the boundary. Because there is no mechanism for this to occur, the frequency must be a constant as a light ray passes from one medium into another. Therefore, because the relationship $v = f\lambda$ (Eq. 16.12) must be valid in both media and because $f_1 = f_2 = f$, we see that

$$v_1 = f\lambda_1 \qquad \text{and} \qquad v_2 = f\lambda_2 \qquad (35.5)$$

Because $v_1 \neq v_2$, it follows that $\lambda_1 \neq \lambda_2$.

We can obtain a relationship between index of refraction and wavelength by dividing the first Equation 35.5 by the second and then using Equation 35.4:

$$\frac{\lambda_1}{\lambda_2} = \frac{v_1}{v_2} = \frac{c/n_1}{c/n_2} = \frac{n_2}{n_1} \qquad (35.6)$$

This gives

$$\lambda_1 n_1 = \lambda_2 n_2$$

If medium 1 is vacuum, or for all practical purposes air, then $n_1 = 1$. Hence, it follows from Equation 35.6 that the index of refraction of any medium can be expressed as the ratio

$$n = \frac{\lambda}{\lambda_n} \qquad (35.7)$$

where λ is the wavelength of light in vacuum and λ_n is the wavelength of light in the medium whose index of refraction is n. From Equation 35.7, we see that because $n > 1$, $\lambda_n < \lambda$.

We are now in a position to express Equation 35.3 in an alternative form. If we replace the v_2/v_1 term in Equation 35.3 with n_1/n_2 from Equation 35.6, we obtain

$$n_1 \sin \theta_1 = n_2 \sin \theta_2 \qquad (35.8)$$

The experimental discovery of this relationship is usually credited to Willebrord Snell (1591–1627) and is therefore known as **Snell's law of refraction.** We shall examine this equation further in Sections 35.6 and 35.9.

▲ **PITFALL PREVENTION**

35.3 An Inverse Relationship

The index of refraction is *inversely* proportional to the wave speed. As the wave speed v decreases, the index of refraction n increases. Thus, the higher the index of refraction of a material, the more it *slows down* light from its speed in vacuum. The more the light slows down, the more θ_2 differs from θ_1 in Equation 35.8.

Snell's law of refraction

Quick Quiz 35.3 Light passes from a material with index of refraction 1.3 into one with index of refraction 1.2. Compared to the incident ray, the refracted ray (a) bends toward the normal (b) is undeflected (c) bends away from the normal.

Quick Quiz 35.4 As light from the Sun enters the atmosphere, it refracts due to the small difference between the speeds of light in air and in vacuum. The *optical* length of the day is defined as the time interval between the instant when the top of the Sun is just visibly observed above the horizon to the instant at which the top of the Sun just disappears below the horizon. The *geometric* length of the day is defined as the time interval between the instant when a geometric straight line drawn from the observer to the top of the Sun just clears the horizon to the instant at which this line just dips below the horizon. Which is longer, (a) the optical length of a day, or (b) the geometric length of a day?

Example 35.3   An Index of Refraction Measurement

A beam of light of wavelength 550 nm traveling in air is incident on a slab of transparent material. The incident beam makes an angle of 40.0° with the normal, and the refracted beam makes an angle of 26.0° with the normal. Find the index of refraction of the material.

Solution Using Snell's law of refraction (Eq. 35.8) with these data, and taking $n_1 = 1.00$ for air, we have

$$n_1 \sin \theta_1 = n_2 \sin \theta_2$$

$$n_2 = \frac{n_1 \sin \theta_1}{\sin \theta_2} = (1.00) \frac{\sin 40.0°}{\sin 26.0°}$$

$$= \frac{0.643}{0.438} = \boxed{1.47}$$

From Table 35.1, we see that the material could be fused quartz.

Example 35.4   Angle of Refraction for Glass

A light ray of wavelength 589 nm traveling through air is incident on a smooth, flat slab of crown glass at an angle of 30.0° to the normal, as sketched in Figure 35.15. Find the angle of refraction.

Solution We rearrange Snell's law of refraction to obtain

$$\sin \theta_2 = \frac{n_1}{n_2} \sin \theta_1$$

From Table 35.1, we find that $n_1 = 1.00$ for air and $n_2 = 1.52$ for crown glass. Therefore,

$$\sin \theta_2 = \left(\frac{1.00}{1.52}\right) \sin 30.0° = 0.329$$

$$\theta_2 = \sin^{-1}(0.329) = \boxed{19.2°}$$

Because this is less than the incident angle of 30°, the refracted ray is bent toward the normal, as expected. Its

change in direction is called the *angle of deviation* and is given by $\delta = |\theta_1 - \theta_2| = 30.0° - 19.2° = 10.8°$.

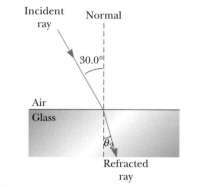

Figure 35.15 (Example 35.4) Refraction of light by glass.

Example 35.5   Laser Light in a Compact Disc

A laser in a compact disc player generates light that has a wavelength of 780 nm in air.

(A) Find the speed of this light once it enters the plastic of a compact disc ($n = 1.55$).

Solution We expect to find a value less than 3.00×10^8 m/s because $n > 1$. We can obtain the speed of light in the plastic by using Equation 35.4:

$$v = \frac{c}{n} = \frac{3.00 \times 10^8 \text{ m/s}}{1.55}$$

$$v = \boxed{1.94 \times 10^8 \text{ m/s}}$$

(B) What is the wavelength of this light in the plastic?

Solution We use Equation 35.7 to calculate the wavelength in plastic, noting that we are given the wavelength in air to be $\lambda = 780$ nm:

$$\lambda_n = \frac{\lambda}{n} = \frac{780 \text{ nm}}{1.55} = \boxed{503 \text{ nm}}$$

Example 35.6   Light Passing Through a Slab   Interactive

A light beam passes from medium 1 to medium 2, with the latter medium being a thick slab of material whose index of refraction is n_2 (Fig. 35.16a). Show that the emerging beam is parallel to the incident beam.

Solution First, let us apply Snell's law of refraction to the upper surface:

$$(1) \qquad \sin \theta_2 = \frac{n_1}{n_2} \sin \theta_1$$

Applying this law to the lower surface gives

$$(2) \qquad \sin \theta_3 = \frac{n_2}{n_1} \sin \theta_2$$

Substituting Equation (1) into Equation (2) gives

$$\sin \theta_3 = \frac{n_2}{n_1} \left(\frac{n_1}{n_2} \sin \theta_1\right) = \sin \theta_1$$

Therefore, $\theta_3 = \theta_1$, and the slab does not alter the direction of the beam. It does, however, offset the beam parallel to itself by the distance d shown in Figure 35.16a.

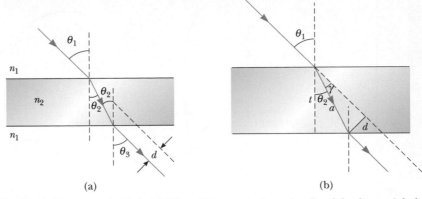

(a)   (b)

Figure 35.16 (Example 35.6) (a) When light passes through a flat slab of material, the emerging beam is parallel to the incident beam, and therefore $\theta_1 = \theta_3$. The dashed line drawn parallel to the ray coming out the bottom of the slab represents the path the light would take if the slab were not there. (b) A magnification of the area of the light path inside the slab.

What If? What if the thickness t of the slab is doubled? Does the offset distance d also double?

Answer Consider the magnification of the area of the light path within the slab in Figure 35.16b. The distance a is the hypotenuse of two right triangles. From the gold triangle, we see

$$a = \frac{t}{\cos \theta_2}$$

and from the blue triangle,

$$d = a \sin \gamma = a \sin(\theta_1 - \theta_2)$$

Combining these equations, we have

$$d = \frac{t}{\cos \theta_2} \sin(\theta_1 - \theta_2)$$

For a given incident angle θ_1, the refracted angle θ_2 is determined solely by the index of refraction, so the offset distance d is proportional to t. If the thickness doubles, so does the offset distance.

 *Explore refraction through slabs of various thicknesses at the Interactive Worked Example link at* **http://www.pse6.com.**

35.6 Huygens's Principle

In this section, we develop the laws of reflection and refraction by using a geometric method proposed by Huygens in 1678. **Huygens's principle** is a geometric construction for using knowledge of an earlier wave front to determine the position of a new wave front at some instant. In Huygens's construction,

all points on a given wave front are taken as point sources for the production of spherical secondary waves, called wavelets, which propagate outward through a medium with speeds characteristic of waves in that medium. After some time interval has passed, the new position of the wave front is the surface tangent to the wavelets.

▲ **PITFALL PREVENTION**

35.4 Of What Use Is Huygens's Principle?

At this point, the importance of Huygens's principle may not be evident. Predicting the position of a future wave front may not seem to be very critical. However, we will use Huygens's principle in later chapters to explain additional wave phenomena for light.

First, consider a plane wave moving through free space, as shown in Figure 35.17a. At $t = 0$, the wave front is indicated by the plane labeled AA'. In Huygens's construction, each point on this wave front is considered a point source. For clarity, only three points on AA' are shown. With these points as sources for the wavelets, we draw circles, each of radius $c\,\Delta t$, where c is the speed of light in vacuum and Δt is some time interval during which the wave propagates. The surface drawn tangent to these wavelets is the plane BB', which is the wave front at a later time, and is parallel to AA'. In a similar manner, Figure 35.17b shows Huygens's construction for a spherical wave.

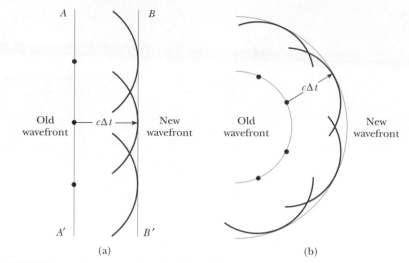

Figure 35.17 Huygens's construction for (a) a plane wave propagating to the right and (b) a spherical wave propagating to the right.

Huygens's Principle Applied to Reflection and Refraction

The laws of reflection and refraction were stated earlier in this chapter without proof. We now derive these laws, using Huygens's principle.

For the law of reflection, refer to Figure 35.18a. The line AB represents a wave front of the incident light just as ray 1 strikes the surface. At this instant, the wave at A sends out a Huygens wavelet (the circular arc centered on A) toward D. At the same time, the wave at B emits a Huygens wavelet (the circular arc centered on B) toward C. Figure 35.18a shows these wavelets after a time interval Δt, after which ray 2 strikes the surface. Because both rays 1 and 2 move with the same speed, we must have $AD = BC = c\,\Delta t$.

The remainder of our analysis depends on geometry, as summarized in Figure 35.18b, in which we isolate the triangles ABC and ADC. Note that these two triangles are congruent because they have the same hypotenuse AC and because $AD = BC$. From Figure 35.18b, we have

$$\cos \gamma = \frac{BC}{AC} \qquad \text{and} \qquad \cos \gamma' = \frac{AD}{AC}$$

where, comparing Figures 35.18a and 35.18b, we see that $\gamma = 90° - \theta_1$ and $\gamma' = 90° - \theta_1'$. Because $AD = BC$, we have

$$\cos \gamma = \cos \gamma'$$

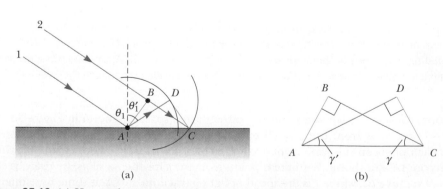

Figure 35.18 (a) Huygens's construction for proving the law of reflection. At the instant that ray 1 strikes the surface, it sends out a Huygens wavelet from A and ray 2 sends out a Huygens wavelet from B. We choose a radius of the wavelet to be $c\,\Delta t$, where Δt is the time interval for ray 2 to travel from B to C. (b) Triangle ADC is congruent to triangle ABC.

Therefore,

$$\gamma = \gamma'$$

$$90° - \theta_1 = 90° - \theta_1'$$

and

$$\theta_1 = \theta_1'$$

which is the law of reflection.

Now let us use Huygens's principle and Figure 35.19 to derive Snell's law of refraction. We focus our attention on the instant ray 1 strikes the surface and the subsequent time interval until ray 2 strikes the surface. During this time interval, the wave at A sends out a Huygens wavelet (the arc centered on A) toward D. In the same time interval, the wave at B sends out a Huygens wavelet (the arc centered on B) toward C. Because these two wavelets travel through different media, the radii of the wavelets are different. The radius of the wavelet from A is $AD = v_2 \Delta t$, where v_2 is the wave speed in the second medium. The radius of the wavelet from B is $BC = v_1 \Delta t$, where v_1 is the wave speed in the original medium.

From triangles ABC and ADC, we find that

$$\sin \theta_1 = \frac{BC}{AC} = \frac{v_1 \Delta t}{AC} \quad \text{and} \quad \sin \theta_2 = \frac{AD}{AC} = \frac{v_2 \Delta t}{AC}$$

If we divide the first equation by the second, we obtain

$$\frac{\sin \theta_1}{\sin \theta_2} = \frac{v_1}{v_2}$$

But from Equation 35.4 we know that $v_1 = c/n_1$ and $v_2 = c/n_2$. Therefore,

$$\frac{\sin \theta_1}{\sin \theta_2} = \frac{c/n_1}{c/n_2} = \frac{n_2}{n_1}$$

$$n_1 \sin \theta_1 = n_2 \sin \theta_2$$

which is Snell's law of refraction.

35.7 Dispersion and Prisms

An important property of the index of refraction n is that, for a given material, the index varies with the wavelength of the light passing through the material, as Figure 35.20 shows. This behavior is called **dispersion.** Because n is a function of wavelength, Snell's law of refraction indicates that light of different wavelengths is bent at different angles when incident on a refracting material.

As we see from Figure 35.20, the index of refraction generally decreases with increasing wavelength. This means that violet light bends more than red light does when passing into a refracting material. To understand the effects that dispersion can have on light, consider what happens when light strikes a prism, as shown in Figure 35.21. A ray of single-wavelength light incident on the prism from the left emerges refracted from its original direction of travel by an angle δ, called the **angle of deviation.**

Now suppose that a beam of *white light* (a combination of all visible wavelengths) is incident on a prism, as illustrated in Figure 35.22. The rays that emerge spread out in a series of colors known as the **visible spectrum.** These colors, in order of decreasing wavelength, are red, orange, yellow, green, blue, and violet. Clearly, the angle of deviation δ depends on wavelength. Violet light deviates the most, red the least, and the remaining colors in the visible spectrum fall between these extremes. Newton showed that each color has a particular angle of deviation and that the colors can be recombined to form the original white light.

The dispersion of light into a spectrum is demonstrated most vividly in nature by the formation of a rainbow, which is often seen by an observer positioned between the Sun

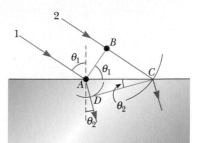

Figure 35.19 Huygens's construction for proving Snell's law of refraction. At the instant that ray 1 strikes the surface, it sends out a Huygens wavelet from A and ray 2 sends out a Huygens wavelet from B. The two wavelets have different radii because they travel in different media.

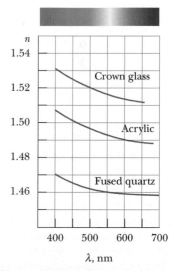

Figure 35.20 Variation of index of refraction with vacuum wavelength for three materials.

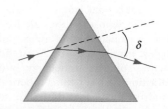

Figure 35.21 A prism refracts a single-wavelength light ray through an angle δ.

Figure 35.22 White light enters a glass prism at the upper left. A reflected beam of light comes out of the prism just below the incoming beam. The beam moving toward the lower right shows distinct colors. Different colors are refracted at different angles because the index of refraction of the glass depends on wavelength. Violet light deviates the most; red light deviates the least.

David Parker/Science Photo Library/Photo Researchers, Inc.

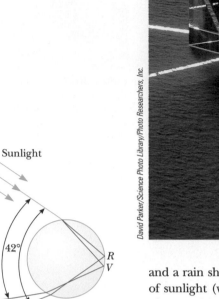

Active Figure 35.23 Path of sunlight through a spherical raindrop. Light following this path contributes to the visible rainbow.

At the Active Figures link at http://www.pse6.com, you can vary the point at which the sunlight enters the raindrop to verify that the angles shown are the maximum angles.

⚠ **PITFALL PREVENTION**

35.5 A Rainbow of Many Light Rays

Pictorial representations such as Figure 35.23 are subject to misinterpretation. The figure shows one ray of light entering the raindrop and undergoing reflection and refraction, exiting the raindrop in a range of 40° to 42° from the entering ray. This might be interpreted incorrectly as meaning that *all* light entering the raindrop exits in this small range of angles. In reality, light exits the raindrop over a much larger range of angles, from 0° to 42°. A careful analysis of the reflection and refraction from the spherical raindrop shows that the range of 40° to 42° is where the *highest-intensity light* exits the raindrop.

and a rain shower. To understand how a rainbow is formed, consider Figure 35.23. A ray of sunlight (which is white light) passing overhead strikes a drop of water in the atmosphere and is refracted and reflected as follows: It is first refracted at the front surface of the drop, with the violet light deviating the most and the red light the least. At the back surface of the drop, the light is reflected and returns to the front surface, where it again undergoes refraction as it moves from water into air. The rays leave the drop such that the angle between the incident white light and the most intense returning violet ray is 40° and the angle between the white light and the most intense returning red ray is 42°. This small angular difference between the returning rays causes us to see a colored bow.

Now suppose that an observer is viewing a rainbow, as shown in Figure 35.24. If a raindrop high in the sky is being observed, the most intense red light returning from the drop can reach the observer because it is deviated the most, but the most intense violet light passes over the observer because it is deviated the least. Hence, the observer sees this drop as being red. Similarly, a drop lower in the sky would direct the most intense violet light toward the observer and appears to be violet. (The most intense red light from this drop would pass below the eye of the observer and not be

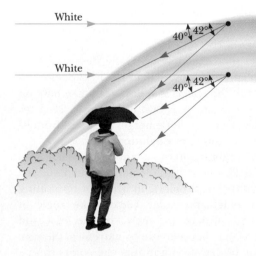

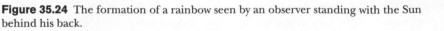

Figure 35.24 The formation of a rainbow seen by an observer standing with the Sun behind his back.

seen.) The most intense light from other colors of the spectrum would reach the observer from raindrops lying between these two extreme positions.

The opening photograph for this chapter shows a *double rainbow*. The secondary rainbow is fainter than the primary rainbow and the colors are reversed. The secondary rainbow arises from light that makes two reflections from the interior surface before exiting the raindrop. In the laboratory, rainbows have been observed in which the light makes over 30 reflections before exiting the water drop. Because each reflection involves some loss of light due to refraction out of the water drop, the intensity of these higher-order rainbows is small compared to the intensity of the primary rainbow.

> **Quick Quiz 35.5** Lenses in a camera use refraction to form an image on a film. Ideally, you want all the colors in the light from the object being photographed to be refracted by the same amount. Of the materials shown in Figure 35.20, which would you choose for a camera lens? (a) crown glass (b) acrylic (c) fused quartz (d) impossible to determine

Example 35.7   Measuring *n* Using a Prism

Although we do not prove it here, the minimum angle of deviation δ_{min} for a prism occurs when the angle of incidence θ_1 is such that the refracted ray inside the prism makes the same angle with the normal to the two prism faces,[1] as shown in Figure 35.25. Obtain an expression for the index of refraction of the prism material.

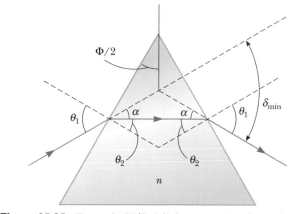

Figure 35.25 (Example 35.7) A light ray passing through a prism at the minimum angle of deviation δ_{min}.

Solution Using the geometry shown in Figure 35.25, we find that $\theta_2 = \Phi/2$, where Φ is the apex angle and

$$\theta_1 = \theta_2 + \alpha = \frac{\Phi}{2} + \frac{\delta_{min}}{2} = \frac{\Phi + \delta_{min}}{2}$$

From Snell's law of refraction, with $n_1 - 1$ because medium 1 is air, we have

$$\sin \theta_1 = n \sin \theta_2$$

$$\sin\left(\frac{\Phi + \delta_{min}}{2}\right) = n \sin(\Phi/2)$$

$$n = \frac{\sin\left(\dfrac{\Phi + \delta_{min}}{2}\right)}{\sin(\Phi/2)} \qquad (35.9)$$

Hence, knowing the apex angle Φ of the prism and measuring δ_{min}, we can calculate the index of refraction of the prism material. Furthermore, we can use a hollow prism to determine the values of n for various liquids filling the prism.

35.8 Total Internal Reflection

An interesting effect called **total internal reflection** can occur when light is directed from a medium having a given index of refraction toward one having a lower index of refraction. Consider a light beam traveling in medium 1 and meeting the boundary between medium 1 and medium 2, where n_1 is greater than n_2 (Fig. 35.26a). Various possible directions of the beam are indicated by rays 1 through 5. The refracted rays are bent away from the normal because n_1 is greater than n_2. At some particular angle of incidence θ_c, called the **critical angle,** the refracted light ray moves parallel to the boundary so that $\theta_2 = 90°$ (Fig. 35.26b).

---

[1]   The details of this proof are available in texts on optics.

Normal

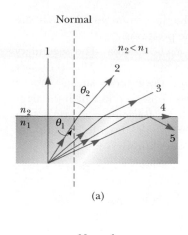

(a)

Normal

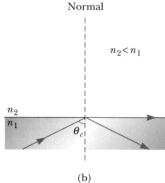

(b)

Active Figure 35.26 (a) Rays travel from a medium of index of refraction n_1 into a medium of index of refraction n_2, where $n_2 < n_1$. As the angle of incidence θ_1 increases, the angle of refraction θ_2 increases until θ_2 is 90° (ray 4). For even larger angles of incidence, total internal reflection occurs (ray 5). (b) The angle of incidence producing an angle of refraction equal to 90° is the critical angle θ_c. At this angle of incidence, all of the energy of the incident light is reflected.

At the Active Figures link at http://www.pse6.com, you can vary the incident angle and see the effect on the refracted ray and the distribution of incident energy between the reflected and refracted rays.

For angles of incidence greater than θ_c, the beam is entirely reflected at the boundary, as shown by ray 5 in Figure 35.26a. This ray is reflected at the boundary as it strikes the surface. This ray and all those like it obey the law of reflection; that is, for these rays, the angle of incidence equals the angle of reflection.

We can use Snell's law of refraction to find the critical angle. When $\theta_1 = \theta_c$, $\theta_2 = 90°$ and Equation 35.8 gives

$$n_1 \sin \theta_c = n_2 \sin 90° = n_2$$

Critical angle for total internal reflection

$$\sin \theta_c = \frac{n_2}{n_1} \qquad (\text{for } n_1 > n_2) \qquad (35.10)$$

This equation can be used only when n_1 is greater than n_2. That is, **total internal reflection occurs only when light is directed from a medium of a given index of refraction toward a medium of lower index of refraction.** If n_1 were less than n_2, Equation 35.10 would give $\sin \theta_c > 1$; this is a meaningless result because the sine of an angle can never be greater than unity.

The critical angle for total internal reflection is small when n_1 is considerably greater than n_2. For example, the critical angle for a diamond in air is 24°. Any ray inside the diamond that approaches the surface at an angle greater than this is completely reflected back into the crystal. This property, combined with proper faceting, causes diamonds to sparkle. The angles of the facets are cut so that light is "caught" inside the crystal through multiple internal reflections. These multiple reflections give the light a long path through the medium, and substantial dispersion of colors occurs. By the time the light exits through the top surface of the crystal, the rays associated with different colors have been fairly widely separated from one another.

Cubic zirconia also has a high index of refraction and can be made to sparkle very much like a genuine diamond. If a suspect jewel is immersed in corn syrup, the difference in *n* for the cubic zirconia and that for the syrup is small, and the critical angle is therefore great. This means that more rays escape sooner, and as a result the sparkle completely disappears. A real diamond does not lose all of its sparkle when placed in corn syrup.

Quick Quiz 35.6 In Figure 35.27, five light rays enter a glass prism from the left. How many of these rays undergo total internal reflection at the slanted surface of the prism? (a) 1 (b) 2 (c) 3 (d) 4 (e) 5.

Quick Quiz 35.7 Suppose that the prism in Figure 35.27 can be rotated in the plane of the paper. In order for *all five* rays to experience total internal reflection from the slanted surface, should the prism be rotated (a) clockwise or (b) counterclockwise?

Quick Quiz 35.8 A beam of white light is incident on a crown glass–air interface as shown in Figure 35.26a. The incoming beam is rotated clockwise, so that the incident angle θ increases. Because of dispersion in the glass, some colors of light experience total internal reflection (ray 4 in Figure 35.26a) before other colors, so that the beam refracting out of the glass is no longer white. The last color to refract out of the upper surface is (a) violet (b) green (c) red (d) impossible to determine.

Figure 35.27 (Quick Quiz 35.6 and 35.7) Five nonparallel light rays enter a glass prism from the left.

Example 35.8   A View from the Fish's Eye

Find the critical angle for an air–water boundary. (The index of refraction of water is 1.33.)

Solution We can use Figure 35.26 to solve this problem, with the air above the water having index of refraction n_2 and the water having index of refraction n_1. Applying Equation 35.10, we find that

$$\sin \theta_c = \frac{n_2}{n_1} = \frac{1}{1.33} = 0.752$$

$$\theta_c = \boxed{48.8°}$$

What If? What if a fish in a still pond looks upward toward the water's surface at different angles relative to the surface, as in Figure 35.28? What does it see?

Answer Because the path of a light ray is reversible, light traveling from medium 2 into medium 1 in Figure 35.26a follows the paths shown, but in the *opposite* direction. A fish looking upward toward the water surface, as in Figure 35.28, can see out of the water if it looks toward the surface at an angle less than the critical angle. Thus, for example, when the fish's line of vision makes an angle of 40° with the normal to the surface, light from above the water reaches the fish's eye. At 48.8°, the critical angle for water, the light has to skim along the water's surface before being refracted to the fish's eye; at this angle, the fish can in principle see the whole shore of the pond. At angles greater than the critical angle, the light reaching the fish comes by means of internal reflection at the surface. Thus, at 60°, the fish sees a reflection of the bottom of the pond.

Figure 35.28 (Example 35.8) **What If?** A fish looks upward toward the water surface.

(*Left*) Strands of glass optical fibers are used to carry voice, video, and data signals in telecommunication networks. (*Right*) A bundle of optical fibers is illuminated by a laser.

Figure 35.29 Light travels in a curved transparent rod by multiple internal reflections.

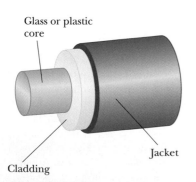

Glass or plastic core

Jacket

Cladding

Figure 35.30 The construction of an optical fiber. Light travels in the core, which is surrounded by a cladding and a protective jacket.

Optical Fibers

Another interesting application of total internal reflection is the use of glass or transparent plastic rods to "pipe" light from one place to another. As indicated in Figure 35.29, light is confined to traveling within a rod, even around curves, as the result of successive total internal reflections. Such a light pipe is flexible if thin fibers are used rather than thick rods. A flexible light pipe is called an **optical fiber.** If a bundle of parallel fibers is used to construct an optical transmission line, images can be transferred from one point to another. This technique is used in a sizable industry known as *fiber optics*.

A practical optical fiber consists of a transparent core surrounded by a *cladding*, a material that has a lower index of refraction than the core. The combination may be surrounded by a plastic *jacket* to prevent mechanical damage. Figure 35.30 shows a cutaway view of this construction. Because the index of refraction of the cladding is less than that of the core, light traveling in the core experiences total internal reflection if it arrives at the interface between the core and the cladding at an angle of incidence that exceeds the critical angle. In this case, light "bounces" along the core of the optical fiber, losing very little of its intensity as it travels.

Any loss in intensity in an optical fiber is due essentially to reflections from the two ends and absorption by the fiber material. Optical fiber devices are particularly useful for viewing an object at an inaccessible location. For example, physicians often use such devices to examine internal organs of the body or to perform surgery without making large incisions. Optical fiber cables are replacing copper wiring and coaxial cables for telecommunications because the fibers can carry a much greater volume of telephone calls or other forms of communication than electrical wires can.

35.9 Fermat's Principle

Pierre de Fermat (1601–1665) developed a general principle that can be used to determine the path that light follows as it travels from one point to another. **Fermat's principle** states that **when a light ray travels between any two points, its path is**

the one that requires the smallest time interval. An obvious consequence of this principle is that the paths of light rays traveling in a homogeneous medium are straight lines because a straight line is the shortest distance between two points.

Let us illustrate how Fermat's principle can be used to derive Snell's law of refraction. Suppose that a light ray is to travel from point P in medium 1 to point Q in medium 2 (Fig. 35.31), where P and Q are at perpendicular distances a and b, respectively, from the interface. The speed of light is c/n_1 in medium 1 and c/n_2 in medium 2. Using the geometry of Figure 35.31, and assuming that light leaves P at $t = 0$, we see that the time at which the ray arrives at Q is

$$t = \frac{r_1}{v_1} + \frac{r_2}{v_2} = \frac{\sqrt{a^2 + x^2}}{c/n_1} + \frac{\sqrt{b^2 + (d-x)^2}}{c/n_2} \qquad (35.11)$$

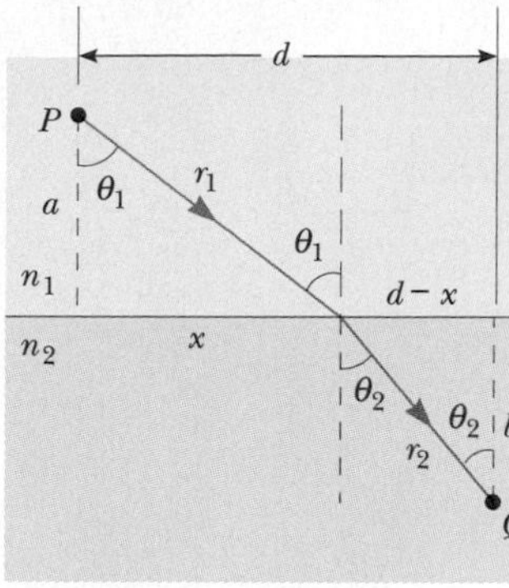

To obtain the value of x for which t has its minimum value, we take the derivative of t with respect to x and set the derivative equal to zero:

$$\frac{dt}{dx} = \frac{n_1}{c} \frac{d}{dx} \sqrt{a^2 + x^2} + \frac{n_2}{c} \frac{d}{dx} \sqrt{b^2 + (d-x)^2}$$

$$= \frac{n_1}{c} \left(\tfrac{1}{2}\right) \frac{2x}{(a^2 + x^2)^{1/2}} + \frac{n_2}{c} \left(\tfrac{1}{2}\right) \frac{2(d-x)(-1)}{[b^2 + (d-x)^2]^{1/2}}$$

$$= \frac{n_1 x}{c(a^2 + x^2)^{1/2}} - \frac{n_2(d-x)}{c[b^2 + (d-x)^2]^{1/2}} = 0$$

or

$$\frac{n_1 x}{(a^2 + x^2)^{1/2}} = \frac{n_2(d-x)}{[b^2 + (d-x)^2]^{1/2}} \qquad (35.12)$$

From Figure 35.31,

$$\sin \theta_1 = \frac{x}{(a^2 + x^2)^{1/2}} \qquad \sin \theta_2 = \frac{d-x}{[b^2 + (d-x)^2]^{1/2}}$$

Substituting these expressions into Equation 35.12, we find that

$$n_1 \sin \theta_1 = n_2 \sin \theta_2$$

which is Snell's law of refraction.

This situation is equivalent to the problem of deciding where a lifeguard who can run faster than he can swim should enter the water to help a swimmer in distress. If he enters the water too directly (in other words, at a very small value of θ_1 in Figure 35.31), the distance x is smaller than the value of x that gives the minimum value of the time interval needed for the guard to move from the starting point on the sand to the swimmer. As a result, he spends too little time running and too much time swimming. The guard's optimum location for entering the water so that he can reach the swimmer in the shortest time is at that interface point that gives the value of x that satisfies Equation 35.12.

It is a simple matter to use a similar procedure to derive the law of reflection (see Problem 65).

Figure 35.31 Geometry for deriving Snell's law of refraction using Fermat's principle.

SUMMARY

In geometric optics, we use the **ray approximation,** in which a wave travels through a uniform medium in straight lines in the direction of the rays.

The **law of reflection** states that for a light ray traveling in air and incident on a smooth surface, the angle of reflection θ_1' equals the angle of incidence θ_1:

$$\theta_1' = \theta_1 \qquad (35.2)$$

Take a practice test for this chapter by clicking on the Practice Test link at http://www.pse6.com.

Light crossing a boundary as it travels from medium 1 to medium 2 is **refracted,** or bent. The angle of refraction θ_2 is defined by the relationship

$$\frac{\sin \theta_2}{\sin \theta_1} = \frac{v_2}{v_1} = \text{constant} \tag{35.3}$$

The **index of refraction** n of a medium is defined by the ratio

$$n \equiv \frac{c}{v} \tag{35.4}$$

where c is the speed of light in a vacuum and v is the speed of light in the medium. In general, n varies with wavelength and is given by

$$n = \frac{\lambda}{\lambda_n} \tag{35.7}$$

where λ is the vacuum wavelength and λ_n is the wavelength in the medium. As light travels from one medium to another, its frequency remains the same.

Snell's law of refraction states that

$$n_1 \sin \theta_1 = n_2 \sin \theta_2 \tag{35.8}$$

where n_1 and n_2 are the indices of refraction in the two media. The incident ray, the reflected ray, the refracted ray, and the normal to the surface all lie in the same plane.

Total internal reflection occurs when light travels from a medium of high index of refraction to one of lower index of refraction. The **critical angle** θ_c for which total internal reflection occurs at an interface is given by

$$\sin \theta_c = \frac{n_2}{n_1} \qquad \text{(for } n_1 > n_2) \tag{35.10}$$

QUESTIONS

1. Light of wavelength λ is incident on a slit of width d. Under what conditions is the ray approximation valid? Under what circumstances does the slit produce enough diffraction to make the ray approximation invalid?

2. Why do astronomers looking at distant galaxies talk about looking backward in time?

3. A solar eclipse occurs when the Moon passes between the Earth and the Sun. Use a diagram to show why some areas of the Earth see a total eclipse, other areas see a partial eclipse, and most areas see no eclipse.

4. The display windows of some department stores are slanted slightly inward at the bottom. This is to decrease the glare from streetlights or the Sun, which would make it difficult for shoppers to see the display inside. Sketch a light ray reflecting from such a window to show how this technique works.

5. You take a child for walks around the neighborhood. She loves to listen to echoes from houses when she shouts or when you clap loudly. A house with a large flat front wall can produce an echo if you stand straight in front of it and reasonably far away. Draw a bird's-eye view of the situation to explain the production of the echo. Shade in the area where you can stand to hear the echo. **What If?** The child helps you to discover that a house with an L-shaped floor plan can produce echoes if you are standing in a wider range of locations. You can be standing at any reasonably distant location from which you can see the inside corner. Explain the echo in this case and draw another diagram for comparison. **What If?** What if the two wings of the house are not perpendicular? Will you and the child, standing close together, hear echoes? **What If?** What if a rectangular house and its garage have a breezeway between them, so that their perpendicular walls do not meet in an inside corner? Will this structure produce strong echoes for people in a wide range of locations? Explain your answers with diagrams.

6. The F-117A stealth fighter (Figure Q35.6) is specifically designed to be a *non*-retroreflector of radar. What aspects of its design help accomplish this? *Suggestion:* Answer the previous question as preparation for this one. Note that the bottom of the plane is flat and that all of the flat exterior panels meet at odd angles.

Figure Q35.6

7. Sound waves have much in common with light waves, including the properties of reflection and refraction. Give examples of these phenomena for sound waves.

8. Does a light ray traveling from one medium into another always bend toward the normal, as shown in Figure 35.10a? Explain.

9. As light travels from one medium to another, does the wavelength of the light change? Does the frequency change? Does the speed change? Explain.

10. A laser beam passing through a nonhomogeneous sugar solution follows a curved path. Explain.

11. A laser beam with vacuum wavelength 632.8 nm is incident from air onto a block of Lucite as shown in Figure 35.10b. The line of sight of the photograph is perpendicular to the plane in which the light moves. Find the speed, frequency, and wavelength of the light in the Lucite.

12. Suppose blue light were used instead of red light in the experiment shown in Figure 35.10b. Would the refracted beam be bent at a larger or smaller angle?

13. The level of water in a clear, colorless glass is easily observed with the naked eye. The level of liquid helium in a clear glass vessel is extremely difficult to see with the naked eye. Explain.

14. In Example 35.6 we saw that light entering a slab with parallel sides will emerge offset, but still parallel to the incoming beam. Our assumption was that the index of refraction of the material did not vary with wavelength. If the slab were made of crown glass (see Fig. 35.20), what would the outgoing beam look like?

15. Explain why a diamond sparkles more than a glass crystal of the same shape and size.

16. Explain why an oar partially in the water appears bent.

17. Total internal reflection is applied in the periscope of a submarine to let the user "see around corners." In this device, two prisms are arranged as shown in Figure Q35.17, so that an incident beam of light follows the path shown. Parallel tilted silvered mirrors could be used, but glass prisms with no silvered surfaces give higher light throughput. Propose a reason for the higher efficiency.

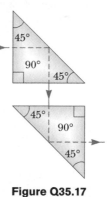

Figure Q35.17

18. Under certain circumstances, sound can be heard over extremely great distances. This frequently happens over a body of water, where the air near the water surface is cooler than the air higher up. Explain how the refraction of sound waves in such a situation could increase the distance over which the sound can be heard.

19. When two colors of light (X and Y) are sent through a glass prism, X is bent more than Y. Which color travels more slowly in the prism?

20. Retroreflection by transparent spheres, mentioned in Section 35.4 in the text, can be observed with dewdrops. To do so, look at the shadow of your head where it falls on dewy grass. Compare your observations to the reactions of two other people: The Renaissance artist Benvenuto Cellini described the phenomenon and his reaction in his *Autobiography,* at the end of Part One. The American philosopher Henry David Thoreau did the same in *Walden,* "Baker Farm," paragraph two. Try to find a person you know who has seen the halo—what did they think?

21. Why does the arc of a rainbow appear with red on top and violet on the bottom?

22. How is it possible that a complete circle of a rainbow can sometimes be seen from an airplane? With a stepladder, a lawn sprinkler, and a sunny day, how can you show the complete circle to children?

23. Is it possible to have total internal reflection for light incident from air on water? Explain.

24. Under what conditions is a mirage formed? On a hot day, what are we seeing when we observe "water on the road"?

PROBLEMS

1, 2, 3 = straightforward, intermediate, challenging ☐ = full solution available in the *Student Solutions Manual and Study Guide*

🌀 = coached solution with hints available at http://www.pse6.com 💻 = computer useful in solving problem

▨ = paired numerical and symbolic problems

Section 35.1 The Nature of Light
Section 35.2 Measurements of the Speed of Light

1. The *Apollo 11* astronauts set up a panel of efficient corner-cube retroreflectors on the Moon's surface. The speed of light can be found by measuring the time interval required for a laser beam to travel from Earth, reflect from the panel, and return to Earth. If this interval is measured to be 2.51 s, what is the measured speed of light? Take the center-to-center distance from Earth to Moon to be 3.84×10^8 m, and do not ignore the sizes of the Earth and Moon.

2. As a result of his observations, Roemer concluded that eclipses of Io by Jupiter were delayed by 22 min during a 6 month period as the Earth moved from the point in its orbit where it is closest to Jupiter to the diametrically opposite point where it is farthest from Jupiter. Using 1.50×10^8 km as the average radius of the Earth's orbit around the Sun, calculate the speed of light from these data.

3. In an experiment to measure the speed of light using the apparatus of Fizeau (see Fig. 35.2), the distance between light source and mirror was 11.45 km and the wheel had 720 notches. The experimentally determined value of c was 2.998×10^8 m/s. Calculate the minimum angular speed of the wheel for this experiment.

4. Figure P35.4 shows an apparatus used to measure the speed distribution of gas molecules. It consists of two slotted rotating disks separated by a distance d, with the slots displaced by the angle θ. Suppose the speed of light is measured by sending a light beam from the left through this apparatus. (a) Show that a light beam will be seen in the detector (that is, will make it through both slots) only if its speed is given by $c = \omega d / \theta$, where ω is the angular

speed of the disks and θ is measured in radians. (b) What is the measured speed of light if the distance between the two slotted rotating disks is 2.50 m, the slot in the second disk is displaced 1/60 of one degree from the slot in the first disk, and the disks are rotating at 5 555 rev/s?

Section 35.3 The Ray Approximation in Geometric Optics
Section 35.4 Reflection
Section 35.5 Refraction

> *Note:* You may look up indices of refraction in Table 35.1.

5. A dance hall is built without pillars and with a horizontal ceiling 7.20 m above the floor. A mirror is fastened flat against one section of the ceiling. Following an earthquake, the mirror is in place and unbroken. An engineer makes a quick check of whether the ceiling is sagging by directing a vertical beam of laser light up at the mirror and observing its reflection on the floor. (a) Show that if the mirror has rotated to make an angle ϕ with the horizontal, the normal to the mirror makes an angle ϕ with the vertical. (b) Show that the reflected laser light makes an angle 2ϕ with the vertical. (c) If the reflected laser light makes a spot on the floor 1.40 cm away from the point vertically below the laser, find the angle ϕ.

6. The two mirrors illustrated in Figure P35.6 meet at a right angle. The beam of light in the vertical plane P strikes mirror 1 as shown. (a) Determine the distance the

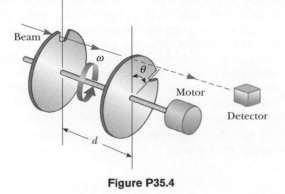

Figure P35.4

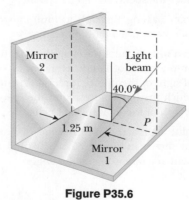

Figure P35.6

reflected light beam travels before striking mirror 2. (b) In what direction does the light beam travel after being reflected from mirror 2?

7. Two flat rectangular mirrors, both perpendicular to a horizontal sheet of paper, are set edge to edge with their reflecting surfaces perpendicular to each other. (a) A light ray in the plane of the paper strikes one of the mirrors at an arbitrary angle of incidence θ_1. Prove that the final direction of the ray, after reflection from both mirrors, is opposite to its initial direction. In a clothing store, such a pair of mirrors shows you an image of yourself as others see you, with no apparent right–left reversal. (b) **What If?** Now assume that the paper is replaced with a third flat mirror, touching edges with the other two and perpendicular to both. The set of three mirrors is called a *corner-cube reflector*. A ray of light is incident from any direction within the octant of space bounded by the reflecting surfaces. Argue that the ray will reflect once from each mirror and that its final direction will be opposite to its original direction. The *Apollo 11* astronauts placed a panel of corner cube retroreflectors on the Moon. Analysis of timing data taken with it reveals that the radius of the Moon's orbit is increasing at the rate of 3.8 cm/yr as it loses kinetic energy because of tidal friction.

8. How many times will the incident beam shown in Figure P35.8 be reflected by each of the parallel mirrors?

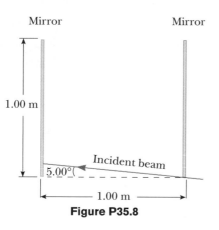

Figure P35.8

9. The distance of a lightbulb from a large plane mirror is twice the distance of a person from the plane mirror. Light from the bulb reaches the person by two paths. It travels to the mirror at an angle of incidence θ, and reflects from the mirror to the person. It also travels directly to the person without reflecting off the mirror. The total distance traveled by the light in the first case is twice the distance traveled by the light in the second case. Find the value of the angle θ.

10. A narrow beam of sodium yellow light, with wavelength 589 nm in vacuum, is incident from air onto a smooth water surface at an angle of incidence of 35.0°. Determine the angle of refraction and the wavelength of the light in water.

11. *Compare this problem with the preceding problem.* A plane sound wave in air at 20°C, with wavelength 589 mm, is incident

on a smooth surface of water at 25°C, at an angle of incidence of 3.50°. Determine the angle of refraction for the sound wave and the wavelength of the sound in water.

12. The wavelength of red helium–neon laser light in air is 632.8 nm. (a) What is its frequency? (b) What is its wavelength in glass that has an index of refraction of 1.50? (c) What is its speed in the glass?

13. An underwater scuba diver sees the Sun at an apparent angle of 45.0° above the horizon. What is the actual elevation angle of the Sun above the horizon?

14. A ray of light is incident on a flat surface of a block of crown glass that is surrounded by water. The angle of refraction is 19.6°. Find the angle of reflection.

15. A laser beam is incident at an angle of 30.0° from the vertical onto a solution of corn syrup in water. If the beam is refracted to 19.24° from the vertical, (a) what is the index of refraction of the syrup solution? Suppose the light is red, with vacuum wavelength 632.8 nm. Find its (b) wavelength, (c) frequency, and (d) speed in the solution.

16. Find the speed of light in (a) flint glass, (b) water, and (c) cubic zirconia.

17. A light ray initially in water enters a transparent substance at an angle of incidence of 37.0°, and the transmitted ray is refracted at an angle of 25.0°. Calculate the speed of light in the transparent substance.

18. An opaque cylindrical tank with an open top has a diameter of 3.00 m and is completely filled with water. When the afternoon Sun reaches an angle of 28.0° above the horizon, sunlight ceases to illuminate any part of the bottom of the tank. How deep is the tank?

19. A ray of light strikes a flat block of glass ($n = 1.50$) of thickness 2.00 cm at an angle of 30.0° with the normal. Trace the light beam through the glass, and find the angles of incidence and refraction at each surface.

20. Unpolarized light in vacuum is incident onto a sheet of glass with index of refraction n. The reflected and refracted rays are perpendicular to each other. Find the angle of incidence. This angle is called *Brewster's angle* or the *polarizing angle*. In this situation the reflected light is linearly polarized, with its electric field restricted to be perpendicular to the plane containing the rays and the normal.

21. When the light illustrated in Figure P35.21 passes through the glass block, it is shifted laterally by the distance d. Taking $n = 1.50$, find the value of d.

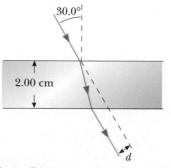

Figure P35.21 Problems 21 and 22.

22. Find the time interval required for the light to pass through the glass block described in the previous problem.

23. The light beam shown in Figure P35.23 makes an angle of 20.0° with the normal line NN' in the linseed oil. Determine the angles θ and θ'. (The index of refraction of linseed oil is 1.48.)

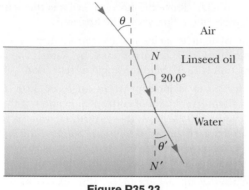

Figure P35.23

24. Three sheets of plastic have unknown indices of refraction. Sheet 1 is placed on top of sheet 2, and a laser beam is directed onto the sheets from above so that it strikes the interface at an angle of 26.5° with the normal. The refracted beam in sheet 2 makes an angle of 31.7° with the normal. The experiment is repeated with sheet 3 on top of sheet 2, and, with the same angle of incidence, the refracted beam makes an angle of 36.7° with the normal. If the experiment is repeated again with sheet 1 on top of sheet 3, what is the expected angle of refraction in sheet 3? Assume the same angle of incidence.

25. When you look through a window, by how much time is the light you see delayed by having to go through glass instead of air? Make an order-of-magnitude estimate on the basis of data you specify. By how many wavelengths is it delayed?

26. Light passes from air into flint glass. (a) What angle of incidence must the light have if the component of its velocity perpendicular to the interface is to remain constant? (b) **What If?** Can the component of velocity parallel to the interface remain constant during refraction?

27. The reflecting surfaces of two intersecting flat mirrors are at an angle θ ($0° < \theta < 90°$), as shown in Figure P35.27. For a light ray that strikes the horizontal mirror, show that the emerging ray will intersect the incident ray at an angle $\beta = 180° - 2\theta$.

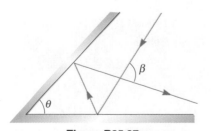

Figure P35.27

Section 35.6 Huygens's Principle

28. The speed of a water wave is described by $v = \sqrt{gd}$, where d is the water depth, assumed to be small compared to the wavelength. Because their speed changes, water waves refract when moving into a region of different depth. Sketch a map of an ocean beach on the eastern side of a landmass. Show contour lines of constant depth under water, assuming reasonably uniform slope. (a) Suppose that waves approach the coast from a storm far away to the north-northeast. Demonstrate that the waves will move nearly perpendicular to the shoreline when they reach the beach. (b) Sketch a map of a coastline with alternating bays and headlands, as suggested in Figure P35.28. Again make a reasonable guess about the shape of contour lines of constant depth. Suppose that waves approach the coast, carrying energy with uniform density along originally straight wavefronts. Show that the energy reaching the coast is concentrated at the headlands and has lower intensity in the bays.

Figure P35.28

Section 35.7 Dispersion and Prisms

Note: The apex angle of a prism is the angle between the surface at which light enters the prism and the second surface the light encounters.

29. A narrow white light beam is incident on a block of fused quartz at an angle of 30.0°. Find the angular width of the light beam inside the quartz.

30. Light of wavelength 700 nm is incident on the face of a fused quartz prism at an angle of 75.0° (with respect to the normal to the surface). The apex angle of the prism is 60.0°. Use the value of n from Figure 35.20 and calculate the angle (a) of refraction at this first surface, (b) of incidence at the second surface, (c) of refraction at the second surface, and (d) between the incident and emerging rays.

31. A prism that has an apex angle of 50.0° is made of cubic zirconia, with $n = 2.20$. What is its angle of minimum deviation?

32. A triangular glass prism with apex angle 60.0° has an index of refraction of 1.50. (a) Show that if its angle of incidence on the first surface is $\theta_1 = 48.6°$, light will pass symmetrically through the prism, as shown in

Figure 35.25. (b) Find the angle of deviation δ_{min} for $\theta_1 = 48.6°$. (c) **What If?** Find the angle of deviation if the angle of incidence on the first surface is 45.6°. (d) Find the angle of deviation if $\theta_1 = 51.6°$.

33. A triangular glass prism with apex angle $\Phi = 60.0°$ has an index of refraction $n = 1.50$ (Fig. P35.33). What is the smallest angle of incidence θ_1 for which a light ray can emerge from the other side?

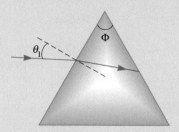

Figure P35.33 Problems 33 and 34.

34. A triangular glass prism with apex angle Φ has index of refraction n. (See Fig. P35.33.) What is the smallest angle of incidence θ_1 for which a light ray can emerge from the other side?

35. The index of refraction for violet light in silica flint glass is 1.66, and that for red light is 1.62. What is the angular dispersion of visible light passing through a prism of apex angle 60.0° if the angle of incidence is 50.0°? (See Fig. P35.35.)

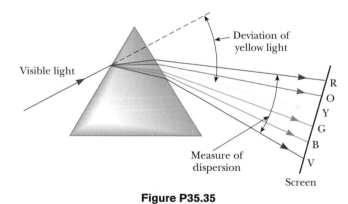

Figure P35.35

Section 35.8   Total Internal Reflection

36. For 589-nm light, calculate the critical angle for the following materials surrounded by air: (a) diamond, (b) flint glass, and (c) ice.

37. Repeat Problem 36 when the materials are surrounded by water.

38. Determine the maximum angle θ for which the light rays incident on the end of the pipe in Figure P35.38 are subject to total internal reflection along the walls of the pipe. Assume that the pipe has an index of refraction of 1.36 and the outside medium is air.

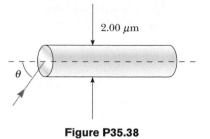

Figure P35.38

39. Consider a common mirage formed by super-heated air just above a roadway. A truck driver whose eyes are 2.00 m above the road, where $n = 1.000\ 3$, looks forward. She perceives the illusion of a patch of water ahead on the road, where her line of sight makes an angle of 1.20° below the horizontal. Find the index of refraction of the air just above the road surface. (*Suggestion:* Treat this as a problem in total internal reflection.)

40. An optical fiber has index of refraction n and diameter d. It is surrounded by air. Light is sent into the fiber along its axis, as shown in Figure P35.40. (a) Find the smallest outside radius R permitted for a bend in the fiber if no light is to escape. (b) **What If?** Does the result for part (a) predict reasonable behavior as d approaches zero? As n increases? As n approaches 1? (c) Evaluate R assuming the fiber diameter is 100 μm and its index of refraction is 1.40.

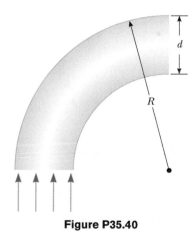

Figure P35.40

41. A large Lucite cube ($n = 1.59$) has a small air bubble (a defect in the casting process) below one surface. When a penny (diameter 1.90 cm) is placed directly over the bubble on the outside of the cube, the bubble cannot be seen by looking down into the cube at any angle. However, when a dime (diameter 1.75 cm) is placed directly over it, the bubble can be seen by looking down into the cube. What is the range of the possible depths of the air bubble beneath the surface?

42. A room contains air in which the speed of sound is 343 m/s. The walls of the room are made of concrete, in which the speed of sound is 1 850 m/s. (a) Find the critical angle for total internal reflection of sound at the concrete–air boundary. (b) In which medium must the sound be traveling in order to undergo total internal reflection? (c) "A bare concrete wall is a highly efficient mirror for sound." Give evidence for or against this statement.

43. In about 1965, engineers at the Toro Company invented a gasoline gauge for small engines, diagrammed in Figure P35.43. The gauge has no moving parts. It consists of a flat slab of transparent plastic fitting vertically into a slot in the cap on the gas tank. None of the plastic has a reflective coating. The plastic projects from the horizontal top down nearly to the bottom of the opaque tank. Its lower edge is cut with facets making angles of 45° with the horizontal. A lawnmower operator looks down from above and sees a boundary between bright and dark on the gauge. The location of the boundary, across the width of the plastic, indicates the quantity of gasoline in the tank. Explain how the gauge works. Explain the design requirements, if any, for the index of refraction of the plastic.

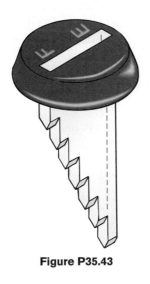

Figure P35.43

Section 35.9 Fermat's Principle

44. 🖥 The shoreline of a lake runs east and west. A swimmer gets into trouble 20.0 m out from shore and 26.0 m to the east of a lifeguard, whose station is 16.0 m in from the shoreline. The lifeguard takes negligible time to accelerate. He can run at 7.00 m/s and swim at 1.40 m/s. To reach the swimmer as quickly as possible, in what direction should the lifeguard start running? You will need to solve a transcendental equation numerically.

Additional Problems

45. Figure P35.45 shows a desk ornament globe containing a photograph. The flat photograph is in air, inside a vertical slot located behind a water-filled compartment having the shape of one half of a cylinder. Suppose you are looking at the center of the photograph and then rotate the globe about a vertical axis. You find that the center of the photograph disappears when you rotate the globe beyond a certain maximum angle (Fig. P35.45b). Account for this phenomenon and calculate the maximum angle. Briefly describe what you would see when you turn the globe beyond this angle.

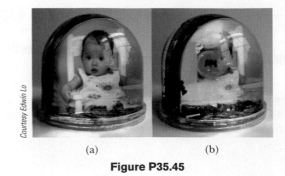

(a)   (b)

Figure P35.45

46. A light ray enters the atmosphere of a planet where it descends vertically to the surface a distance h below. The index of refraction where the light enters the atmosphere is 1.000, and it increases linearly to the surface where it has the value n. (a) How long does it take the ray to traverse this path? (b) Compare this to the time interval required in the absence of an atmosphere.

47. A narrow beam of light is incident from air onto the surface of glass with index of refraction 1.56. Find the angle of incidence for which the corresponding angle of refraction is half the angle of incidence. (*Suggestion:* You might want to use the trigonometric identity $\sin 2\theta = 2 \sin \theta \cos \theta$.)

48. 🖥 (a) Consider a horizontal interface between air above and glass of index 1.55 below. Draw a light ray incident from the air at angle of incidence 30.0°. Determine the angles of the reflected and refracted rays and show them on the diagram. (b) **What If?** Suppose instead that the light ray is incident from the glass at angle of incidence 30.0°. Determine the angles of the reflected and refracted rays and show all three rays on a new diagram. (c) For rays incident from the air onto the air–glass surface, determine and tabulate the angles of reflection and refraction for all the angles of incidence at 10.0° intervals from 0° to 90.0°. (d) Do the same for light rays coming up to the interface through the glass.

49. 🌐 A small underwater pool light is 1.00 m below the surface. The light emerging from the water forms a circle on the water surface. What is the diameter of this circle?

50. One technique for measuring the angle of a prism is shown in Figure P35.50. A parallel beam of light is directed on the angle so that parts of the beam reflect from opposite sides. Show that the angular separation of the two reflected beams is given by $B = 2A$.

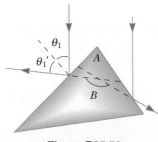

Figure P35.50

51. The walls of a prison cell are perpendicular to the four cardinal compass directions. On the first day of spring, light from the rising Sun enters a rectangular window in

the eastern wall. The light traverses 2.37 m horizontally to shine perpendicularly on the wall opposite the window. A young prisoner observes the patch of light moving across this western wall and for the first time forms his own understanding of the rotation of the Earth. (a) With what speed does the illuminated rectangle move? (b) The prisoner holds a small square mirror flat against the wall at one corner of the rectangle of light. The mirror reflects light back to a spot on the eastern wall close beside the window. How fast does the smaller square of light move across that wall? (c) Seen from a latitude of 40.0° north, the rising Sun moves through the sky along a line making a 50.0° angle with the southeastern horizon. In what direction does the rectangular patch of light on the western wall of the prisoner's cell move? (d) In what direction does the smaller square of light on the eastern wall move?

52. Figure P35.52 shows a top view of a square enclosure. The inner surfaces are plane mirrors. A ray of light enters a small hole in the center of one mirror. (a) At what angle θ must the ray enter in order to exit through the hole after being reflected once by each of the other three mirrors? (b) **What If?** Are there other values of θ for which the ray can exit after multiple reflections? If so, make a sketch of one of the ray's paths.

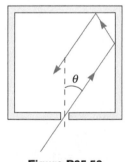

Figure P35.52

53. A hiker stands on an isolated mountain peak near sunset and observes a rainbow caused by water droplets in the air 8.00 km away. The valley is 2.00 km below the mountain peak and entirely flat. What fraction of the complete circular arc of the rainbow is visible to the hiker? (See Fig. 35.24.)

54. A 4.00-m-long pole stands vertically in a lake having a depth of 2.00 m. The Sun is 40.0° above the horizontal. Determine the length of the pole's shadow on the bottom of the lake. Take the index of refraction for water to be 1.33.

55. A laser beam strikes one end of a slab of material, as shown in Figure P35.55. The index of refraction of the slab is 1.48. Determine the number of internal reflections of the beam before it emerges from the opposite end of the slab.

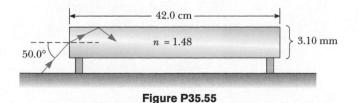

Figure P35.55

56. When light is incident normally on the interface between two transparent optical media, the intensity of the reflected light is given by the expression

$$S_1' = \left(\frac{n_2 - n_1}{n_2 + n_1}\right)^2 S_1$$

In this equation S_1 represents the average magnitude of the Poynting vector in the incident light (the incident intensity), S_1' is the reflected intensity, and n_1 and n_2 are the refractive indices of the two media. (a) What fraction of the incident intensity is reflected for 589-nm light normally incident on an interface between air and crown glass? (b) **What If?** Does it matter in part (a) whether the light is in the air or in the glass as it strikes the interface?

57. Refer to Problem 56 for its description of the reflected intensity of light normally incident on an interface between two transparent media. (a) When light is normally incident on an interface between vacuum and a transparent medium of index n, show that the intensity S_2 of the transmitted light is given by $S_2/S_1 = 4n/(n + 1)^2$. (b) Light travels perpendicularly through a diamond slab, surrounded by air, with parallel surfaces of entry and exit. Apply the transmission fraction in part (a) to find the approximate overall transmission through the slab of diamond, as a percentage. Ignore light reflected back and forth within the slab.

58. **What If?** This problem builds upon the results of Problems 56 and 57. Light travels perpendicularly through a diamond slab, surrounded by air, with parallel surfaces of entry and exit. The intensity of the transmitted light is what fraction of the incident intensity? Include the effects of light reflected back and forth inside the slab.

59. The light beam in Figure P35.59 strikes surface 2 at the critical angle. Determine the angle of incidence θ_1.

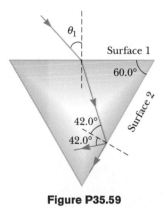

Figure P35.59

60. Builders use a leveling instrument with the beam from a fixed helium–neon laser reflecting in a horizontal plane from a small flat mirror mounted on an accurately vertical rotating shaft. The light is sufficiently bright and the rotation rate is sufficiently high that the reflected light appears as a horizontal line wherever it falls on a wall. (a) Assume the mirror is at the center of a circular grain elevator of radius R. The mirror spins with constant angular velocity ω_m. Find the speed of the spot of laser light on the wall. (b) **What If?** Assume the spinning mirror is at a perpendicular distance d from point O on a flat vertical wall. When the spot of laser light on the wall is at distance x from point O, what is its speed?

61. A light ray of wavelength 589 nm is incident at an angle θ on the top surface of a block of polystyrene, as shown in Figure P35.61. (a) Find the maximum value of θ for which the refracted ray undergoes total internal reflection at the left vertical face of the block. **What If?** Repeat the calculation for the case in which the polystyrene block is immersed in (b) water and (c) carbon disulfide.

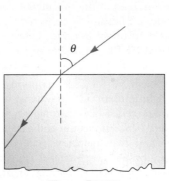

Figure P35.61

62. Refer to Quick Quiz 35.4. By how much does the duration of an optical day exceed that of a geometric day? Model the Earth's atmosphere as uniform, with index of refraction 1.000 293, a sharply defined upper surface, and depth 8 614 m. Assume that the observer is at the Earth's equator, so that the apparent path of the rising and setting Sun is perpendicular to the horizon.

63. A shallow glass dish is 4.00 cm wide at the bottom, as shown in Figure P35.63. When an observer's eye is placed as shown, the observer sees the edge of the bottom of the empty dish. When this dish is filled with water, the observer sees the center of the bottom of the dish. Find the height of the dish.

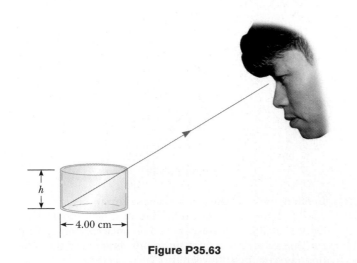

Figure P35.63

64. A ray of light passes from air into water. For its deviation angle $\delta = |\theta_1 - \theta_2|$ to be 10.0°, what must be its angle of incidence?

65. Derive the law of reflection (Eq. 35.2) from Fermat's principle. (See the procedure outlined in Section 35.9 for the derivation of the law of refraction from Fermat's principle.)

66. A material having an index of refraction n is surrounded by a vacuum and is in the shape of a quarter circle of radius R (Fig. P35.66). A light ray parallel to the base of the material is incident from the left at a distance L above the base and emerges from the material at the angle θ. Determine an expression for θ.

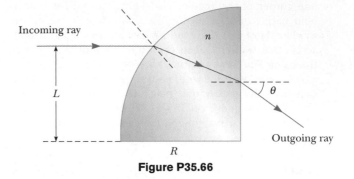

Figure P35.66

67. A transparent cylinder of radius $R = 2.00$ m has a mirrored surface on its right half, as shown in Figure P35.67. A light ray traveling in air is incident on the left side of the cylinder. The incident light ray and exiting light ray are parallel and $d = 2.00$ m. Determine the index of refraction of the material.

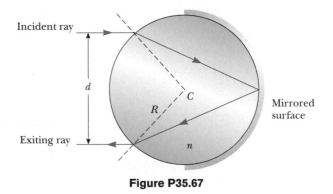

Figure P35.67

68. Suppose that a luminous sphere of radius R_1 (such as the Sun) is surrounded by a uniform atmosphere of radius R_2 and index of refraction n. When the sphere is viewed from a location far away in vacuum, what is its apparent radius? You will need to distinguish between the two cases (a) $R_2 > nR_1$ and (b) $R_2 < nR_1$.

69. A. H. Pfund's method for measuring the index of refraction of glass is illustrated in Figure P35.69. One face of a slab of thickness t is painted white, and a small hole scraped clear at point P serves as a source of diverging rays when the slab is

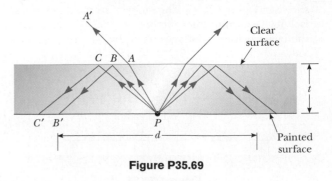

Figure P35.69

illuminated from below. Ray PBB' strikes the clear surface at the critical angle and is totally reflected, as are rays such as PCC'. Rays such as PAA' emerge from the clear surface. On the painted surface there appears a dark circle of diameter d, surrounded by an illuminated region, or halo. (a) Derive an equation for n in terms of the measured quantities d and t. (b) What is the diameter of the dark circle if $n = 1.52$ for a slab 0.600 cm thick? (c) If white light is used, the critical angle depends on color caused by dispersion. Is the inner edge of the white halo tinged with red light or violet light? Explain.

70. A light ray traveling in air is incident on one face of a right-angle prism of index of refraction $n = 1.50$ as shown in Figure P35.70, and the ray follows the path shown in the figure. Assuming $\theta = 60.0°$ and the base of the prism is mirrored, determine the angle ϕ made by the outgoing ray with the normal to the right face of the prism.

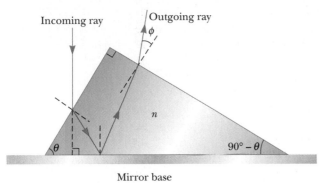

Figure P35.70

71. A light ray enters a rectangular block of plastic at an angle $\theta_1 = 45.0°$ and emerges at an angle $\theta_2 = 76.0°$, as shown in Figure P35.71. (a) Determine the index of refraction of the plastic. (b) If the light ray enters the plastic at a point $L = 50.0$ cm from the bottom edge, how long does it take the light ray to travel through the plastic?

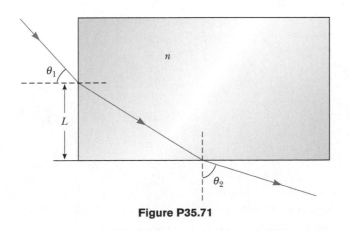

Figure P35.71

72. 💻 Students allow a narrow beam of laser light to strike a water surface. They arrange to measure the angle of refraction for selected angles of incidence and record the data shown in the accompanying table. Use the data to verify Snell's law of refraction by plotting the sine of the angle of incidence versus the sine of the angle of refraction. Use the resulting plot to deduce the index of refraction of water.

Angle of Incidence (degrees)	Angle of Refraction (degrees)
10.0	7.5
20.0	15.1
30.0	22.3
40.0	28.7
50.0	35.2
60.0	40.3
70.0	45.3
80.0	47.7

Answers to Quick Quizzes

35.1 (d). The light rays from the actor's face must reflect from the mirror and into the camera. If these light rays are reversed, light from the camera reflects from the mirror into the eyes of the actor.

35.2 Beams ② and ④ are reflected; beams ③ and ⑤ are refracted.

35.3 (c). Because the light is entering a material in which the index of refraction is lower, the speed of light is higher and the light bends away from the normal.

35.4 (a). Due to the refraction of light by air, light rays from the Sun deviate slightly downward toward the surface of the Earth as the light enters the atmosphere. Thus, in the morning, light rays from the upper edge of the Sun arrive at your eyes before the geometric line from your eyes to the top of the Sun clears the horizon. In the evening, light rays from the top of the Sun continue to arrive at your eyes even after the geometric line from your eyes to the top of the Sun dips below the horizon.

35.5 (c). An ideal camera lens would have an index of refraction that does not vary with wavelength so that all colors would be bent through the same angle by the lens. Of the three choices, fused quartz has the least variation in n across the visible spectrum.

35.6 (b). The two bright rays exiting the bottom of the prism on the right in Figure 35.27 result from total internal reflection at the right face of the prism. Notice that there is no refracted light exiting the slanted side for these rays. The light from the other three rays is divided into reflected and refracted parts.

35.7 (b). Counterclockwise rotation of the prism will cause the rays to strike the slanted side of the prism at a larger angle. When all five rays strike at an angle larger than the critical angle, they will all undergo total internal reflection.

35.8 (c). When the outgoing beam approaches the direction parallel to the straight side, the incident angle is approaching the critical angle for total internal reflection. The index of refraction for light at the violet end of the visible spectrum is larger than that at the red end. Thus, as the outgoing beam approaches the straight side, the violet light experiences total internal reflection first, followed by the other colors. The red light is the last to experience total internal reflection.

Chapter 36

Image Formation

▲ The light rays coming from the leaves in the background of this scene did not form a focused image on the film of the camera that took this photograph. Consequently, the background appears very blurry. Light rays passing though the raindrop, however, have been altered so as to form a focused image of the background leaves on the film. In this chapter, we investigate the formation of images as light rays reflect from mirrors and refract through lenses. (Don Hammond/CORBIS)

This chapter is concerned with the images that result when light rays encounter flat and curved surfaces. We find that images can be formed either by reflection or by refraction and that we can design mirrors and lenses to form images with desired characteristics. We continue to use the ray approximation and to assume that light travels in straight lines. Both of these steps lead to valid predictions in the field called *geometric optics*. In subsequent chapters, we shall concern ourselves with interference and diffraction effects—the objects of study in the field of *wave optics*.

36.1 Images Formed by Flat Mirrors

We begin by considering the simplest possible mirror, the flat mirror. Consider a point source of light placed at O in Figure 36.1, a distance p in front of a flat mirror. The distance p is called the **object distance.** Light rays leave the source and are reflected from the mirror. Upon reflection, the rays continue to diverge (spread apart). The dashed lines in Figure 36.1 are extensions of the diverging rays back to a point of intersection at I. The diverging rays appear to the viewer to come from the point I behind the mirror. Point I is called the **image** of the object at O. Regardless of the system under study, we always locate images by extending diverging rays back to a point at which they intersect. **Images are located either at a point from which rays of light *actually* diverge or at a point from which they *appear* to diverge.** Because the rays in Figure 36.1 appear to originate at I, which is a distance q behind the mirror, this is the location of the image. The distance q is called the **image distance.**

Images are classified as **real** or **virtual. A real image is formed when light rays pass through and diverge from the image point; a virtual image is formed when the light rays do not pass through the image point but only appear to diverge from that point.** The image formed by the mirror in Figure 36.1 is virtual. The image of an object seen in a flat mirror is *always* virtual. Real images can be displayed on a

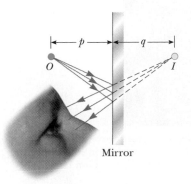

Mirror

Figure 36.1 An image formed by reflection from a flat mirror. The image point I is located behind the mirror a perpendicular distance q from the mirror (the image distance). The image distance has the same magnitude as the object distance p.

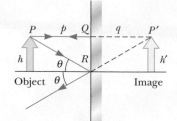

Active Figure 36.2 A geometric construction that is used to locate the image of an object placed in front of a flat mirror. Because the triangles PQR and $P'QR$ are congruent, $|p| = |q|$ and $h = h'$.

At the Active Figures link at http://www.pse6.com, *you can move the object and see the effect on the image.*

Lateral magnification

> ⚠ **PITFALL PREVENTION**
>
> ### 36.1 Magnification Does Not Necessarily Imply Enlargement
>
> For optical elements other than flat mirrors, the magnification defined in Equation 36.1 can result in a number with magnitude larger *or* smaller than 1. Thus, despite the cultural usage of the word *magnification* to mean *enlargement,* the image could be smaller than the object.

screen (as at a movie), but virtual images cannot be displayed on a screen. We shall see an example of a real image in Section 36.2.

We can use the simple geometry in Figure 36.2 to examine the properties of the images of extended objects formed by flat mirrors. Even though there are an infinite number of choices of direction in which light rays could leave each point on the object, we need to choose only two rays to determine where an image is formed. One of those rays starts at P, follows a horizontal path to the mirror, and reflects back on itself. The second ray follows the oblique path PR and reflects as shown, according to the law of reflection. An observer in front of the mirror would trace the two reflected rays back to the point at which they appear to have originated, which is point P' behind the mirror. A continuation of this process for points other than P on the object would result in a virtual image (represented by a yellow arrow) behind the mirror. Because triangles PQR and $P'QR$ are congruent, $PQ = P'Q$. We conclude that **the image formed by an object placed in front of a flat mirror is as far behind the mirror as the object is in front of the mirror.**

Geometry also reveals that the object height h equals the image height h'. Let us define **lateral magnification** M of an image as follows:

$$M \equiv \frac{\text{Image height}}{\text{Object height}} = \frac{h'}{h} \tag{36.1}$$

This is a general definition of the lateral magnification for an image from any type of mirror. (This equation is also valid for images formed by lenses, which we study in Section 36.4.) For a flat mirror, $M = 1$ for any image because $h' = h$.

Finally, note that a flat mirror produces an image that has an *apparent* left–right reversal. You can see this reversal by standing in front of a mirror and raising your right hand, as shown in Figure 36.3. The image you see raises its left hand. Likewise, your hair appears to be parted on the side opposite your real part, and a mole on your right cheek appears to be on your left cheek.

This reversal is not *actually* a left–right reversal. Imagine, for example, lying on your left side on the floor, with your body parallel to the mirror surface. Now your head is on the left and your feet are on the right. If you shake your feet, the image does not shake its head! If you raise your right hand, however, the image again raises its left hand. Thus, the mirror again appears to produce a left–right reversal but in the up–down direction!

The reversal is actually a *front–back reversal*, caused by the light rays going forward toward the mirror and then reflecting back from it. An interesting exercise is to stand in front of a mirror while holding an overhead transparency in front of you so that you can read the writing on the transparency. You will also be able to read the writing on the image of the transparency. You may have had a similar experience if you have attached a transparent decal with words on it to the rear window of your car. If the

Figure 36.3 The image in the mirror of a person's right hand is reversed front to back. This makes the right hand appear to be a left hand. Notice that the thumb is on the left side of both real hands and on the left side of the image. That the thumb is not on the right side of the image indicates that there is no left-to-right reversal.

decal can be read from outside the car, you can also read it when looking into your rearview mirror from inside the car.

We conclude that the image that is formed by a flat mirror has the following properties.

- The image is as far behind the mirror as the object is in front.
- The image is unmagnified, virtual, and upright. (By upright we mean that, if the object arrow points upward as in Figure 36.2, so does the image arrow.)
- The image has front–back reversal.

Quick Quiz 36.1 In the overhead view of Figure 36.4, the image of the stone seen by observer 1 is at *C*. At which of the five points *A*, *B*, *C*, *D*, or *E* does observer 2 see the image?

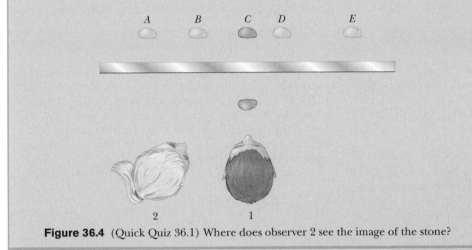

Figure 36.4 (Quick Quiz 36.1) Where does observer 2 see the image of the stone?

Quick Quiz 36.2 You are standing about 2 m away from a mirror. The mirror has water spots on its surface. True or false: It is possible for you to see the water spots and your image both in focus at the same time.

Conceptual Example 36.1   Multiple Images Formed by Two Mirrors

Two flat mirrors are perpendicular to each other, as in Figure 36.5, and an object is placed at point *O*. In this situation, multiple images are formed. Locate the positions of these images.

Solution The image of the object is at I_1 in mirror 1 and at I_2 in mirror 2. In addition, a third image is formed at I_3. This third image is the image of I_1 in mirror 2 or, equivalently, the image of I_2 in mirror 1. That is, the image at I_1 (or I_2) serves as the object for I_3. Note that to form this image at I_3, the rays reflect twice after leaving the object at *O*.

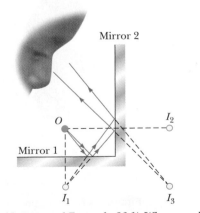

Figure 36.5 (Conceptual Example 36.1) When an object is placed in front of two mutually perpendicular mirrors as shown, three images are formed.

Conceptual Example 36.2 The Levitated Professor

The professor in the box shown in Figure 36.6 appears to be balancing himself on a few fingers, with his feet off the floor. He can maintain this position for a long time, and he appears to defy gravity. How was this illusion created?

Solution This is one of many magicians' optical illusions that make use of a mirror. The box in which the professor stands is a cubical frame that contains a flat vertical mirror positioned in a diagonal plane of the frame. The professor straddles the mirror so that one foot, which you see, is in front of the mirror, and the other foot, which you cannot see, is behind the mirror. When he raises the foot in front of the mirror, the reflection of that foot also rises, so he appears to float in air.

Courtesy of Henry Leap and Jim Lehman

Figure 36.6 (Conceptual Example 36.2) An optical illusion.

Conceptual Example 36.3 The Tilting Rearview Mirror

Most rearview mirrors in cars have a day setting and a night setting. The night setting greatly diminishes the intensity of the image in order that lights from trailing vehicles do not blind the driver. How does such a mirror work?

Solution Figure 36.7 shows a cross-sectional view of a rearview mirror for each setting. The unit consists of a reflective coating on the back of a wedge of glass. In the day setting (Fig. 36.7a), the light from an object behind the car strikes the glass wedge at point 1. Most of the light enters the wedge, refracting as it crosses the front surface, and reflects from the back surface to return to the front surface, where it is refracted again as it re-enters the air as ray *B* (for *bright*). In addition, a small portion of the light is reflected at the front surface of the glass, as indicated by ray *D* (for *dim*).

This dim reflected light is responsible for the image that is observed when the mirror is in the night setting (Fig. 36.7b). In this case, the wedge is rotated so that the path followed by the bright light (ray *B*) does not lead to the eye. Instead, the dim light reflected from the front surface of the wedge travels to the eye, and the brightness of trailing headlights does not become a hazard.

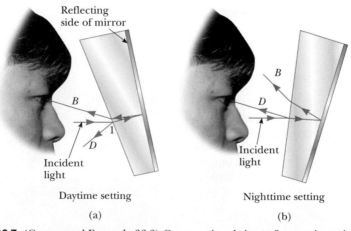

Figure 36.7 (Conceptual Example 36.3) Cross-sectional views of a rearview mirror. (a) With the day setting, the silvered back surface of the mirror reflects a bright ray *B* into the driver's eyes. (b) With the night setting, the glass of the unsilvered front surface of the mirror reflects a dim ray *D* into the driver's eyes.

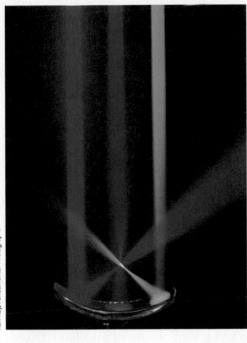

Ken Kay/Fundamental Photographs

Figure 36.8 Red, blue, and green light rays are reflected by a curved mirror. Note that the three colored beams meet at a point.

36.2 Images Formed by Spherical Mirrors

Concave Mirrors

A **spherical mirror,** as its name implies, has the shape of a section of a sphere. This type of mirror focuses incoming parallel rays to a point, as demonstrated by the colored light rays in Figure 36.8. Figure 36.9a shows a cross section of a spherical mirror, with its surface represented by the solid, curved black line. (The blue band represents the structural support for the mirrored surface, such as a curved piece of glass on which the silvered surface is deposited.) Such a mirror, in which light is reflected from the inner, concave surface, is called a **concave mirror.** The mirror has a radius of curvature R, and its center of curvature is point C. Point V is the center of the spherical section, and a line through C and V is called the **principal axis** of the mirror.

Now consider a point source of light placed at point O in Figure 36.9b, where O is any point on the principal axis to the left of C. Two diverging rays that originate at O are shown. After reflecting from the mirror, these rays converge and cross at the image point I. They then continue to diverge from I as if an object were there. As a result, at point I we have a real image of the light source at O.

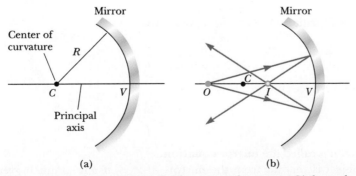

(a)   (b)

Figure 36.9 (a) A concave mirror of radius R. The center of curvature C is located on the principal axis. (b) A point object placed at O in front of a concave spherical mirror of radius R, where O is any point on the principal axis farther than R from the mirror surface, forms a real image at I. If the rays diverge from O at small angles, they all reflect through the same image point.

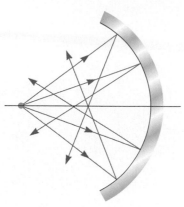

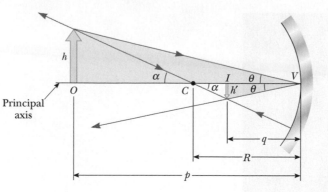

Figure 36.11 The image formed by a spherical concave mirror when the object *O* lies outside the center of curvature *C*. This geometric construction is used to derive Equation 36.4.

Figure 36.10 Rays diverging from the object at large angles from the principal axis reflect from a spherical concave mirror to intersect the principal axis at different points, resulting in a blurred image. This condition is called *spherical aberration.*

We shall consider in this section only rays that diverge from the object and make a small angle with the principal axis. Such rays are called **paraxial rays.** All paraxial rays reflect through the image point, as shown in Figure 36.9b. Rays that are far from the principal axis, such as those shown in Figure 36.10, converge to other points on the principal axis, producing a blurred image. This effect, which is called **spherical aberration,** is present to some extent for any spherical mirror and is discussed in Section 36.5.

We can use Figure 36.11 to calculate the image distance q from a knowledge of the object distance p and radius of curvature R. By convention, these distances are measured from point V. Figure 36.11 shows two rays leaving the tip of the object. One of these rays passes through the center of curvature C of the mirror, hitting the mirror perpendicular to the mirror surface and reflecting back on itself. The second ray strikes the mirror at its center (point V) and reflects as shown, obeying the law of reflection. The image of the tip of the arrow is located at the point where these two rays intersect. From the gold right triangle in Figure 36.11, we see that $\tan\theta = h/p$, and from the blue right triangle we see that $\tan\theta = -h'/q$. The negative sign is introduced because the image is inverted, so h' is taken to be negative. Thus, from Equation 36.1 and these results, we find that the magnification of the image is

$$M = \frac{h'}{h} = -\frac{q}{p} \tag{36.2}$$

We also note from the two triangles in Figure 36.11 that have α as one angle that

$$\tan\alpha = \frac{h}{p-R} \quad \text{and} \quad \tan\alpha = -\frac{h'}{R-q}$$

from which we find that

$$\frac{h'}{h} = -\frac{R-q}{p-R} \tag{36.3}$$

If we compare Equations 36.2 and 36.3, we see that

$$\frac{R-q}{p-R} = \frac{q}{p}$$

Simple algebra reduces this to

Mirror equation in terms of radius of curvature

$$\frac{1}{p} + \frac{1}{q} = \frac{2}{R} \tag{36.4}$$

This expression is called the **mirror equation.**

If the object is very far from the mirror—that is, if p is so much greater than R that p can be said to approach infinity—then $1/p \approx 0$, and we see from Equation 36.4 that $q \approx R/2$. That is, when the object is very far from the mirror, the image point is halfway between the center of curvature and the center point on the mirror, as shown in Figure 36.12a. The incoming rays from the object are essentially parallel

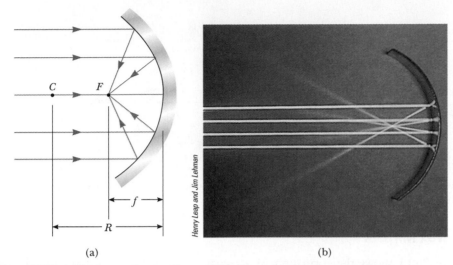

(a)   (b)

Henry Leap and Jim Lehman

Figure 36.12 (a) Light rays from a distant object ($p \rightarrow \infty$) reflect from a concave mirror through the focal point *F*. In this case, the image distance $q \approx R/2 = f$, where *f* is the focal length of the mirror. (b) Reflection of parallel rays from a concave mirror.

in this figure because the source is assumed to be very far from the mirror. We call the image point in this special case the **focal point** *F* and the image distance the **focal length** *f*, where

$$f = \frac{R}{2}$$ (36.5)

In Figure 36.8, the colored beams are traveling parallel to the principal axis and the mirror reflects all three beams to the focal point. Notice that the point at which the three beams intersect and the colors add is white.

Focal length is a parameter particular to a given mirror and therefore can be used to compare one mirror with another. The mirror equation can be expressed in terms of the focal length:

$$\frac{1}{p} + \frac{1}{q} = \frac{1}{f}$$ (36.6)

Notice that the focal length of a mirror depends only on the curvature of the mirror and not on the material from which the mirror is made. This is because the formation of the image results from rays reflected from the surface of the material. The situation is different for lenses; in that case the light actually passes through the material and the focal length depends on the type of material from which the lens is made.

Focal length

Mirror equation in terms of focal length

Courtesy of Thomson Consumer Electronics

A satellite-dish antenna is a concave reflector for television signals from a satellite in orbit around the Earth. The signals are carried by microwaves that, because the satellite is so far away, are parallel when they arrive at the dish. These waves reflect from the dish and are focused on the receiver at the focal point of the dish.

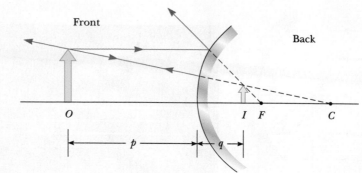

Figure 36.13 Formation of an image by a spherical convex mirror. The image formed by the real object is virtual and upright.

Convex Mirrors

Figure 36.13 shows the formation of an image by a **convex mirror**—that is, one silvered so that light is reflected from the outer, convex surface. This is sometimes called a **diverging mirror** because the rays from any point on an object diverge after reflection as though they were coming from some point behind the mirror. The image in Figure 36.13 is virtual because the reflected rays only appear to originate at the image point, as indicated by the dashed lines. Furthermore, the image is always upright and smaller than the object. This type of mirror is often used in stores to foil shoplifters. A single mirror can be used to survey a large field of view because it forms a smaller image of the interior of the store.

We do not derive any equations for convex spherical mirrors because we can use Equations 36.2, 36.4, and 36.6 for either concave or convex mirrors if we adhere to the following procedure. Let us refer to the region in which light rays move toward the mirror as the *front side* of the mirror, and the other side as the *back side*. For example, in Figures 36.11 and 36.13, the side to the left of the mirrors is the front side, and the side to the right of the mirrors is the back side. Figure 36.14 states the sign conventions for object and image distances, and Table 36.1 summarizes the sign conventions for all quantities.

Ray Diagrams for Mirrors

The positions and sizes of images formed by mirrors can be conveniently determined with *ray diagrams*. These graphical constructions reveal the nature of the image and can be used to check results calculated from the mirror and magnification equations. To draw a ray diagram, we need to know the position of the object and the locations of the mirror's focal point and center of curvature. We then draw three principal rays to locate the image, as shown by the examples in Figure 36.15.

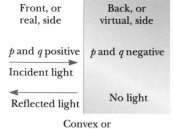

Figure 36.14 Signs of p and q for convex and concave mirrors.

⚠ **PITFALL PREVENTION**

36.3 Watch Your Signs

Success in working mirror problems (as well as problems involving refracting surfaces and thin lenses) is largely determined by proper sign choices when substituting into the equations. The best way to become adept at this is to work a multitude of problems on your own. Watching your instructor or reading the example problems is no substitute for practice.

Table 36.1

Sign Conventions for Mirrors		
Quantity	**Positive When**	**Negative When**
Object location (p)	Object is in front of mirror (real object)	Object is in back of mirror (virtual object)
Image location (q)	Image is in front of mirror (real image)	Image is in back of mirror (virtual image)
Image height (h')	Image is upright	Image is inverted
Focal length (f) and radius (R)	Mirror is concave	Mirror is convex
Magnification (M)	Image is upright	Image is inverted

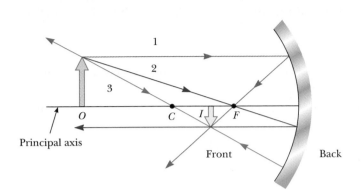

(a)

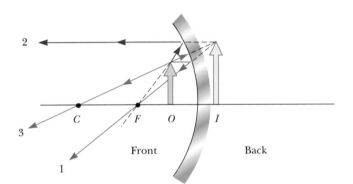

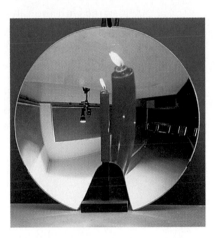

(b)

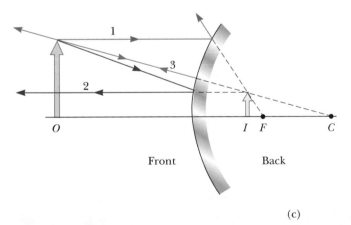

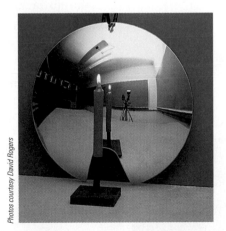

(c)

Photos courtesy David Rogers

Active Figure 36.15 Ray diagrams for spherical mirrors, along with corresponding photographs of the images of candles. (a) When the object is located so that the center of curvature lies between the object and a concave mirror surface, the image is real, inverted, and reduced in size. (b) When the object is located between the focal point and a concave mirror surface, the image is virtual, upright, and enlarged. (c) When the object is in front of a convex mirror, the image is virtual, upright, and reduced in size.

At the Active Figures link at http://www.pse6.com, *you can move the objects and change the focal length of the mirrors to see the effect on the images.*

▲ **PITFALL PREVENTION**

36.4 We Are *Choosing* a Small Number of Rays

A *huge* number of light rays leave each point on an object (and pass through each point on an image). In a principal-ray diagram, which displays the characteristics of the image, we choose only a few rays that follow simply stated rules. Locating the image by calculation complements the diagram.

These rays all start from the same object point and are drawn as follows. We may choose any point on the object; here, we choose the top of the object for simplicity. For concave mirrors (see Figs. 36.15a and 36.15b), we draw the following three principal rays:

- Ray 1 is drawn from the top of the object parallel to the principal axis and is reflected through the focal point *F*.
- Ray 2 is drawn from the top of the object through the focal point and is reflected parallel to the principal axis.
- Ray 3 is drawn from the top of the object through the center of curvature *C* and is reflected back on itself.

The intersection of any two of these rays locates the image. The third ray serves as a check of the construction. The image point obtained in this fashion must always agree with the value of *q* calculated from the mirror equation. With concave mirrors, note what happens as the object is moved closer to the mirror. The real, inverted image in Figure 36.15a moves to the left as the object approaches the focal point. When the object is at the focal point, the image is infinitely far to the left. However, when the object lies between the focal point and the mirror surface, as shown in Figure 36.15b, the image is virtual, upright, and enlarged. This latter situation applies when you use a shaving mirror or a makeup mirror, both of which are concave. Your face is closer to the mirror than the focal point, and you see an upright, enlarged image of your face.

For convex mirrors (see Fig. 36.15c), we draw the following three principal rays:

- Ray 1 is drawn from the top of the object parallel to the principal axis and is reflected *away from* the focal point *F*.
- Ray 2 is drawn from the top of the object toward the focal point on the back side of the mirror and is reflected parallel to the principal axis.
- Ray 3 is drawn from the top of the object toward the center of curvature *C* on the back side of the mirror and is reflected back on itself.

In a convex mirror, the image of an object is always virtual, upright, and reduced in size as shown in Figure 36.15c. In this case, as the object distance decreases, the virtual image increases in size and moves away from the focal point toward the mirror as the object approaches the mirror. You should construct other diagrams to verify how image position varies with object position.

Figure 36.16 (Quick Quiz 36.4) What type of mirror is this?

Quick Quiz 36.3 You wish to reflect sunlight from a mirror onto some paper under a pile of wood in order to start a fire. Which would be the best choice for the type of mirror? (a) flat (b) concave (c) convex.

Quick Quiz 36.4 Consider the image in the mirror in Figure 36.16. Based on the appearance of this image, you would conclude that (a) the mirror is concave and the image is real. (b) the mirror is concave and the image is virtual. (c) the mirror is convex and the image is real. (d) the mirror is convex and the image is virtual.

Example 36.4 The Image formed by a Concave Mirror

Assume that a certain spherical mirror has a focal length of + 10.0 cm. Locate and describe the image for object distances of

(A) 25.0 cm,

(B) 10.0 cm, and

(C) 5.00 cm.

Solution Because the focal length is positive, we know that this is a concave mirror (see Table 36.1).

(A) This situation is analogous to that in Figure 36.15a; hence, we expect the image to be real. We find the image distance by using Equation 36.6:

$$\frac{1}{p} + \frac{1}{q} = \frac{1}{f}$$

$$\frac{1}{25.0 \text{ cm}} + \frac{1}{q} = \frac{1}{10.0 \text{ cm}}$$

$$q = 16.7 \text{ cm}$$

The magnification of the image is given by Equation 36.2:

$$M = -\frac{q}{p} = -\frac{16.7 \text{ cm}}{25.0 \text{ cm}} = -0.668$$

The fact that the absolute value of M is less than unity tells us that the image is smaller than the object, and the negative sign for M tells us that the image is inverted. Because q is positive, the image is located on the front side of the mirror and is real.

(B) When the object distance is 10.0 cm, the object is located at the focal point. Now we find that

$$\frac{1}{10.0 \text{ cm}} + \frac{1}{q} = \frac{1}{10.0 \text{ cm}}$$

$$q = \infty$$

which means that rays originating from an object positioned at the focal point of a mirror are reflected so that the image is formed at an infinite distance from the mirror; that is, the rays travel parallel to one another after reflection. This is the situation in a flashlight, where the bulb filament is placed at the focal point of a reflector, producing a parallel beam of light.

(C) When the object is at $p = 5.00$ cm, it lies halfway between the focal point and the mirror surface, as shown in Figure 36.15b. Thus, we expect a magnified, virtual, upright

image. In this case, the mirror equation gives

$$\frac{1}{5.00 \text{ cm}} + \frac{1}{q} = \frac{1}{10.0 \text{ cm}}$$

$$q = -10.0 \text{ cm}$$

The image is virtual because it is located behind the mirror, as expected. The magnification of the image is

$$M = -\frac{q}{p} = -\left(\frac{-10.0 \text{ cm}}{5.00 \text{ cm}}\right) = +2.00$$

The image is twice as large as the object, and the positive sign for M indicates that the image is upright (see Fig. 36.15b).

What If? Suppose you set up the candle and mirror apparatus illustrated in Figure 36.15a and described in part (A) of the example. While adjusting the apparatus, you accidentally strike the candle with your elbow so that it begins to slide toward the mirror at velocity v_p. How fast does the image of the candle move?

Answer We solve the mirror equation, Equation 36.6, for q:

$$q = \frac{fp}{p - f}$$

Differentiating this equation with respect to time gives us the velocity of the image $v_q = dq/dt$:

$$v_q = \frac{dq}{dt} = \frac{d}{dt}\left(\frac{fp}{p - f}\right) = -\frac{f^2}{(p - f)^2}\frac{dp}{dt} = -\frac{f^2 v_p}{(p - f)^2}$$

For the object position of 25.0 cm in part (A), the velocity of the image is

$$v_q = -\frac{f^2 v_p}{(p - f)^2} = -\frac{(10.0 \text{ cm})^2 v_p}{(25.0 \text{ cm} - 10.0 \text{ cm})^2} = -0.444 v_p$$

Thus, the speed of the image is less than that of the object in this case.

We can see two interesting behaviors of this function for v_q. First, note that the velocity is negative regardless of the value of p or f. Thus, if the object moves toward the mirror, the image moves toward the left in Figure 36.15 without regard for the side of the focal point at which the object is located or whether the mirror is concave or convex. Second, in the limit of $p \rightarrow 0$, the velocity v_q approaches $-v_p$. As the object moves very close to the mirror, the mirror looks like a plane mirror, the image is as far behind the mirror as the object is in front, and both the object and the image move with the same speed.

🌐 *Investigate the image formed for various object positions and mirror focal lengths at the Interactive Worked Example link at* **http://www.pse6.com.**

Example 36.5 The Image from a Convex Mirror

An anti-shoplifting mirror, as shown in Figure 36.17, shows an image of a woman who is located 3.0 m from the mirror. The focal length of the mirror is − 0.25 m. Find

(A) the position of her image and

(B) the magnification of the image.

Solution (A) This situation is depicted in Figure 36.15c. We should expect to find an upright, reduced, virtual image. To find the image position, we use Equation 36.6:

$$\frac{1}{p} + \frac{1}{q} = \frac{1}{f} = \frac{1}{-0.25 \text{ m}}$$

$$\frac{1}{q} = \frac{1}{-0.25 \text{ m}} - \frac{1}{3.0 \text{ m}}$$

$$q = \boxed{-0.23 \text{ m}}$$

The negative value of q indicates that her image is virtual, or behind the mirror, as shown in Figure 36.15c.

(B) The magnification of the image is

$$M = -\frac{q}{p} = -\left(\frac{-0.23 \text{ m}}{3.0 \text{ m}}\right) = \boxed{+0.077}$$

The image is much smaller than the woman, and it is upright because M is positive.

Figure 36.17 (Example 36.5) Convex mirrors, often used for security in department stores, provide wide-angle viewing.

Investigate the image formed for various object positions and mirror focal lengths at the Interactive Worked Example link at http://www.pse6.com.

36.3 Images Formed by Refraction

In this section we describe how images are formed when light rays are refracted at the boundary between two transparent materials. Consider two transparent media having indices of refraction n_1 and n_2, where the boundary between the two media is a spherical surface of radius R (Fig. 36.18). We assume that the object at O is in the medium for which the index of refraction is n_1. Let us consider the paraxial rays leaving O. As we shall see, all such rays are refracted at the spherical surface and focus at a single point I, the image point.

Figure 36.19 shows a single ray leaving point O and refracting to point I. Snell's law of refraction applied to this ray gives

$$n_1 \sin \theta_1 = n_2 \sin \theta_2$$

Because θ_1 and θ_2 are assumed to be small, we can use the small-angle approximation $\sin \theta \approx \theta$ (with angles in radians) and say that

$$n_1 \theta_1 = n_2 \theta_2$$

Now we use the fact that an exterior angle of any triangle equals the sum of the two opposite interior angles. Applying this rule to triangles OPC and PIC in Figure 36.19 gives

$$\theta_1 = \alpha + \beta$$

$$\beta = \theta_2 + \gamma$$

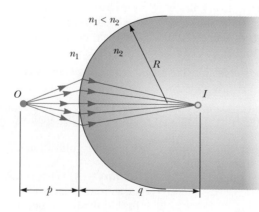

Figure 36.18 An image formed by refraction at a spherical surface. Rays making small angles with the principal axis diverge from a point object at O and are refracted through the image point I.

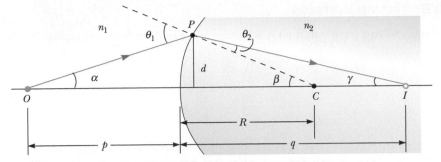

Figure 36.19 Geometry used to derive Equation 36.8, assuming that $n_1 < n_2$.

If we combine all three expressions and eliminate θ_1 and θ_2, we find that

$$n_1\alpha + n_2\gamma = (n_2 - n_1)\beta \tag{36.7}$$

From Figure 36.19, we see three right triangles that have a common vertical leg of length d. For paraxial rays (unlike the relatively large-angle ray shown in Fig. 36.19), the horizontal legs of these triangles are approximately p for the triangle containing angle α, R for the triangle containing angle β, and q for the triangle containing angle γ. In the small-angle approximation, $\tan\theta \approx \theta$, so we can write the approximate relationships from these triangles as follows:

$$\tan\alpha \approx \alpha \approx \frac{d}{p} \qquad \tan\beta \approx \beta \approx \frac{d}{R} \qquad \tan\gamma \approx \gamma \approx \frac{d}{q}$$

We substitute these expressions into Equation 36.7 and divide through by d to give

$$\frac{n_1}{p} + \frac{n_2}{q} = \frac{n_2 - n_1}{R} \tag{36.8}$$

Relation between object and image distance for a refracting surface

For a fixed object distance p, the image distance q is independent of the angle that the ray makes with the axis. This result tells us that all paraxial rays focus at the same point I.

As with mirrors, we must use a sign convention if we are to apply this equation to a variety of cases. We define the side of the surface in which light rays originate as the front side. The other side is called the back side. Real images are formed by refraction in back of the surface, in contrast with mirrors, where real images are formed in front of the reflecting surface. Because of the difference in location of real images, the refraction sign conventions for q and R are opposite the reflection sign conventions. For example, q and R are both positive in Figure 36.19. The sign conventions for spherical refracting surfaces are summarized in Table 36.2.

We derived Equation 36.8 from an assumption that $n_1 < n_2$ in Figure 36.19. This assumption is not necessary, however. Equation 36.8 is valid regardless of which index of refraction is greater.

Table 36.2

Sign Conventions for Refracting Surfaces		
Quantity	**Positive When**	**Negative When**
Object location (p)	Object is in front of surface (real object)	Object is in back of surface (virtual object)
Image location (q)	Image is in back of surface (real image)	Image is in front of surface (virtual image)
Image height (h')	Image is upright	Image is inverted
Radius (R)	Center of curvature is in back of surface	Center of curvature is in front of surface

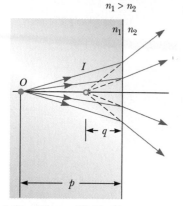

$n_1 > n_2$

Active Figure 36.20 The image formed by a flat refracting surface is virtual and on the same side of the surface as the object. All rays are assumed to be paraxial.

At the Active Figures link at http://www.pse6.com, *you can move the object to see the effect on the location of the image.*

Flat Refracting Surfaces

If a refracting surface is flat, then R is infinite and Equation 36.8 reduces to

$$\frac{n_1}{p} = -\frac{n_2}{q}$$

$$q = -\frac{n_2}{n_1} p \tag{36.9}$$

From this expression we see that the sign of q is opposite that of p. Thus, according to Table 36.2, **the image formed by a flat refracting surface is on the same side of the surface as the object.** This is illustrated in Figure 36.20 for the situation in which the object is in the medium of index n_1 and n_1 is greater than n_2. In this case, a virtual image is formed between the object and the surface. If n_1 is less than n_2, the rays in the back side diverge from each other at lesser angles than those in Figure 36.20. As a result, the virtual image is formed to the left of the object.

Quick Quiz 36.5 In Figure 36.18, what happens to the image point I as the object point O is moved to the right from very far away to very close to the refracting surface? (a) It is always to the right of the surface. (b) It is always to the left of the surface. (c) It starts off to the left and at some position of O, I moves to the right of the surface. (d) It starts off to the right and at some position of O, I moves to the left of the surface.

Quick Quiz 36.6 In Figure 36.20, what happens to the image point I as the object point O moves toward the right-hand surface of the material of index of refraction n_1? (a) It always remains between O and the surface, arriving at the surface just as O does. (b) It moves toward the surface more slowly than O so that eventually O passes I. (c) It approaches the surface and then moves to the right of the surface.

Conceptual Example 36.6   Let's Go Scuba Diving!

It is well known that objects viewed under water with the naked eye appear blurred and out of focus. However, a scuba diver using a mask has a clear view of underwater objects. Explain how this works, using the facts that the indices of refraction of the cornea, water, and air are 1.376, 1.333, and 1.00029, respectively.

Solution Because the cornea and water have almost identical indices of refraction, very little refraction occurs

when a person under water views objects with the naked eye. In this case, light rays from an object focus behind the retina, resulting in a blurred image. When a mask is used, the air space between the eye and the mask surface provides the normal amount of refraction at the eye–air interface, and the light from the object focuses on the retina.

Example 36.7   Gaze into the Crystal Ball

A set of coins is embedded in a spherical plastic paperweight having a radius of 3.0 cm. The index of refraction of the plastic is $n_1 = 1.50$. One coin is located 2.0 cm from the edge of the sphere (Fig. 36.21). Find the position of the image of the coin.

Solution Because $n_1 > n_2$, where $n_2 = 1.00$ is the index of refraction for air, the rays originating from the coin are refracted away from the normal at the surface and diverge outward. Hence, the image is formed inside the paperweight and is *virtual*. Applying Equation 36.8 and noting

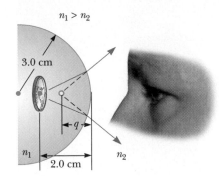

$n_1 > n_2$

3.0 cm

n_1

2.0 cm

n_2

Figure 36.21 (Example 36.7) Light rays from a coin embedded in a plastic sphere form a virtual image between the surface of the object and the sphere surface. Because the object is inside the sphere, the front of the refracting surface is the *interior* of the sphere.

from Table 36.2 that R is negative, we obtain

$$\frac{n_1}{p} + \frac{n_2}{q} = \frac{n_2 - n_1}{R}$$

$$\frac{1.50}{2.0 \text{ cm}} + \frac{1}{q} = \frac{1.00 - 1.50}{-3.0 \text{ cm}}$$

$$q = \boxed{-1.7 \text{ cm}}$$

The negative sign for q indicates that the image is in front of the surface—in other words, in the same medium as the object, as shown in Figure 36.21. Being in the same medium as the object, the image must be virtual. (See Table 36.2.) The coin appears to be closer to the paperweight surface than it actually is.

Example 36.8 The One That Got Away

A small fish is swimming at a depth d below the surface of a pond (Fig. 36.22). What is the apparent depth of the fish, as viewed from directly overhead?

Solution Because the refracting surface is flat, R is infinite. Hence, we can use Equation 36.9 to determine the location of the image with $p = d$. Using the indices of refraction given in Figure 36.22, we obtain

$$q = -\frac{n_2}{n_1} p = -\frac{1.00}{1.33} d = \boxed{-0.752d}$$

Because q is negative, the image is virtual, as indicated by the dashed lines in Figure 36.22. The apparent depth is approximately three-fourths the actual depth.

What If? What if you look more carefully at the fish and measure its apparent *height*, from its upper fin to its lower fin? Is the apparent height h' of the fish different from the actual height h?

Answer Because all points on the fish appear to be fractionally closer to the observer, we would predict that the height would be smaller. If we let the distance d in Figure 36.22 be measured to the top fin and the distance to the bottom fin be $d + h$, then the images of the top and bottom of the fish are located at

$$q_{\text{top}} = -0.752d$$

$$q_{\text{bottom}} = -0.752(d + h)$$

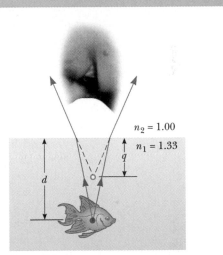

$n_2 = 1.00$

$n_1 = 1.33$

q

d

Figure 36.22 (Example 36.8) The apparent depth q of the fish is less than the true depth d. All rays are assumed to be paraxial.

The apparent height h' of the fish is

$$h' = q_{\text{top}} - q_{\text{bottom}} = -0.752d - [-0.752(d + h)]$$

$$= 0.752h$$

and the fish appears to be approximately three-fourths its actual height.

36.4 Thin Lenses

Lenses are commonly used to form images by refraction in optical instruments, such as cameras, telescopes, and microscopes. We can use what we just learned about images formed by refracting surfaces to help us locate the image formed by a lens. We recognize that light passing through a lens experiences refraction at two surfaces. The development we shall follow is based on the notion that **the image**

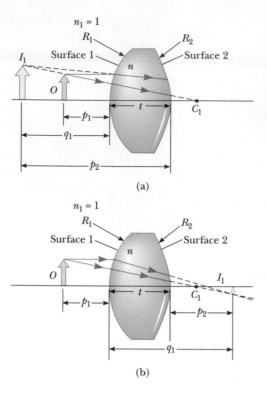

Figure 36.23 To locate the image formed by a lens, we use the virtual image at I_1 formed by surface 1 as the object for the image formed by surface 2. The point C_1 is the center of curvature of surface 1. (a) The image due to surface 1 is virtual so that I_1 is to the left of the surface. (b) The image due to surface 1 is real so that I_1 is to the right of the surface.

formed by one refracting surface serves as the object for the second surface. We shall analyze a thick lens first and then let the thickness of the lens be approximately zero.

Consider a lens having an index of refraction n and two spherical surfaces with radii of curvature R_1 and R_2, as in Figure 36.23. (Note that R_1 is the radius of curvature of the lens surface that the light from the object reaches first and that R_2 is the radius of curvature of the other surface of the lens.) An object is placed at point O at a distance p_1 in front of surface 1.

Let us begin with the image formed by surface 1. Using Equation 36.8 and assuming that $n_1 = 1$ because the lens is surrounded by air, we find that the image I_1 formed by surface 1 satisfies the equation

$$\frac{1}{p_1} + \frac{n}{q_1} = \frac{n-1}{R_1} \tag{36.10}$$

where q_1 is the position of the image due to surface 1. If the image due to surface 1 is virtual (Fig. 36.23a), q_1 is negative, and it is positive if the image is real (Fig. 36.23b).

Now we apply Equation 36.8 to surface 2, taking $n_1 = n$ and $n_2 = 1$. (We make this switch in index because the light rays approaching surface 2 are *in the material of the lens,* and this material has index n.) Taking p_2 as the object distance for surface 2 and q_2 as the image distance gives

$$\frac{n}{p_2} + \frac{1}{q_2} = \frac{1-n}{R_2} \tag{36.11}$$

We now introduce mathematically the fact that the image formed by the first surface acts as the object for the second surface. We do this by noting from Figure 36.23 that p_2, measured from surface 2, is related to q_1 as follows:

Virtual image from surface 1 (Fig. 36.23a): $p_2 = -q_1 + t$ (q_1 is negative)

Real image from surface 1 (Fig. 36.23b): $p_2 = -q_1 + t$ (q_1 is positive)

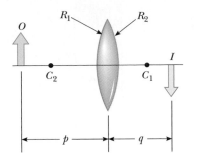

Figure 36.24 Simplified geometry for a thin lens.

where t is the thickness of the lens. For a *thin* lens (one whose thickness is small compared to the radii of curvature), we can neglect t. In this approximation, we see that $p_2 = -q_1$ for either type of image from surface 1. (If the image from surface 1 is real, the image acts as a virtual object, so p_2 is negative.) Hence, Equation 36.11 becomes

$$-\frac{n}{q_1} + \frac{1}{q_2} = \frac{1-n}{R_2}$$ (36.12)

Adding Equations 36.10 and 36.12, we find that

$$\frac{1}{p_1} + \frac{1}{q_2} = (n-1)\left(\frac{1}{R_1} - \frac{1}{R_2}\right)$$ (36.13)

For a thin lens, we can omit the subscripts on p_1 and q_2 in Equation 36.13 and call the object distance p and the image distance q, as in Figure 36.24. Hence, we can write Equation 36.13 in the form

$$\frac{1}{p} + \frac{1}{q} = (n-1)\left(\frac{1}{R_1} - \frac{1}{R_2}\right)$$ (36.14)

This expression relates the image distance q of the image formed by a thin lens to the object distance p and to the lens properties (index of refraction and radii of curvature). It is valid only for paraxial rays and only when the lens thickness is much less than R_1 and R_2.

The **focal length** f of a thin lens is the image distance that corresponds to an infinite object distance, just as with mirrors. Letting p approach ∞ and q approach f in Equation 36.14, we see that the inverse of the focal length for a thin lens is

$$\frac{1}{f} = (n-1)\left(\frac{1}{R_1} - \frac{1}{R_2}\right)$$ (36.15)   **Lens makers' equation**

This relationship is called the **lens makers' equation** because it can be used to determine the values of R_1 and R_2 that are needed for a given index of refraction and a desired focal length f. Conversely, if the index of refraction and the radii of curvature of a lens are given, this equation enables a calculation of the focal length. If the lens is immersed in something other than air, this same equation can be used, with n interpreted as the *ratio* of the index of refraction of the lens material to that of the surrounding fluid.

Using Equation 36.15, we can write Equation 36.14 in a form identical to Equation 36.6 for mirrors:

$$\frac{1}{p} + \frac{1}{q} = \frac{1}{f}$$ (36.16)   **Thin lens equation**

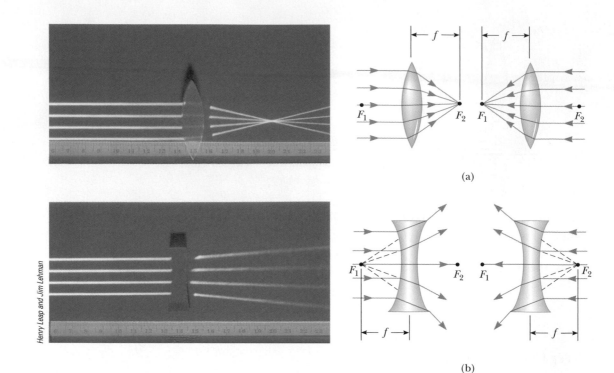

(a)

(b)

Henny Leap and Jim Lehman

Figure 36.25 (*Left*) Effects of a converging lens (top) and a diverging lens (bottom) on parallel rays. (*Right*) Parallel light rays pass through (a) a converging lens and (b) a diverging lens. The focal length is the same for light rays passing through a given lens in either direction. Both focal points F_1 and F_2 are the same distance from the lens.

Front	Back
p positive	p negative
q negative	q positive
Incident light →	Refracted light →

Figure 36.26 A diagram for obtaining the signs of p and q for a thin lens. (This diagram also applies to a refracting surface.)

▲ **PITFALL PREVENTION**

36.5 A Lens Has Two Focal Points but Only One Focal Length

A lens has a focal point on each side, front and back. However, there is only one focal length—each of the two focal points is located the same distance from the lens (Fig. 36.25). This can be seen mathematically by interchanging R_1 and R_2 in Equation 36.15 (and changing the signs of the radii because back and front have been interchanged). As a result, the lens forms an image of an object at the same point if it is turned around. In practice this might not happen, because real lenses are not infinitesimally thin.

This equation, called the **thin lens equation**, can be used to relate the image distance and object distance for a thin lens.

Because light can travel in either direction through a lens, each lens has two focal points, one for light rays passing through in one direction and one for rays passing through in the other direction. This is illustrated in Figure 36.25 for a biconvex lens (two convex surfaces, resulting in a converging lens) and a biconcave lens (two concave surfaces, resulting in a diverging lens).

Figure 36.26 is useful for obtaining the signs of p and q, and Table 36.3 gives the sign conventions for thin lenses. Note that these sign conventions are the same as those for refracting surfaces (see Table 36.2). Applying these rules to a biconvex lens, we see that when $p > f$, the quantities p, q, and R_1 are positive, and R_2 is negative. Therefore, p, q, and f are all positive when a converging lens forms a real image of an object. For a biconcave lens, p and R_2 are positive and q and R_1 are negative, with the result that f is negative.

Table 36.3

Sign Conventions for Thin Lenses

Quantity	Positive When	Negative When
Object location (p)	Object is in front of lens (real object)	Object is in back of lens (virtual object)
Image location (q)	Image is in back of lens (real image)	Image is in front of lens (virtual image)
Image height (h')	Image is upright	Image is inverted
R_1 and R_2	Center of curvature is in back of lens	Center of curvature is in front of lens
Focal length (f)	Converging lens	Diverging lens

Various lens shapes are shown in Figure 36.27. Note that a converging lens is thicker at the center than at the edge, whereas a diverging lens is thinner at the center than at the edge.

Magnification of Images

Consider a thin lens through which light rays from an object pass. As with mirrors (Eq. 36.2), we could analyze a geometric construction to show that the lateral magnification of the image is

$$M = \frac{h'}{h} = -\frac{q}{p}$$

From this expression, it follows that when M is positive, the image is upright and on the same side of the lens as the object. When M is negative, the image is inverted and on the side of the lens opposite the object.

Ray Diagrams for Thin Lenses

Ray diagrams are convenient for locating the images formed by thin lenses or systems of lenses. They also help clarify our sign conventions. Figure 36.28 shows such diagrams for three single-lens situations.

To locate the image of a *converging* lens (Fig. 36.28a and b), the following three rays are drawn from the top of the object:

- Ray 1 is drawn parallel to the principal axis. After being refracted by the lens, this ray passes through the focal point on the back side of the lens.
- Ray 2 is drawn through the center of the lens and continues in a straight line.
- Ray 3 is drawn through the focal point on the front side of the lens (or as if coming from the focal point if $p < f$) and emerges from the lens parallel to the principal axis.

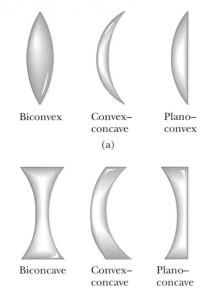

Figure 36.27 Various lens shapes. (a) Converging lenses have a positive focal length and are thickest at the middle. (b) Diverging lenses have a negative focal length and are thickest at the edges.

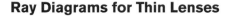

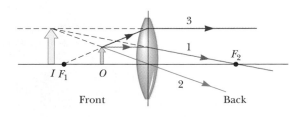

(a)   (b)

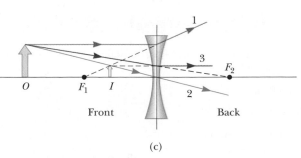

(c)

Active Figure 36.28 Ray diagrams for locating the image formed by a thin lens. (a) When the object is in front of and outside the focal point of a converging lens, the image is real, inverted, and on the back side of the lens. (b) When the object is between the focal point and a converging lens, the image is virtual, upright, larger than the object, and on the front side of the lens. (c) When an object is anywhere in front of a diverging lens, the image is virtual, upright, smaller than the object, and on the front side of the lens.

At the Active Figures link at http://www.pse6.com, you can move the objects and change the focal length of the lenses to see the effect on the images.

To locate the image of a *diverging* lens (Fig. 36.28c), the following three rays are drawn from the top of the object:

> • Ray 1 is drawn parallel to the principal axis. After being refracted by the lens, this ray emerges directed away from the focal point on the front side of the lens.
>
> • Ray 2 is drawn through the center of the lens and continues in a straight line.
>
> • Ray 3 is drawn in the direction toward the focal point on the back side of the lens and emerges from the lens parallel to the principal axis.

For the converging lens in Figure 36.28a, where the object is to the left of the focal point $(p > f)$, the image is real and inverted. When the object is between the focal point and the lens $(p < f)$, as in Figure 36.28b, the image is virtual and upright. For a diverging lens (see Fig. 36.28c), the image is always virtual and upright, regardless of where the object is placed. These geometric constructions are reasonably accurate only if the distance between the rays and the principal axis is much less than the radii of the lens surfaces.

Note that refraction occurs only at the surfaces of the lens. A certain lens design takes advantage of this fact to produce the *Fresnel lens*, a powerful lens without great thickness. Because only the surface curvature is important in the refracting qualities of the lens, material in the middle of a Fresnel lens is removed, as shown in the cross sections of lenses in Figure 36.29. Because the edges of the curved segments cause some distortion, Fresnel lenses are usually used only in situations in which image quality is less important than reduction of weight. A classroom overhead projector often uses a Fresnel lens; the circular edges between segments of the lens can be seen by looking closely at the light projected onto a screen.

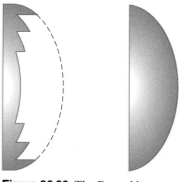

Figure 36.29 The Fresnel lens on the left has the same focal length as the thick lens on the right but is made of much less glass.

Quick Quiz 36.7 What is the focal length of a pane of window glass? (a) zero (b) infinity (c) the thickness of the glass (d) impossible to determine

Quick Quiz 36.8 Diving masks often have a lens built into the glass for divers who do not have perfect vision. This allows the individual to dive without the necessity for glasses, because the lenses in the faceplate perform the necessary refraction to provide clear vision. The proper design allows the diver to see clearly with the mask on *both* under water and in the open air. Normal eyeglasses have lenses that are curved on both the front and back surfaces. The lenses in a diving mask should be curved (a) only on the front surface (b) only on the back surface (c) on both the front and back surfaces.

Example 36.9   Images Formed by a Converging Lens   Interactive

A converging lens of focal length 10.0 cm forms images of objects placed

(A) 30.0 cm,

(B) 10.0 cm, and

(C) 5.00 cm from the lens.

In each case, construct a ray diagram, find the image distance and describe the image.

Solution

(A) First we construct a ray diagram as shown in Figure 36.30a. The diagram shows that we should expect a real, inverted, smaller image to be formed on the back side of the lens. The thin lens equation, Equation 36.16, can be used to find the image distance:

$$\frac{1}{p} + \frac{1}{q} = \frac{1}{f}$$

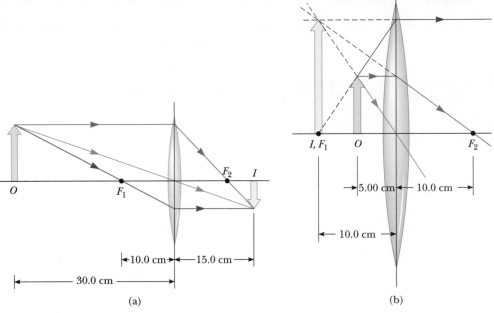

Figure 36.30 (Example 36.9) An image is formed by a converging lens. (a) The object is farther from the lens than the focal point. (b) The object is closer to the lens than the focal point.

$$\frac{1}{30.0 \text{ cm}} + \frac{1}{q} = \frac{1}{10.0 \text{ cm}}$$

$$q = \boxed{+15.0 \text{ cm}}$$

The positive sign for the image distance tells us that the image is indeed real and on the back side of the lens. The magnification of the image is

$$M = -\frac{q}{p} = -\frac{15.0 \text{ cm}}{30.0 \text{ cm}} = \boxed{-0.500}$$

Thus, the image is reduced in height by one half, and the negative sign for M tells us that the image is inverted.

(B) No calculation is necessary for this case because we know that, when the object is placed at the focal point, the image is formed at infinity. This is readily verified by substituting $p = 10.0$ cm into the thin lens equation.

(C) We now move inside the focal point. The ray diagram in Figure 36.30b shows that in this case the lens acts as a magnifying glass; that is, the image is magnified, upright, on the same side of the lens as the object, and virtual. Because the object distance is 5.00 cm, the thin lens equation gives

$$\frac{1}{5.00 \text{ cm}} + \frac{1}{q} = \frac{1}{10.0 \text{ cm}}$$

$$q = \boxed{-10.0 \text{ cm}}$$

and the magnification of the image is

$$M = -\frac{q}{p} = -\left(\frac{-10.0 \text{ cm}}{5.00 \text{ cm}}\right) = \boxed{+2.00}$$

The negative image distance tells us that the image is virtual and formed on the side of the lens from which the light is incident, the front side. The image is enlarged, and the positive sign for M tells us that the image is upright.

What If? What if the object moves right up to the lens surface, so that $p \to 0$? Where is the image?

Answer In this case, because $p \ll R$, where R is either of the radii of the surfaces of the lens, the curvature of the lens can be ignored and it should appear to have the same effect as a plane piece of material. This would suggest that the image is just on the front side of the lens, at $q = 0$. We can verify this mathematically by rearranging the thin lens equation:

$$\frac{1}{q} = \frac{1}{f} - \frac{1}{p}$$

If we let $p \to 0$, the second term on the right becomes very large compared to the first and we can neglect $1/f$. The equation becomes

$$\frac{1}{q} = -\frac{1}{p}$$

$$q = -p = 0$$

Thus, q is on the front side of the lens (because it has the opposite sign as p), and just at the lens surface.

Investigate the image formed for various object positions and lens focal lengths at the Interactive Worked Example link at http://www.pse6.com.

Example 36.10   The Case of a Diverging Lens

Repeat Example 36.9 for a *diverging* lens of focal length 10.0 cm.

Solution

(A) We begin by constructing a ray diagram as in Figure 36.31a taking the object distance to be 30.0 cm. The diagram shows that we should expect an image that is virtual, smaller than the object, and upright. Let us now apply the thin lens equation with $p = 30.0$ cm:

$$\frac{1}{p} + \frac{1}{q} = \frac{1}{f}$$

$$\frac{1}{30.0 \text{ cm}} + \frac{1}{q} = \frac{1}{-10.0 \text{ cm}}$$

$$q = \boxed{-7.50 \text{ cm}}$$

The magnification of the image is

$$M = -\frac{q}{p} = -\left(\frac{-7.50 \text{ cm}}{30.0 \text{ cm}}\right) = \boxed{+0.250}$$

This result confirms that the image is virtual, smaller than the object, and upright.

(B) When the object is at the focal point, the ray diagram appears as in Figure 36.31b. In the thin lens equation, using $p = 10.0$ cm, we have

$$\frac{1}{10.0 \text{ cm}} + \frac{1}{q} = \frac{1}{-10.0 \text{ cm}}$$

$$q = \boxed{-5.00 \text{ cm}}$$

The magnification of the image is

$$M = -\frac{q}{p} = -\left(\frac{-5.00 \text{ cm}}{10.0 \text{ cm}}\right) = \boxed{+0.500}$$

Notice the difference between this situation and that for a converging lens. For a diverging lens, an object at the focal point does not produce an image infinitely far away.

(C) When the object is inside the focal point, at $p = 5.00$ cm, the ray diagram in Figure 36.31c shows that we expect a virtual image that is smaller than the object and upright. In

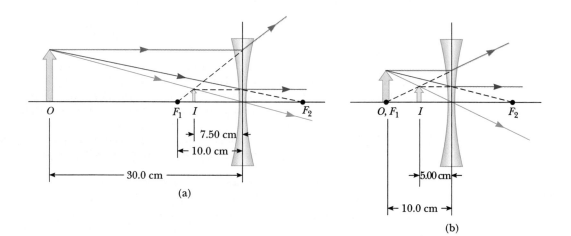

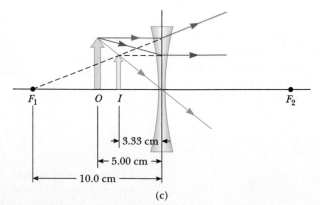

Figure 36.31 (Example 36.10) An image is formed by a diverging lens. (a) The object is farther from the lens than the focal point. (b) The object is at the focal point. (c) The object is closer to the lens than the focal point.

this case, the thin lens equation gives

$$\frac{1}{5.00 \text{ cm}} + \frac{1}{q} = \frac{1}{-10.0 \text{ cm}}$$

$$q = \boxed{-3.33 \text{ cm}}$$

and the magnification of the image is

$$M = -\left(\frac{-3.33 \text{ cm}}{5.00 \text{ cm}}\right) = \boxed{+0.667}$$

This confirms that the image is virtual, smaller than the object, and upright.

Investigate the image formed for various object positions and lens focal lengths at the Interactive Worked Example link at **http://www.pse6.com.**

Example 36.11 A Lens Under Water

A converging glass lens ($n = 1.52$) has a focal length of 40.0 cm in air. Find its focal length when it is immersed in water, which has an index of refraction of 1.33.

Solution We can use the lens makers' equation (Eq. 36.15) in both cases, noting that R_1 and R_2 remain the same in air and water:

$$\frac{1}{f_{\text{air}}} = (n - 1)\left(\frac{1}{R_1} - \frac{1}{R_2}\right)$$

$$\frac{1}{f_{\text{water}}} = (n' - 1)\left(\frac{1}{R_1} - \frac{1}{R_2}\right)$$

where n' is the ratio of the index of refraction of glass to that of water: $n' = 1.52/1.33 = 1.14$. Dividing the first

equation by the second gives

$$\frac{f_{\text{water}}}{f_{\text{air}}} = \frac{n - 1}{n' - 1} = \frac{1.52 - 1}{1.14 - 1} = 3.71$$

Because $f_{\text{air}} = 40.0$ cm, we find that

$$f_{\text{water}} = 3.71 f_{\text{air}} = 3.71(40.0 \text{ cm}) = \boxed{148 \text{ cm}}$$

The focal length of any lens is increased by a factor $(n - 1)/(n' - 1)$ when the lens is immersed in a fluid, where n' is the ratio of the index of refraction n of the lens material to that of the fluid.

Combination of Thin Lenses

If two thin lenses are used to form an image, the system can be treated in the following manner. First, the image formed by the first lens is located as if the second lens were not present. Then a ray diagram is drawn for the second lens, with the image formed by the first lens now serving as the object for the second lens. The second image formed is the final image of the system. If the image formed by the first lens lies on the back side of the second lens, then that image is treated as a **virtual object** for the second lens (that is, in the thin lens equation, p is negative). The same procedure can be extended to a system of three or more lenses. Because the magnification due to the second lens is performed on the magnified image due to the first lens, the overall magnification of the image due to the combination of lenses is the product of the individual magnifications.

Let us consider the special case of a system of two lenses of focal lengths f_1 and f_2 in contact with each other. If $p_1 = p$ is the object distance for the combination, application of the thin lens equation (Eq. 36.16) to the first lens gives

$$\frac{1}{p} + \frac{1}{q_1} = \frac{1}{f_1}$$

Light from a distant object is brought into focus by two converging lenses.

where q_1 is the image distance for the first lens. Treating this image as the object for the second lens, we see that the object distance for the second lens must be $p_2 = -q_1$. (The distances are the same because the lenses are in contact and assumed to be infinitesimally thin. The object distance is negative because the object is virtual.) Therefore, for the second lens,

$$\frac{1}{p_2} + \frac{1}{q_2} = \frac{1}{f_2}$$

$$-\frac{1}{q_1} + \frac{1}{q} = \frac{1}{f_2}$$

where $q = q_2$ is the final image distance from the second lens, which is the image distance for the combination. Adding the equations for the two lenses eliminates q_1 and gives

$$\frac{1}{p} + \frac{1}{q} = \frac{1}{f_1} + \frac{1}{f_2}$$

If we consider replacing the combination with a single lens that will form an image at the same location, we see that its focal length is related to the individual focal lengths by

Focal length for a combination of two thin lenses in contact

$$\frac{1}{f} = \frac{1}{f_1} + \frac{1}{f_2} \qquad (36.17)$$

Therefore, **two thin lenses in contact with each other are equivalent to a single thin lens having a focal length given by Equation 36.17.**

Example 36.12   Where Is the Final Image?   `Interactive`

Two thin converging lenses of focal lengths $f_1 = 10.0$ cm and $f_2 = 20.0$ cm are separated by 20.0 cm, as illustrated in Figure 36.32a. An object is placed 30.0 cm to the left of lens 1. Find the position and the magnification of the final image.

Solution Conceptualize by imagining light rays passing through the first lens and forming a real image (because $p > f$) in the absence of the second lens. Figure 36.32b shows these light rays forming the inverted image I_1. Once the light rays converge to the image point, they do not stop. They continue through the image point and interact with the second lens. The rays leaving the image point behave in the same way as the rays leaving an object. Thus, the image of the first lens serves as the object of the second lens. We categorize this problem as one in which we apply the thin lens equation, but in stepwise fashion to the two lenses.

To analyze the problem, we first draw a ray diagram (Figure 36.32b) showing where the image from the first lens falls and how it acts as the object for the second lens. The location of the image formed by lens 1 is found from the thin lens equation:

$$\frac{1}{p_1} + \frac{1}{q_1} = \frac{1}{f}$$

$$\frac{1}{30.0 \text{ cm}} + \frac{1}{q_1} = \frac{1}{10.0 \text{ cm}}$$

$$q_1 = \boxed{+15.0 \text{ cm}}$$

The magnification of this image is

$$M_1 = -\frac{q_1}{p_1} = -\frac{15.0 \text{ cm}}{30.0 \text{ cm}} = \boxed{-0.500}$$

The image formed by this lens acts as the object for the second lens. Thus, the object distance for the second lens is $20.0 \text{ cm} - 15.0 \text{ cm} = 5.00$ cm. We again apply the thin lens equation to find the location of the final image:

$$\frac{1}{5.00 \text{ cm}} + \frac{1}{q_2} = \frac{1}{20.0 \text{ cm}}$$

$$q_2 = \boxed{-6.67 \text{ cm}}$$

The magnification of the second image is

$$M_2 = -\frac{q_2}{p_2} = -\frac{(-6.67 \text{ cm})}{5.00 \text{ cm}} = \boxed{+1.33}$$

Thus, the overall magnification of the system is

$$M = M_1 M_2 = (-0.500)(1.33) = \boxed{-0.667}$$

To finalize the problem, note that the negative sign on the overall magnification indicates that the final image is inverted with respect to the initial object. The fact that the absolute value of the magnification is less than one tells us that the final image is smaller than the object. The fact that q_2 is negative tells us that the final image is on the front, or left, side of lens 2. All of these conclusions are consistent with the ray diagram in Figure 36.32b.

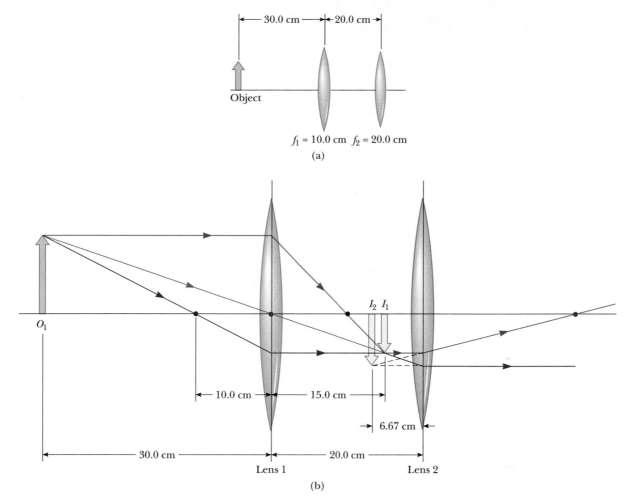

Figure 36.32 (Example 36.12) (a) A combination of two converging lenses. (b) The ray diagram showing the location of the final image due to the combination of lenses. The black dots are the focal points of lens 1 while the red dots are the focal points of lens 2.

What If? Suppose we want to create an upright image with this system of two lenses. How must the second lens be moved in order to achieve this?

Answer Because the object is farther from the first lens than the focal length of that lens, we know that the first image is inverted. Consequently, we need the second lens to invert the image once again so that the final image is upright. An inverted image is only formed by a converging lens if the object is outside the focal point. Thus, the image due to the first lens must be to the left of the focal point of the second lens in Figure 36.32b. To make this happen, we must move the second lens at least as far away from the first lens as the sum $q_1 + f_2 = 15.0$ cm $+ 20.0$ cm $= 35.0$ cm.

Investigate the image formed by a combination of two lenses at the Interactive Worked Example link at **http://www.pse6.com.**

Conceptual Example 36.13 Watch Your *p*'s and *q*'s!

Use a spreadsheet or a similar tool to create two graphs of image distance as a function of object distance—one for a lens for which the focal length is 10 cm and one for a lens for which the focal length is − 10 cm.

Solution The graphs are shown in Figure 36.33. In each graph, a gap occurs where $p = f$, which we shall discuss. Note the similarity in the shapes—a result of the fact that image and object distances for both lenses are related according to the same equation—the thin lens equation.

The curve in the upper right portion of the $f = +10$ cm graph corresponds to an object located on the *front* side of a lens, which we have drawn as the left side of the lens in our previous diagrams. When the object is at positive infinity, a real image forms at the focal point on the back side (the positive side) of the lens, $q = f$. (The incoming rays are parallel in this case.) As the object moves closer to the lens, the image

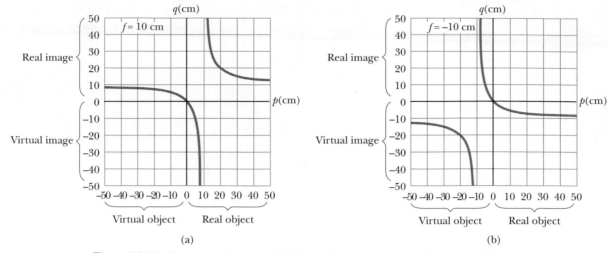

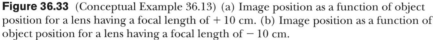

Figure 36.33 (Conceptual Example 36.13) (a) Image position as a function of object position for a lens having a focal length of + 10 cm. (b) Image position as a function of object position for a lens having a focal length of − 10 cm.

moves farther from the lens, corresponding to the upward path of the curve. This continues until the object is located at the focal point on the near side of the lens. At this point, the rays leaving the lens are parallel, making the image infinitely far away. This is described in the graph by the asymptotic approach of the curve to the line $p = f = 10$ cm.

As the object moves inside the focal point, the image becomes virtual and located near $q = -\infty$. We are now following the curve in the lower left portion of Figure 36.33a. As the object moves closer to the lens, the virtual image also moves closer to the lens. As $p \to 0$, the image distance q also approaches 0. Now imagine that we bring the object to the back side of the lens, where $p < 0$. The object is now a virtual object, so it must have been formed by some other lens. For all locations of the virtual object, the image

distance is positive and less than the focal length. The final image is real, and its position approaches the focal point as p becomes more and more negative.

The $f = -10$ cm graph shows that a distant real object forms an image at the focal point on the front side of the lens. As the object approaches the lens, the image remains virtual and moves closer to the lens. But as we continue toward the left end of the p axis, the object becomes virtual. As the position of this virtual object approaches the focal point, the image recedes toward infinity. As we pass the focal point, the image shifts from a location at positive infinity to one at negative infinity. Finally, as the virtual object continues moving away from the lens, the image is virtual, starts moving in from negative infinity, and approaches the focal point.

36.5 Lens Aberrations

Our analysis of mirrors and lenses assumes that rays make small angles with the principal axis and that the lenses are thin. In this simple model, all rays leaving a point source focus at a single point, producing a sharp image. Clearly, this is not always true. When the approximations used in this analysis do not hold, imperfect images are formed.

A precise analysis of image formation requires tracing each ray, using Snell's law at each refracting surface and the law of reflection at each reflecting surface. This procedure shows that the rays from a point object do not focus at a single point, with the result that the image is blurred. The departures of actual images from the ideal predicted by our simplified model are called **aberrations.**

Spherical Aberrations

Spherical aberrations occur because the focal points of rays far from the principal axis of a spherical lens (or mirror) are different from the focal points of rays of the same wavelength passing near the axis. Figure 36.34 illustrates spherical aberration for parallel rays passing through a converging lens. Rays passing through points near the center of

Figure 36.34 Spherical aberration caused by a converging lens. Does a diverging lens cause spherical aberration?

the lens are imaged farther from the lens than rays passing through points near the edges. Figure 36.10 earlier in the chapter showed a similar situation for a spherical mirror.

Many cameras have an adjustable aperture to control light intensity and reduce spherical aberration. (An aperture is an opening that controls the amount of light passing through the lens.) Sharper images are produced as the aperture size is reduced because with a small aperture only the central portion of the lens is exposed to the light; as a result, a greater percentage of the rays are paraxial. At the same time, however, less light passes through the lens. To compensate for this lower light intensity, a longer exposure time is used.

In the case of mirrors, spherical aberration can be minimized through the use of a parabolic reflecting surface rather than a spherical surface. Parabolic surfaces are not used often, however, because those with high-quality optics are very expensive to make. Parallel light rays incident on a parabolic surface focus at a common point, regardless of their distance from the principal axis. Parabolic reflecting surfaces are used in many astronomical telescopes to enhance image quality.

Chromatic Aberrations

The fact that different wavelengths of light refracted by a lens focus at different points gives rise to chromatic aberrations. In Chapter 35 we described how the index of refraction of a material varies with wavelength. For instance, when white light passes through a lens, violet rays are refracted more than red rays (Fig. 36.35). From this we see that the focal length of a lens is greater for red light than for violet light. Other wavelengths (not shown in Fig. 36.35) have focal points intermediate between those of red and violet.

Chromatic aberration for a diverging lens also results in a shorter focal length for violet light than for red light, but on the front side of the lens. Chromatic aberration can be greatly reduced by combining a converging lens made of one type of glass and a diverging lens made of another type of glass.

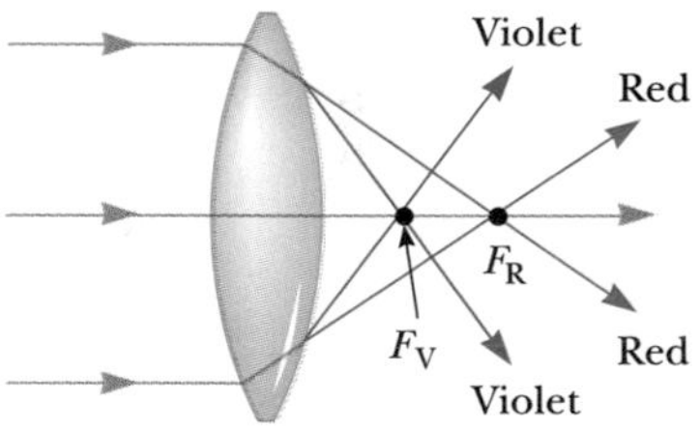

Figure 36.35 Chromatic aberration caused by a converging lens. Rays of different wavelengths focus at different points.

Quick Quiz 36.9 A curved mirrored surface can have (a) spherical aberration but not chromatic aberration (b) chromatic aberration but not spherical aberration (c) both spherical aberration and chromatic aberration.

36.6   The Camera

The photographic **camera** is a simple optical instrument whose essential features are shown in Figure 36.36. It consists of a light-tight chamber, a converging lens that produces a real image, and a film behind the lens to receive the image. One focuses the camera by varying the distance between lens and film. This is accomplished with an adjustable bellows in antique cameras and with some other mechanical arrangement in contemporary models. For proper focusing—which is necessary for the formation of sharp images—the lens-to-film distance depends on the object distance as well as on the focal length of the lens.

The shutter, positioned behind the lens, is a mechanical device that is opened for selected time intervals, called *exposure times*. One can photograph moving objects by using short exposure times or photograph dark scenes (with low light levels) by using long exposure times. If this adjustment were not available, it would be impossible to take stop-action photographs. For example, a rapidly moving vehicle could move enough in the time interval during which the shutter is open to produce a blurred image. Another major cause of blurred images is the movement of the camera while the shutter is open. To prevent such movement, either short exposure times or a tripod should be used, even for stationary objects. Typical shutter speeds (that is, exposure times) are $(1/30)$s, $(1/60)$s, $(1/125)$s, and $(1/250)$s. For handheld cameras,

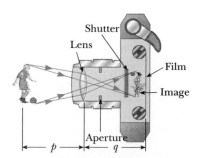

Figure 36.36 Cross-sectional view of a simple camera. Note that in reality, $p \gg q$.

the use of slower speeds can result in blurred images (due to movement), but the use of faster speeds reduces the gathered light intensity. In practice, stationary objects are normally shot with an intermediate shutter speed of $(1/60)$s.

More expensive cameras have an aperture of adjustable diameter to further control the intensity of the light reaching the film. As noted earlier, when an aperture of small diameter is used, only light from the central portion of the lens reaches the film; in this way spherical aberration is reduced.

The intensity I of the light reaching the film is proportional to the area of the lens. Because this area is proportional to the square of the diameter D, we conclude that I is also proportional to D^2. Light intensity is a measure of the rate at which energy is received by the film per unit area of the image. Because the area of the image is proportional to q^2 and $q \approx f$ (when $p \gg f$, so p can be approximated as infinite), we conclude that the intensity is also proportional to $1/f^2$, and thus $I \propto D^2/f^2$. The brightness of the image formed on the film depends on the light intensity, so we see that the image brightness depends on both the focal length and the diameter of the lens.

The ratio f/D is called the **f-number** of a lens:

$$f\text{-number} \equiv \frac{f}{D} \tag{36.18}$$

Hence, the intensity of light incident on the film varies according to the following proportionality:

$$I \propto \frac{1}{(f/D)^2} \propto \frac{1}{(f\text{-number})^2} \tag{36.19}$$

The f-number is often given as a description of the lens "speed." The lower the f-number, the wider the aperture and the higher the rate at which energy from the light exposes the film—thus, a lens with a low f-number is a "fast" lens. The conventional notation for an f-number is "$f/$" followed by the actual number. For example, "$f/4$" means an f-number of 4—it *does not* mean to divide f by 4! Extremely fast lenses, which have f-numbers as low as approximately $f/1.2$, are expensive because it is very difficult to keep aberrations acceptably small with light rays passing through a large area of the lens. Camera lens systems (that is, combinations of lenses with adjustable apertures) are often marked with multiple f-numbers, usually $f/2.8$, $f/4$, $f/5.6$, $f/8$, $f/11$, and $f/16$. Any one of these settings can be selected by adjusting the aperture, which changes the value of D. Increasing the setting from one f-number to the next higher value (for example, from $f/2.8$ to $f/4$) decreases the area of the aperture by a factor of two. The lowest f-number setting on a camera lens corresponds to a wide-open aperture and the use of the maximum possible lens area.

Simple cameras usually have a fixed focal length and a fixed aperture size, with an f-number of about $f/11$. This high value for the f-number allows for a large **depth of field,** meaning that objects at a wide range of distances from the lens form reasonably sharp images on the film. In other words, the camera does not have to be focused.

Digital cameras are similar to the cameras we have described here except that the light does not form an image on photographic film. The image in a digital camera is formed on a *charge-coupled device* (CCD), which digitizes the image, turning it into binary code, as we discussed for sound in Section 17.5. (The CCD is described in Section 40.2.) The digital information is then stored on a memory chip for playback on the screen of the camera, or it can be downloaded to a computer and sent to a friend or relative through the Internet.

Quick Quiz 36.10 A camera can be modeled as a simple converging lens that focuses an image on the film, acting as the screen. A camera is initially focused on a distant object. To focus the image of an object close to the camera, the lens must be (a) moved away from the film. (b) left where it is. (c) moved toward the film.

Example 36.14   Finding the Correct Exposure Time

The lens of a certain 35-mm camera (where 35 mm is the width of the film strip) has a focal length of 55 mm and a speed (an *f*-number) of *f*/1.8. The correct exposure time for this speed under certain conditions is known to be (1/500) s.

(A) Determine the diameter of the lens.

Solution From Equation 36.18, we find that

$$D = \frac{f}{f\text{-number}} = \frac{55 \text{ mm}}{1.8} = \boxed{31 \text{ mm}}$$

(B) Calculate the correct exposure time if the *f*-number is changed to *f*/4 under the same lighting conditions.

Solution The total light energy hitting the film is proportional to the product of the intensity and the exposure time. If *I* is the light intensity reaching the film, then in a time interval Δt the energy per unit area received by the film is proportional to $I \Delta t$. Comparing the two situations, we require that $I_1 \Delta t_1 = I_2 \Delta t_2$, where Δt_1 is the correct exposure time for *f*/1.8 and Δt_2 is the correct exposure time for *f*/4. Using this result together with Equation 36.19, we find that

$$\frac{\Delta t_1}{(f_1\text{-number})^2} = \frac{\Delta t_2}{(f_2\text{-number})^2}$$

$$\Delta t_2 = \left(\frac{f_2\text{-number}}{f_1\text{-number}} \right)^2 \Delta t_1 = \left(\frac{4}{1.8} \right)^2 \left(\frac{1}{500} \text{ s} \right) \approx \boxed{\frac{1}{100} \text{ s}}$$

As the aperture size is reduced, exposure time must increase.

36.7   The Eye

Like a camera, a normal eye focuses light and produces a sharp image. However, the mechanisms by which the eye controls the amount of light admitted and adjusts to produce correctly focused images are far more complex, intricate, and effective than those in even the most sophisticated camera. In all respects, the eye is a physiological wonder.

Figure 36.37 shows the basic parts of the human eye. Light entering the eye passes through a transparent structure called the *cornea* (Fig. 36.38), behind which are a clear liquid (the *aqueous humor*), a variable aperture (the *pupil*, which is an opening in the *iris*), and the *crystalline lens*. Most of the refraction occurs at the outer surface of the eye, where the cornea is covered with a film of tears. Relatively little refraction occurs in the crystalline lens because the aqueous humor in contact with the lens has an average index of refraction close to that of the lens. The iris, which is the colored portion

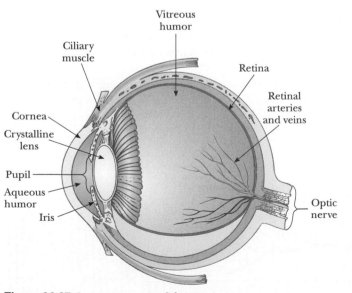

Figure 36.37 Important parts of the eye.

From Lennart Nilsson, in collaboration with Jan Lindberg, Behold Man: A Photographic Journey of Discovery Inside the Body, Boston, Little, Brown & Co., 1974

Figure 36.38 Close-up photograph of the cornea of the human eye.

of the eye, is a muscular diaphragm that controls pupil size. The iris regulates the amount of light entering the eye by dilating the pupil in low-light conditions and contracting the pupil in high-light conditions. The f-number range of the eye is from about $f/2.8$ to $f/16$.

The cornea–lens system focuses light onto the back surface of the eye, the *retina,* which consists of millions of sensitive receptors called *rods* and *cones.* When stimulated by light, these receptors send impulses via the optic nerve to the brain, where an image is perceived. By this process, a distinct image of an object is observed when the image falls on the retina.

The eye focuses on an object by varying the shape of the pliable crystalline lens through an amazing process called **accommodation.** An important component of accommodation is the *ciliary muscle,* which is situated in a circle around the rim of the lens. Thin filaments, called *zonules,* run from this muscle to the edge of the lens. When the eye is focused on a distant object, the ciliary muscle is relaxed, tightening the zonules that attach the muscle to the edge of the lens. The force of the zonules causes the lens to flatten, increasing its focal length. For an object distance of infinity, the focal length of the eye is equal to the fixed distance between lens and retina, about 1.7 cm. The eye focuses on nearby objects by tensing the ciliary muscle, which relaxes the zonules. This action allows the lens to bulge a bit, and its focal length decreases, resulting in the image being focused on the retina. All these lens adjustments take place so swiftly that we are not even aware of the change.

Accommodation is limited in that objects very close to the eye produce blurred images. The **near point** is the closest distance for which the lens can accommodate to focus light on the retina. This distance usually increases with age and has an average value of 25 cm. Typically, at age 10 the near point of the eye is about 18 cm. It increases to about 25 cm at age 20, to 50 cm at age 40, and to 500 cm or greater at age 60. The **far point** of the eye represents the greatest distance for which the lens of the relaxed eye can focus light on the retina. A person with normal vision can see very distant objects and thus has a far point that can be approximated as infinity.

Recall that the light leaving the mirror in Figure 36.8 becomes white where it comes together but then diverges into separate colors again. Because nothing but air exists at the point where the rays cross (and hence nothing exists to cause the colors to separate again), seeing white light as a result of a combination of colors must be a visual illusion. In fact, this is the case. Only three types of color-sensitive cells are present in the retina; they are called red, green, and blue cones because of the peaks of the color ranges to which they respond (Fig. 36.39). If the red and green cones are stimulated simultaneously (as would be the case if yellow light were shining on them), the brain interprets what we see as yellow. If all three types of cones are stimulated by the separate colors red, blue, and green, as in Figure 36.8, we see white. If all three types of cones are stimulated by light that contains *all* colors, such as sunlight, we again see white light.

Color televisions take advantage of this visual illusion by having only red, green, and blue dots on the screen. With specific combinations of brightness in these three

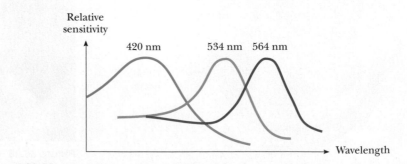

Figure 36.39 Approximate color sensitivity of the three types of cones in the retina.

primary colors, our eyes can be made to see any color in the rainbow. Thus, the yellow lemon you see in a television commercial is not really yellow, it is red and green! The paper on which this page is printed is made of tiny, matted, translucent fibers that scatter light in all directions; the resultant mixture of colors appears white to the eye. Snow, clouds, and white hair are not really white. In fact, there is no such thing as a white pigment. The appearance of these things is a consequence of the scattering of light containing all colors, which we interpret as white.

Conditions of the Eye

When the eye suffers a mismatch between the focusing range of the lens–cornea system and the length of the eye, with the result that light rays from a near object reach the retina before they converge to form an image, as shown in Figure 36.40a, the condition is known as **farsightedness** (or *hyperopia*). A farsighted person can usually see faraway objects clearly but not nearby objects. Although the near point of a normal eye is approximately 25 cm, the near point of a farsighted person is much farther away. The refracting power in the cornea and lens is insufficient to focus the light from all but distant objects satisfactorily. The condition can be corrected by placing a converging lens in front of the eye, as shown in Figure 36.40b. The lens refracts the incoming rays more toward the principal axis before entering the eye, allowing them to converge and focus on the retina.

A person with **nearsightedness** (or *myopia*), another mismatch condition, can focus on nearby objects but not on faraway objects. The far point of the nearsighted eye is not infinity and may be less than 1 m. The maximum focal length of the nearsighted eye is insufficient to produce a sharp image on the retina, and rays from a distant object converge to a focus in front of the retina. They then continue past that point, diverging before they finally reach the retina and causing blurred vision

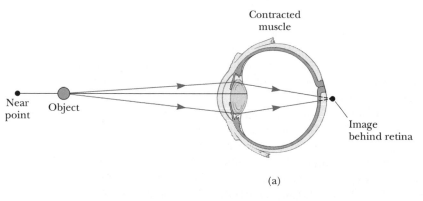

(a)

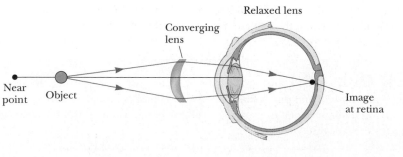

(b)

Figure 36.40 (a) When a farsighted eye looks at an object located between the near point and the eye, the image point is behind the retina, resulting in blurred vision. The eye muscle contracts to try to bring the object into focus. (b) Farsightedness is corrected with a converging lens.

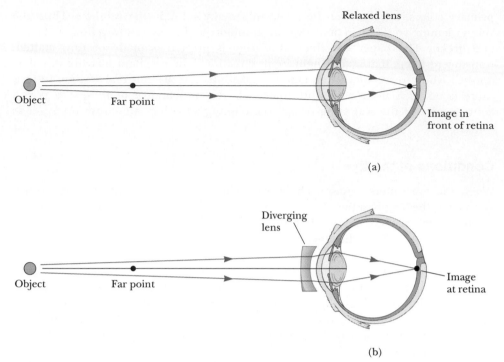

Figure 36.41 (a) When a nearsighted eye looks at an object that lies beyond the eye's far point, the image is formed in front of the retina, resulting in blurred vision. (b) Nearsightedness is corrected with a diverging lens.

(Fig. 36.41a). Nearsightedness can be corrected with a diverging lens, as shown in Figure 36.41b. The lens refracts the rays away from the principal axis before they enter the eye, allowing them to focus on the retina.

Beginning in middle age, most people lose some of their accommodation ability as the ciliary muscle weakens and the lens hardens. Unlike farsightedness, which is a mismatch between focusing power and eye length, **presbyopia** (literally, "old-age vision") is due to a reduction in accommodation ability. The cornea and lens do not have sufficient focusing power to bring nearby objects into focus on the retina. The symptoms are the same as those of farsightedness, and the condition can be corrected with converging lenses.

In the eye defect known as **astigmatism,** light from a point source produces a line image on the retina. This condition arises when either the cornea or the lens or both are not perfectly symmetric. Astigmatism can be corrected with lenses that have different curvatures in two mutually perpendicular directions.

Optometrists and ophthalmologists usually prescribe lenses[1] measured in **diopters:** the **power** P of a lens in diopters equals the inverse of the focal length in meters: $P = 1/f$. For example, a converging lens of focal length $+ 20$ cm has a power of $+ 5.0$ diopters, and a diverging lens of focal length $- 40$ cm has a power of $- 2.5$ diopters.

Quick Quiz 36.11 Two campers wish to start a fire during the day. One camper is nearsighted and one is farsighted. Whose glasses should be used to focus the Sun's rays onto some paper to start the fire? (a) either camper (b) the nearsighted camper (c) the farsighted camper.

---

[1] The word *lens* comes from *lentil,* the name of an Italian legume. (You may have eaten lentil soup.) Early eyeglasses were called "glass lentils" because the biconvex shape of their lenses resembled the shape of a lentil. The first lenses for farsightedness and presbyopia appeared around 1280; concave eyeglasses for correcting nearsightedness did not appear for more than 100 years after that.

Example 36.15   A Case of Nearsightedness

A particular nearsighted person is unable to see objects clearly when they are beyond 2.5 m away (the far point of this particular eye). What should the focal length be in a lens prescribed to correct this problem?

$$\frac{1}{p} + \frac{1}{q} = \frac{1}{\infty} + \frac{1}{-2.5 \text{ m}} = \frac{1}{f}$$

$$f = \boxed{-2.5 \text{ m}}$$

Solution The purpose of the lens in this instance is to "move" an object from infinity to a distance where it can be seen clearly. This is accomplished by having the lens produce an image at the far point. From the thin lens equation, we have

We use a negative sign for the image distance because the image is virtual and in front of the eye. As you should have suspected, the lens must be a diverging lens (one with a negative focal length) to correct nearsightedness.

36.8 The Simple Magnifier

The simple magnifier consists of a single converging lens. As the name implies, this device increases the apparent size of an object.

Suppose an object is viewed at some distance p from the eye, as illustrated in Figure 36.42. The size of the image formed at the retina depends on the angle θ subtended by the object at the eye. As the object moves closer to the eye, θ increases and a larger image is observed. However, an average normal eye cannot focus on an object closer than about 25 cm, the near point (Fig. 36.43a). Therefore, θ is maximum at the near point.

To further increase the apparent angular size of an object, a converging lens can be placed in front of the eye as in Figure 36.43b, with the object located at point O, just inside the focal point of the lens. At this location, the lens forms a virtual, upright, enlarged image. We define **angular magnification** m as the ratio of the angle subtended by an object with a lens in use (angle θ in Fig. 36.43b) to the angle subtended by the object placed at the near point with no lens in use (angle θ_0 in Fig. 36.43a):

$$m \equiv \frac{\theta}{\theta_0} \tag{36.20}$$

The angular magnification is a maximum when the image is at the near point of the eye—that is, when $q = -25$ cm. The object distance corresponding to this image

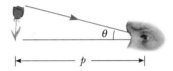

Figure 36.42 The size of the image formed on the retina depends on the angle θ subtended at the eye.

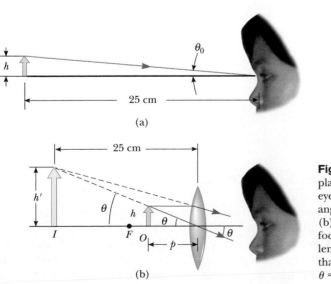

(a)

(b)

Figure 36.43 (a) An object placed at the near point of the eye ($p = 25$ cm) subtends an angle $\theta_0 \approx h/25$ at the eye. (b) An object placed near the focal point of a converging lens produces a magnified image that subtends an angle $\theta \approx h'/25$ at the eye.

distance can be calculated from the thin lens equation:

$$\frac{1}{p} + \frac{1}{-25 \text{ cm}} = \frac{1}{f}$$

$$p = \frac{25f}{25 + f}$$

where f is the focal length of the magnifier in centimeters. If we make the small-angle approximations

$$\tan \theta_0 \approx \theta_0 \approx \frac{h}{25} \quad \text{and} \quad \tan \theta \approx \theta \approx \frac{h}{p} \tag{36.21}$$

Equation 36.20 becomes

$$m_{\text{max}} = \frac{\theta}{\theta_0} = \frac{h/p}{h/25} = \frac{25}{p} = \frac{25}{25f/(25 + f)}$$

$$m_{\text{max}} = 1 + \frac{25 \text{ cm}}{f} \tag{36.22}$$

Although the eye can focus on an image formed anywhere between the near point and infinity, it is most relaxed when the image is at infinity. For the image formed by the magnifying lens to appear at infinity, the object has to be at the focal point of the lens. In this case, Equations 36.21 become

$$\theta_0 \approx \frac{h}{25} \quad \text{and} \quad \theta \approx \frac{h}{f}$$

and the magnification is

$$m_{\text{min}} = \frac{\theta}{\theta_0} = \frac{25 \text{ cm}}{f} \tag{36.23}$$

A simple magnifier, also called a magnifying glass, is used to view an enlarged image of a portion of a map.

George Semple

With a single lens, it is possible to obtain angular magnifications up to about 4 without serious aberrations. Magnifications up to about 20 can be achieved by using one or two additional lenses to correct for aberrations.

Example 36.16   Maximum Magnification of a Lens

What is the maximum magnification that is possible with a lens having a focal length of 10 cm, and what is the magnification of this lens when the eye is relaxed?

Solution The maximum magnification occurs when the image is located at the near point of the eye. Under these circumstances, Equation 36.22 gives

$$m_{\text{max}} = 1 + \frac{25 \text{ cm}}{f} = 1 + \frac{25 \text{ cm}}{10 \text{ cm}} = \boxed{3.5}$$

When the eye is relaxed, the image is at infinity. In this case, we use Equation 36.23:

$$m_{\text{min}} = \frac{25 \text{ cm}}{f} = \frac{25 \text{ cm}}{10 \text{ cm}} = \boxed{2.5}$$

36.9   The Compound Microscope

A simple magnifier provides only limited assistance in inspecting minute details of an object. Greater magnification can be achieved by combining two lenses in a device called a **compound microscope,** a schematic diagram of which is shown in Figure 36.44a. It consists of one lens, the *objective,* that has a very short focal length $f_o < 1$ cm and a second lens, the *eyepiece,* that has a focal length f_e of a few

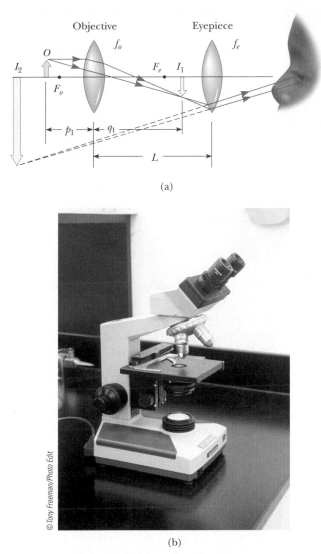

(a)

(b)

Active Figure 36.44 (a) Diagram of a compound microscope, which consists of an objective lens and an eyepiece lens. (b) A compound microscope. The three-objective turret allows the user to choose from several powers of magnification. Combinations of eyepieces with different focal lengths and different objectives can produce a wide range of magnifications.

At the Active Figures link at http://www.pse6.com, you can adjust the focal lengths of the objective and eyepiece lenses to see the effect on the final image.

centimeters. The two lenses are separated by a distance L that is much greater than either f_o or f_e. The object, which is placed just outside the focal point of the objective, forms a real, inverted image at I_1, and this image is located at or close to the focal point of the eyepiece. The eyepiece, which serves as a simple magnifier, produces at I_2 a virtual, enlarged image of I_1. The lateral magnification M_1 of the first image is $-q_1/p_1$. Note from Figure 36.44a that q_1 is approximately equal to L and that the object is very close to the focal point of the objective: $p_1 \approx f_o$. Thus, the lateral magnification by the objective is

$$M_o \approx -\frac{L}{f_o}$$

The angular magnification by the eyepiece for an object (corresponding to the image at I_1) placed at the focal point of the eyepiece is, from Equation 36.23,

$$m_e = \frac{25 \text{ cm}}{f_e}$$

The overall magnification of the image formed by a compound microscope is defined as the product of the lateral and angular magnifications:

$$M = M_o m_e = -\frac{L}{f_o}\left(\frac{25 \text{ cm}}{f_e}\right) \tag{36.24}$$

The negative sign indicates that the image is inverted.

The microscope has extended human vision to the point where we can view previously unknown details of incredibly small objects. The capabilities of this instrument have steadily increased with improved techniques for precision grinding of lenses. A question often asked about microscopes is: "If one were extremely patient and careful, would it be possible to construct a microscope that would enable the human eye to see an atom?" The answer is no, as long as light is used to illuminate the object. The reason is that, for an object under an optical microscope (one that uses visible light) to be seen, the object must be at least as large as a wavelength of light. Because the diameter of any atom is many times smaller than the wavelengths of visible light, the mysteries of the atom must be probed using other types of "microscopes."

The ability to use other types of waves to "see" objects also depends on wavelength. We can illustrate this with water waves in a bathtub. Suppose you vibrate your hand in the water until waves having a wavelength of about 15 cm are moving along the surface. If you hold a small object, such as a toothpick, so that it lies in the path of the waves, it does not appreciably disturb the waves; they continue along their path "oblivious" to it. Now suppose you hold a larger object, such as a toy sailboat, in the path of the 15-cm waves. In this case, the waves are considerably disturbed by the object. Because the toothpick is smaller than the wavelength of the waves, the waves do not "see" it. (The intensity of the scattered waves is low.) Because it is about the same size as the wavelength of the waves, however, the boat creates a disturbance. In other words, the object acts as the source of scattered waves that appear to come from it.

Light waves behave in this same general way. The ability of an optical microscope to view an object depends on the size of the object relative to the wavelength of the light used to observe it. Hence, we can never observe atoms with an optical microscope[2] because their dimensions are small (<0.1 nm) relative to the wavelength of the light (<500 nm).

36.10 The Telescope

Two fundamentally different types of **telescopes** exist; both are designed to aid in viewing distant objects, such as the planets in our Solar System. The **refracting telescope** uses a combination of lenses to form an image, and the **reflecting telescope** uses a curved mirror and a lens.

The lens combination shown in Figure 36.45a is that of a refracting telescope. Like the compound microscope, this telescope has an objective and an eyepiece. The two lenses are arranged so that the objective forms a real, inverted image of a distant object very near the focal point of the eyepiece. Because the object is essentially at infinity, this point at which I_1 forms is the focal point of the objective. The eyepiece then forms, at I_2, an enlarged, inverted image of the image at I_1. In order to provide the largest possible magnification, the image distance for the eyepiece is infinite. This means that the light rays exit the eyepiece lens parallel to the principal axis, and the image of the objective lens must form at the focal point of the eyepiece. Hence, the two lenses are separated by a distance $f_o + f_e$, which corresponds to the length of the telescope tube.

---

[2]   Single-molecule near-field optic studies are routinely performed with visible light having wavelengths of about 500 nm. The technique uses very small apertures to produce images having resolutions as small as 10 nm.

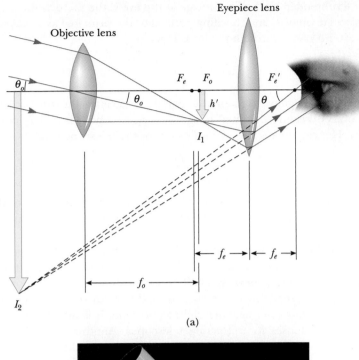

Objective lens

Eyepiece lens

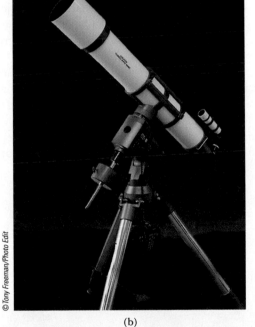

(a)

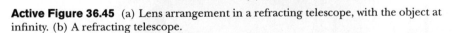

(b)

Active Figure 36.45 (a) Lens arrangement in a refracting telescope, with the object at infinity. (b) A refracting telescope.

At the Active Figures link at http://www.pse6.com, you can adjust the focal lengths of the objective and eyepiece lenses to see the effect on the final image.

The angular magnification of the telescope is given by θ/θ_o, where θ_o is the angle subtended by the object at the objective and θ is the angle subtended by the final image at the viewer's eye. Consider Figure 36.45a, in which the object is a very great distance to the left of the figure. The angle θ_o (to the *left* of the objective) subtended by the object at the objective is the same as the angle (to the *right* of the objective) subtended by the first image at the objective. Thus,

$$\tan \theta_o \approx \theta_o \approx -\frac{h'}{f_o}$$

where the negative sign indicates that the image is inverted.

The angle θ subtended by the final image at the eye is the same as the angle that a ray coming from the tip of I_1 and traveling parallel to the principal axis makes with the principal axis after it passes through the lens. Thus,

$$\tan \theta \approx \theta \approx \frac{h'}{f_e}$$

We have not used a negative sign in this equation because the final image is not inverted; the object creating this final image I_2 is I_1, and both it and I_2 point in the same direction. Hence, the angular magnification of the telescope can be expressed as

$$m = \frac{\theta}{\theta_o} = \frac{h'/f_e}{-h'/f_o} = -\frac{f_o}{f_e} \tag{36.25}$$

and we see that the angular magnification of a telescope equals the ratio of the objective focal length to the eyepiece focal length. The negative sign indicates that the image is inverted.

When we look through a telescope at such relatively nearby objects as the Moon and the planets, magnification is important. However, individual stars in our galaxy are so far away that they always appear as small points of light no matter how great the magnification. A large research telescope that is used to study very distant objects must have a great diameter to gather as much light as possible. It is difficult and expensive to manufacture large lenses for refracting telescopes. Another difficulty with large lenses is that their weight leads to sagging, which is an additional source of aberration. These problems can be partially overcome by replacing the objective with a concave mirror, which results in a reflecting telescope. Because light is reflected from the mirror and does not pass through a lens, the mirror can have rigid supports on the back side. Such supports eliminate the problem of sagging.

Figure 36.46a shows the design for a typical reflecting telescope. Incoming light rays pass down the barrel of the telescope and are reflected by a parabolic mirror at the base. These rays converge toward point A in the figure, where an image would be formed. However, before this image is formed, a small, flat mirror M reflects the light toward an opening in the side of the tube that passes into an eyepiece. This particular design is said to have a Newtonian focus because Newton developed it. Figure 36.46b

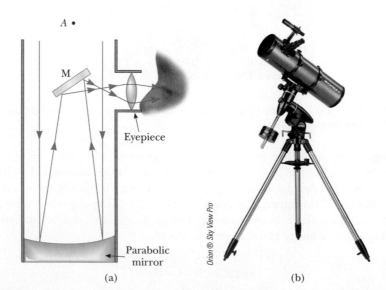

Figure 36.46 (a) A Newtonian-focus reflecting telescope. (b) A reflecting telescope. This type of telescope is shorter than that in Figure 36.45b.

shows such a telescope. Note that in the reflecting telescope the light never passes through glass (except through the small eyepiece). As a result, problems associated with chromatic aberration are virtually eliminated. The reflecting telescope can be made even shorter by orienting the flat mirror so that it reflects the light back toward the objective mirror and the light enters an eyepiece in a hole in the middle of the mirror.

The largest reflecting telescopes in the world are at the Keck Observatory on Mauna Kea, Hawaii. The site includes two telescopes with diameters of 10 m, each containing 36 hexagonally shaped, computer-controlled mirrors that work together to form a large reflecting surface. In contrast, the largest refracting telescope in the world, at the Yerkes Observatory in Williams Bay, Wisconsin, has a diameter of only 1 m.

SUMMARY

Take a practice test for this chapter by clicking on the Practice Test link at http://www.pse6.com.

The **lateral magnification** M of the image due to a mirror or lens is defined as the ratio of the image height h' to the object height h and is equal to the negative of the ratio of the image distance q to the object distance p:

$$M = \frac{h'}{h} = -\frac{q}{p} \qquad (36.1, 36.2)$$

In the paraxial ray approximation, the object distance p and image distance q for a spherical mirror of radius R are related by the **mirror equation:**

$$\frac{1}{p} + \frac{1}{q} = \frac{2}{R} = \frac{1}{f} \qquad (36.4, 36.6)$$

where $f = R/2$ is the **focal length** of the mirror.

An image can be formed by refraction from a spherical surface of radius R. The object and image distances for refraction from such a surface are related by

$$\frac{n_1}{p} + \frac{n_2}{q} = \frac{n_2 - n_1}{R} \qquad (36.8)$$

where the light is incident in the medium for which the index of refraction is n_1 and is refracted in the medium for which the index of refraction is n_2.

The inverse of the **focal length** f of a thin lens surrounded by air is given by the **lens makers' equation:**

$$\frac{1}{f} = (n - 1)\left(\frac{1}{R_1} - \frac{1}{R_2}\right) \qquad (36.15)$$

Converging lenses have positive focal lengths, and **diverging lenses** have negative focal lengths.

For a thin lens, and in the paraxial ray approximation, the object and image distances are related by the **thin lens equation:**

$$\frac{1}{p} + \frac{1}{q} = \frac{1}{f} \qquad (36.16)$$

The ratio of the focal length of a camera lens to the diameter of the lens is called the *f*-**number** of the lens:

$$f\text{-number} \equiv \frac{f}{D} \qquad (36.18)$$

The intensity of light incident on the film in the camera varies according to:

$$I \propto \frac{1}{(f/D)^2} \propto \frac{1}{(f\text{-number})^2} \qquad (36.19)$$

The maximum magnification of a single lens of focal length f used as a simple magnifier is

$$m_{\max} = 1 + \frac{25 \text{ cm}}{f} \tag{36.22}$$

The overall magnification of the image formed by a compound microscope is:

$$M = -\frac{L}{f_o}\left(\frac{25 \text{ cm}}{f_e}\right) \tag{36.24}$$

where f_o and f_e are the focal lengths of the objective and eyepiece lenses, respectively, and L is the distance between the lenses.

The angular magnification of a refracting telescope can be expressed as

$$m = -\frac{f_o}{f_e} \tag{36.25}$$

where f_o and f_e are the focal lengths of the objective and eyepiece lenses, respectively. The angular magnification of a reflecting telescope is given by the same expression where f_o is the focal length of the objective mirror.

QUESTIONS

1. What is wrong with the caption of the cartoon shown in Figure Q36.1?

© 2003 Sidney Harris

Figure Q36.1 "Most mirrors reverse left and right. This one reverses top and bottom."

2. Consider a concave spherical mirror with a real object. Is the image always inverted? Is the image always real? Give conditions for your answers.

3. Repeat the preceding question for a convex spherical mirror.

4. Do the equations $1/p + 1/q = 1/f$ or $M = -q/p$ apply to the image formed by a flat mirror? Explain your answer.

5. Why does a clear stream, such as a creek, always appear to be shallower than it actually is? By how much is its depth apparently reduced?

6. Consider the image formed by a thin converging lens. Under what conditions is the image (a) inverted, (b) upright, (c) real, (d) virtual, (e) larger than the object, and (f) smaller than the object?

7. Repeat Question 6 for a thin diverging lens.

8. Use the lens makers' equation to verify the sign of the focal length of each of the lenses in Figure 36.27.

9. If a solid cylinder of glass or clear plastic is placed above the words LEAD OXIDE and viewed from above as shown

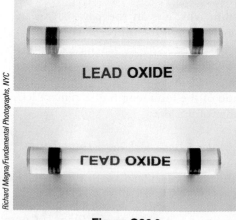

Richard Megna/Fundamental Photographs, NYC

Figure Q36.9

in Figure Q36.9, the LEAD appears inverted but the OXIDE does not. Explain.

10. In Figure 36.28a, assume that the blue object arrow is replaced by one that is much taller than the lens. How many rays from the object will strike the lens? How many principal rays can be drawn in a ray diagram?

11. A zip-lock plastic sandwich bag filled with water can act as a crude converging lens in air. If the bag is filled with air and placed under water, is the effective lens converging or diverging?

12. Explain why a mirror cannot give rise to chromatic aberration.

13. Why do some automobile mirrors have printed on them the statement "Objects in mirror are closer than they appear"? (See Fig. P36.19.)

14. Can a converging lens be made to diverge light if it is placed into a liquid? **What If?** How about a converging mirror?

15. Explain why a fish in a spherical goldfish bowl appears larger than it really is.

16. Why do some emergency vehicles have the symbol ƎƆИA⅃UᙠMA written on the front?

17. A lens forms an image of an object on a screen. What happens to the image if you cover the top half of the lens with paper?

18. Lenses used in eyeglasses, whether converging or diverging, are always designed so that the middle of the lens curves away from the eye, like the center lenses of Figure 36.27a and b. Why?

19. Which glasses in Figure Q36.19 correct nearsightedness and which correct farsightedness?

Figure Q36.19

20. A child tries on either his hyperopic grandfather's or his myopic brother's glasses and complains that "everything looks blurry." Why do the eyes of a person wearing glasses not look blurry? (See Figure Q36.19.)

21. Consider a spherical concave mirror, with the object located to the left of the mirror beyond the focal point. Using ray diagrams, show that the image moves to the left as the object approaches the focal point.

22. In a Jules Verne novel, a piece of ice is shaped to form a magnifying lens to focus sunlight to start a fire. Is this possible?

23. The *f*-number of a camera is the focal length of the lens divided by its aperture (or diameter). How can the *f*-number of the lens be changed? How does changing this number affect the required exposure time?

24. A solar furnace can be constructed by using a concave mirror to reflect and focus sunlight into a furnace enclosure. What factors in the design of the reflecting mirror would guarantee very high temperatures?

25. One method for determining the position of an image, either real or virtual, is by means of *parallax*. If a finger or other object is placed at the position of the image, as shown in Figure Q36.25, and the finger and image are viewed simultaneously (the image is viewed through the lens if it is virtual), the finger and image have the same parallax; that is, if they are viewed from different positions, the image will appear to move along with the finger. Use this method to locate the image formed by a lens. Explain why the method works.

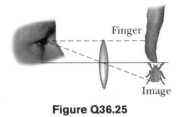

Finger

Image

Figure Q36.25

26. Figure Q36.26 shows a lithograph by M. C. Escher titled *Hand with Reflection Sphere (Self-Portrait in Spherical Mirror)*. Escher had this to say about the work: "The picture

Figure Q36.26

shows a spherical mirror, resting on a left hand. But as a print is the reverse of the original drawing on stone, it was my right hand that you see depicted. (Being left-handed, I needed my left hand to make the drawing.) Such a globe reflection collects almost one's whole surroundings in one disk-shaped image. The whole room, four walls, the floor, and the ceiling, everything, albeit distorted, is compressed into that one small circle. Your own head, or more exactly the point between your eyes, is the absolute center. No matter how you turn or twist yourself, you can't get out of that central point. You are immovably the focus, the unshakable core, of your world." Comment on the accuracy of Escher's description.

27. You can make a corner reflector by placing three flat mirrors in the corner of a room where the ceiling meets the walls. Show that no matter where you are in the room, you can see yourself reflected in the mirrors—upside down.

28. A converging lens of short focal length can take light diverging from a small source and refract it into a beam of parallel rays. A Fresnel lens, as shown in Figure 36.29, is used for this purpose in a lighthouse. A concave mirror can take light diverging from a small source and reflect it into a beam of parallel rays. Is it possible to make a Fresnel mirror? Is this an original idea, or has it already been done? *Suggestion:* Look at the walls and ceiling of an auditorium.

PROBLEMS

1, 2, 3 = straightforward, intermediate, challenging ☐ = full solution available in the *Student Solutions Manual and Study Guide*

🌐 = coached solution with hints available at http://www.pse6.com 💻 = computer useful in solving problem

▨ = paired numerical and symbolic problems

Section 36.1 Images Formed by Flat Mirrors

1. Does your bathroom mirror show you older or younger than you actually are? Compute an order-of-magnitude estimate for the age difference, based on data that you specify.

2. In a church choir loft, two parallel walls are 5.30 m apart. The singers stand against the north wall. The organist faces the south wall, sitting 0.800 m away from it. To enable her to see the choir, a flat mirror 0.600 m wide is mounted on the south wall, straight in front of her. What width of the north wall can she see? *Suggestion:* Draw a top-view diagram to justify your answer.

3. Determine the minimum height of a vertical flat mirror in which a person 5′10″ in height can see his or her full image. (A ray diagram would be helpful.)

4. Two flat mirrors have their reflecting surfaces facing each other, with the edge of one mirror in contact with an edge of the other, so that the angle between the mirrors is α. When an object is placed between the mirrors, a number of images are formed. In general, if the angle α is such that $n\alpha = 360°$, where n is an integer, the number of images formed is $n - 1$. Graphically, find all the image positions for the case $n = 6$ when a point object is between the mirrors (but not on the angle bisector).

5. A person walks into a room with two flat mirrors on opposite walls, which produce multiple images. When the person is located 5.00 ft from the mirror on the left wall and 10.0 ft from the mirror on the right wall, find the distance from the person to the first three images seen in the mirror on the left.

6. A periscope (Figure P36.6) is useful for viewing objects that cannot be seen directly. It finds use in submarines and in watching golf matches or parades from behind a crowd of people. Suppose that the object is a distance p_1 from the upper mirror and that the two flat mirrors are separated by a distance h. (a) What is the distance of the final image from the lower mirror? (b) Is the final image real or virtual? (c) Is it upright or inverted? (d) What is its magnification? (e) Does it appear to be left–right reversed?

Figure P36.6

Section 36.2 Images Formed by Spherical Mirrors

7. A concave spherical mirror has a radius of curvature of 20.0 cm. Find the location of the image for object distances of (a) 40.0 cm, (b) 20.0 cm, and (c) 10.0 cm. For each case, state whether the image is real or virtual and upright or inverted. Find the magnification in each case.

8. At an intersection of hospital hallways, a convex mirror is mounted high on a wall to help people avoid collisions. The mirror has a radius of curvature of 0.550 m. Locate and describe the image of a patient 10.0 m from the mirror. Determine the magnification.

9. A spherical convex mirror has a radius of curvature with a magnitude of 40.0 cm. Determine the position of the virtual image and the magnification for object distances of (a) 30.0 cm and (b) 60.0 cm. (c) Are the images upright or inverted?

10. A large church has a niche in one wall. On the floor plan it appears as a semicircular indentation of radius 2.50 m. A worshiper stands on the center line of the niche, 2.00 m out from its deepest point, and whispers a prayer. Where is the sound concentrated after reflection from the back wall of the niche?

11. A concave mirror has a radius of curvature of 60.0 cm. Calculate the image position and magnification of an object placed in front of the mirror at distances of (a) 90.0 cm and (b) 20.0 cm. (c) Draw ray diagrams to obtain the image characteristics in each case.

12. A concave mirror has a focal length of 40.0 cm. Determine the object position for which the resulting image is upright and four times the size of the object.

13. A certain Christmas tree ornament is a silver sphere having a diameter of 8.50 cm. Determine an object location for which the size of the reflected image is three-fourths the size of the object. Use a principal-ray diagram to arrive at a description of the image.

14. (a) A concave mirror forms an inverted image four times larger than the object. Find the focal length of the mirror, assuming the distance between object and image is 0.600 m. (b) A convex mirror forms a virtual image half the size of the object. Assuming the distance between image and object is 20.0 cm, determine the radius of curvature of the mirror.

15. To fit a contact lens to a patient's eye, a *keratometer* can be used to measure the curvature of the front surface of the eye, the cornea. This instrument places an illuminated object of known size at a known distance p from the cornea. The cornea reflects some light from the object, forming an image of the object. The magnification M of the image is measured by using a small viewing telescope that allows comparison of the image formed by the cornea with a second calibrated image projected into the field of view by a prism arrangement. Determine the radius of curvature of the cornea for the case $p = 30.0$ cm and $M = 0.013\ 0$.

16. An object 10.0 cm tall is placed at the zero mark of a meter stick. A spherical mirror located at some point on the meter stick creates an image of the object that is upright, 4.00 cm tall, and located at the 42.0-cm mark of the meter stick. (a) Is the mirror convex or concave? (b) Where is the mirror? (c) What is the mirror's focal length?

17. A spherical mirror is to be used to form, on a screen located 5.00 m from the object, an image five times the size of the object. (a) Describe the type of mirror required. (b) Where should the mirror be positioned relative to the object?

18. A dedicated sports car enthusiast polishes the inside and outside surfaces of a hubcap that is a section of a sphere. When she looks into one side of the hubcap, she sees an image of her face 30.0 cm in back of the hubcap. She then flips the hubcap over and sees another image of her face 10.0 cm in back of the hubcap. (a) How far is her face from the hubcap? (b) What is the radius of curvature of the hubcap?

19. You unconsciously estimate the distance to an object from the angle it subtends in your field of view. This angle θ in radians is related to the linear height of the object h and to the distance d by $\theta = h/d$. Assume that you are driving a car and another car, 1.50 m high, is 24.0 m behind you. (a) Suppose your car has a flat passenger-side rearview mirror, 1.55 m from your eyes. How far from your eyes is the image of the car following you? (b) What angle does the image subtend in your field of view? (c) **What If?** Suppose instead that your car has a convex rearview mirror with a radius of curvature of magnitude 2.00 m (Fig. P36.19). How far from your eyes is the image of the car behind you? (d) What angle does the image subtend at your eyes? (e) Based on its angular size, how far away does the following car appear to be?

THE FAR SIDE®   By GARY LARSON

Figure P36.19

20. **Review Problem.** A ball is dropped at $t = 0$ from rest 3.00 m directly above the vertex of a concave mirror that has a radius of curvature of 1.00 m and lies in a horizontal plane. (a) Describe the motion of the ball's image in the mirror. (b) At what time do the ball and its image coincide?

Section 36.3   Images Formed by Refraction

21. A cubical block of ice 50.0 cm on a side is placed on a level floor over a speck of dust. Find the location of the image of the speck as viewed from above. The index of refraction of ice is 1.309.

22. A flint glass plate ($n = 1.66$) rests on the bottom of an aquarium tank. The plate is 8.00 cm thick (vertical dimension) and is covered with a layer of water ($n = 1.33$) 12.0 cm deep. Calculate the apparent thickness of the plate as viewed from straight above the water.

23. A glass sphere ($n = 1.50$) with a radius of 15.0 cm has a tiny air bubble 5.00 cm above its center. The sphere is viewed looking down along the extended radius containing the bubble. What is the apparent depth of the bubble below the surface of the sphere?

24. A simple model of the human eye ignores its lens entirely. Most of what the eye does to light happens at the outer surface of the transparent cornea. Assume that this surface has a radius of curvature of 6.00 mm, and assume that the eyeball contains just one fluid with a refractive index of 1.40. Prove that a very distant object will be imaged on the retina, 21.0 mm behind the cornea. Describe the image.

25. One end of a long glass rod ($n = 1.50$) is formed into a convex surface with a radius of curvature of 6.00 cm. An object is located in air along the axis of the rod. Find the image positions corresponding to object distances of (a) 20.0 cm, (b) 10.0 cm, and (c) 3.00 cm from the end of the rod.

26. A transparent sphere of unknown composition is observed to form an image of the Sun on the surface of the sphere opposite the Sun. What is the refractive index of the sphere material?

27. A goldfish is swimming at 2.00 cm/s toward the front wall of a rectangular aquarium. What is the apparent speed of the fish measured by an observer looking in from outside the front wall of the tank? The index of refraction of water is 1.33.

Section 36.4   Thin Lenses

28. A contact lens is made of plastic with an index of refraction of 1.50. The lens has an outer radius of curvature of $+2.00$ cm and an inner radius of curvature of $+2.50$ cm. What is the focal length of the lens?

29. The left face of a biconvex lens has a radius of curvature of magnitude 12.0 cm, and the right face has a radius of curvature of magnitude 18.0 cm. The index of refraction of the glass is 1.44. (a) Calculate the focal length of the lens. (b) **What If?** Calculate the focal length the lens has after is turned around to interchange the radii of curvature of the two faces.

30. A converging lens has a focal length of 20.0 cm. Locate the image for object distances of (a) 40.0 cm, (b) 20.0 cm, and (c) 10.0 cm. For each case, state whether the image is real or virtual and upright or inverted. Find the magnification in each case.

31. A thin lens has a focal length of 25.0 cm. Locate and describe the image when the object is placed (a) 26.0 cm and (b) 24.0 cm in front of the lens.

32. An object located 32.0 cm in front of a lens forms an image on a screen 8.00 cm behind the lens. (a) Find the focal length of the lens. (b) Determine the magnification. (c) Is the lens converging or diverging?

33. The nickel's image in Figure P36.33 has twice the diameter of the nickel and is 2.84 cm from the lens. Determine the focal length of the lens.

Figure P36.33

34. A person looks at a gem with a jeweler's loupe—a converging lens that has a focal length of 12.5 cm. The loupe forms a virtual image 30.0 cm from the lens. (a) Determine the magnification. Is the image upright or inverted? (b) Construct a ray diagram for this arrangement.

35. Suppose an object has thickness dp so that it extends from object distance p to $p + dp$. Prove that the thickness dq of its image is given by $(-q^2/p^2)\,dp$, so that the longitudinal magnification $dq/dp = -M^2$, where M is the lateral magnification.

36. The projection lens in a certain slide projector is a single thin lens. A slide 24.0 mm high is to be projected so that its image fills a screen 1.80 m high. The slide-to-screen distance is 3.00 m. (a) Determine the focal length of the projection lens. (b) How far from the slide should the lens of the projector be placed in order to form the image on the screen?

37. An object is located 20.0 cm to the left of a diverging lens having a focal length $f = -32.0$ cm. Determine (a) the location and (b) the magnification of the image. (c) Construct a ray diagram for this arrangement.

38. An antelope is at a distance of 20.0 m from a converging lens of focal length 30.0 cm. The lens forms an image of the animal. If the antelope runs away from the lens at a speed of 5.00 m/s, how fast does the image move? Does the image move toward or away from the lens?

39. In some types of optical spectroscopy, such as photoluminescence and Raman spectroscopy, a laser beam exits from a pupil and is focused on a sample to stimulate electromagnetic radiation from the sample. The focusing lens usually has an antireflective coating preventing any light loss. Assume a 100-mW laser is located 4.80 m from the lens, which has a focal length of 7.00 cm. (a) How far from the lens should the sample be located so that an image of the laser exit pupil is formed on the surface of the sample? (b) If the diameter of the laser exit pupil is 5.00 mm, what is the diameter of the light spot on the sample? (c) What is the light intensity at the spot?

40. Figure P36.40 shows a thin glass ($n = 1.50$) converging lens for which the radii of curvature are $R_1 = 15.0$ cm and $R_2 = -12.0$ cm. To the left of the lens is a cube having a face area of 100 cm^2. The base of the cube is on the axis of the lens, and the right face is 20.0 cm to the left of the lens. (a) Determine the focal length of the lens. (b) Draw the image of the square face formed by the lens. What type of geometric figure is this? (c) Determine the area of the image.

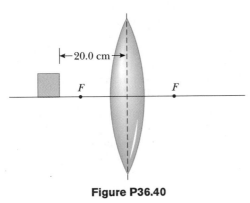

Figure P36.40

41. An object is at a distance d to the left of a flat screen. A converging lens with focal length $f < d/4$ is placed between object and screen. (a) Show that two lens positions exist that form an image on the screen, and determine how far these positions are from the object. (b) How do the two images differ from each other?

42. Figure 36.36 diagrams a cross section of a camera. It has a single lens of focal length 65.0 mm, which is to form an image on the film at the back of the camera. Suppose the position of the lens has been adjusted to focus the image of a distant object. How far and in what direction must the lens be moved to form a sharp image of an object that is 2.00 m away?

43. The South American capybara is the largest rodent on Earth; its body can be 1.20 m long. The smallest rodent is the pygmy mouse found in Texas, with an average body length of 3.60 cm. Assume that a pygmy mouse is observed by looking through a lens placed 20.0 cm from the mouse. The whole image of the mouse is the size of a capybara. Then the lens is moved a certain distance along its axis, and the image of the mouse is the same size as before! How far was the lens moved?

Section 36.5   Lens Aberrations

44. The magnitudes of the radii of curvature are 32.5 cm and 42.5 cm for the two faces of a biconcave lens. The glass has index of refraction 1.53 for violet light and 1.51 for red light. For a very distant object, locate and describe (a) the image formed by violet light, and (b) the image formed by red light.

45. Two rays traveling parallel to the principal axis strike a large plano-convex lens having a refractive index of 1.60 (Fig. P36.45). If the convex face is spherical, a ray near the edge does not pass through the focal point (spherical aberration occurs). Assume this face has a radius of curvature of 20.0 cm and the two rays are at distances $h_1 = 0.500$ cm and $h_2 = 12.0$ cm from the principal axis. Find the difference Δx in the positions where each crosses the principal axis.

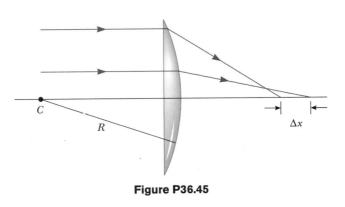

Figure P36.45

Section 36.6   The Camera

46. A camera is being used with a correct exposure at $f/4$ and a shutter speed of $(1/16)$ s. In order to photograph a rapidly moving subject, the shutter speed is changed to $(1/128)$ s. Find the new f-number setting needed to maintain satisfactory exposure.

Section 36.7   The Eye

47. A nearsighted person cannot see objects clearly beyond 25.0 cm (her far point). If she has no astigmatism and contact lenses are prescribed for her, what power and type of lens are required to correct her vision?

48. The accommodation limits for Nearsighted Nick's eyes are 18.0 cm and 80.0 cm. When he wears his glasses, he can see faraway objects clearly. At what minimum distance is he able to see objects clearly?

49. A person sees clearly when he wears eyeglasses that have a power of -4.00 diopters and sit 2.00 cm in front of his eyes. If the person wants to switch to contact lenses, which are placed directly on the eyes, what lens power should be prescribed?

Section 36.8   The Simple Magnifier
Section 36.9   The Compound Microscope
Section 36.10   The Telescope

50. A lens that has a focal length of 5.00 cm is used as a magnifying glass. (a) To obtain maximum magnification, where should the object be placed? (b) What is the magnification?

51. The distance between eyepiece and objective lens in a certain compound microscope is 23.0 cm. The focal length of the eyepiece is 2.50 cm, and that of the objective is 0.400 cm. What is the overall magnification of the microscope?

52. The desired overall magnification of a compound microscope is 140×. The objective alone produces a lateral magnification of 12.0×. Determine the required focal length of the eyepiece.

53. The Yerkes refracting telescope has a 1.00-m diameter objective lens of focal length 20.0 m. Assume it is used with an eyepiece of focal length 2.50 cm. (a) Determine the magnification of the planet Mars as seen through this telescope. (b) Are the Martian polar caps right side up or upside down?

54. Astronomers often take photographs with the objective lens or mirror of a telescope alone, without an eyepiece. (a) Show that the image size h' for this telescope is given by $h' = fh/(f - p)$ where h is the object size, f is the objective focal length, and p is the object distance. (b) **What If?** Simplify the expression in part (a) for the case in which the object distance is much greater than objective focal length. (c) The "wingspan" of the International Space Station is 108.6 m, the overall width of its solar panel configuration. Find the width of the image formed by a telescope objective of focal length 4.00 m when the station is orbiting at an altitude of 407 km.

55. Galileo devised a simple terrestrial telescope that produces an upright image. It consists of a converging objective lens and a diverging eyepiece at opposite ends of the telescope tube. For distant objects, the tube length is equal to the objective focal length minus the absolute value of the eyepiece focal length. (a) Does the user of the telescope see a real or virtual image? (b) Where is the final image? (c) If a telescope is to be constructed with a tube of length 10.0 cm and a magnification of 3.00, what are the focal lengths of the objective and eyepiece?

56. A certain telescope has an objective mirror with an aperture diameter of 200 mm and a focal length of 2 000 mm. It captures the image of a nebula on photographic film at its prime focus with an exposure time of 1.50 min. To produce the same light energy per unit area on the film, what is the required exposure time to photograph the same nebula with a smaller telescope, which has an objective with a diameter of 60.0 mm and a focal length of 900 mm?

Additional Problems

57. The distance between an object and its upright image is 20.0 cm. If the magnification is 0.500, what is the focal length of the lens that is being used to form the image?

58. The distance between an object and its upright image is d. If the magnification is M, what is the focal length of the lens that is being used to form the image?

59. Your friend needs glasses with diverging lenses of focal length -65.0 cm for both eyes. You tell him he looks good

when he doesn't squint, but he is worried about how thick the lenses will be. Assuming the radius of curvature of the first surface is $R_1 = 50.0$ cm and the high-index plastic has a refractive index of 1.66, (a) find the required radius of curvature of the second surface. (b) Assume the lens is ground from a disk 4.00 cm in diameter and 0.100 cm thick at the center. Find the thickness of the plastic at the edge of the lens, measured parallel to the axis. *Suggestion:* Draw a large cross-sectional diagram.

60. A cylindrical rod of glass with index of refraction 1.50 is immersed in water with index 1.33. The diameter of the rod is 9.00 cm. The outer part of each end of the rod has been ground away to form each end into a hemisphere of radius 4.50 cm. The central portion of the rod with straight sides is 75.0 cm long. An object is situated in the water, on the axis of the rod, at a distance of 100 cm from the vertex of the nearer hemisphere. (a) Find the location of the final image formed by refraction at both surfaces. (b) Is the final image real or virtual? Upright or inverted? Enlarged or diminished?

61. A *zoom lens* system is a combination of lenses that produces a variable magnification while maintaining fixed object and image positions. The magnification is varied by moving one or more lenses along the axis. While multiple lenses are used in practice to obtain high-quality images, the effect of zooming in on an object can be demonstrated with a simple two-lens system. An object, two converging lenses, and a screen are mounted on an optical bench. The first lens, which is to the right of the object, has a focal length of 5.00 cm, and the second lens, which is to the right of the first lens, has a focal length of 10.0 cm. The screen is to the right of the second lens. Initially, an object is situated at a distance of 7.50 cm to the left of the first lens, and the image formed on the screen has a magnification of +1.00. (a) Find the distance between the object and the screen. (b) Both lenses are now moved along their common axis, while the object and the screen maintain fixed positions, until the image formed on the screen has a magnification of +3.00. Find the displacement of each lens from its initial position in (a). Can the lenses be displaced in more than one way?

62. The object in Figure P36.62 is midway between the lens and the mirror. The mirror's radius of curvature is 20.0 cm, and the lens has a focal length of -16.7 cm. Considering only the light that leaves the object and travels first toward the mirror, locate the final image formed by this system. Is this image real or virtual? Is it upright or inverted? What is the overall magnification?

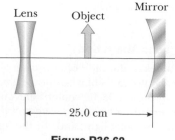

Figure P36.62

63. An object placed 10.0 cm from a concave spherical mirror produces a real image 8.00 cm from the mirror. If the object is moved to a new position 20.0 cm from the mirror, what is the position of the image? Is the latter image real or virtual?

64. In many applications it is necessary to expand or to decrease the diameter of a beam of parallel rays of light. This change can be made by using a converging lens and a diverging lens in combination. Suppose you have a converging lens of focal length 21.0 cm and a diverging lens of focal length − 12.0 cm. How can you arrange these lenses to increase the diameter of a beam of parallel rays? By what factor will the diameter increase?

65. A parallel beam of light enters a glass hemisphere perpendicular to the flat face, as shown in Figure P36.65. The magnitude of the radius is 6.00 cm, and the index of refraction is 1.560. Determine the point at which the beam is focused. (Assume paraxial rays.)

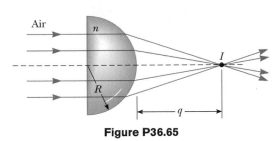

Figure P36.65

66. Review problem. A spherical lightbulb of diameter 3.20 cm radiates light equally in all directions, with power 4.50 W. (a) Find the light intensity at the surface of the bulb. (b) Find the light intensity 7.20 m away from the center of the bulb. (c) At this 7.20-m distance a lens is set up with its axis pointing toward the bulb. The lens has a circular face with a diameter 15.0 cm and has a focal length of 35.0 cm. Find the diameter of the image of the bulb. (d) Find the light intensity at the image.

67. An object is placed 12.0 cm to the left of a diverging lens of focal length − 6.00 cm. A converging lens of focal length 12.0 cm is placed a distance d to the right of the diverging lens. Find the distance d so that the final image is at infinity. Draw a ray diagram for this case.

68. An observer to the right of the mirror–lens combination shown in Figure P36.68 sees two real images that are the same size and in the same location. One image is upright and the other is inverted. Both images are 1.50 times larger than the object. The lens has a focal length of 10.0 cm. The lens and mirror are separated by 40.0 cm. Determine the focal length of the mirror. Do not assume that the figure is drawn to scale.

69. The disk of the Sun subtends an angle of 0.533° at the Earth. What are the position and diameter of the solar image formed by a concave spherical mirror with a radius of curvature of 3.00 m?

70. Assume the intensity of sunlight is 1.00 kW/m² at a particular location. A highly reflecting concave mirror is to be pointed toward the Sun to produce a power of at least 350 W at the image. (a) Find the required radius R_a of the circular face area of the mirror. (b) Now suppose the light intensity is to be at least 120 kW/m² at the image. Find the required relationship between R_a and the radius of curvature R of the mirror. The disk of the Sun subtends an angle of 0.533° at the Earth.

71. In a darkened room, a burning candle is placed 1.50 m from a white wall. A lens is placed between candle and wall at a location that causes a larger, inverted image to form on the wall. When the lens is moved 90.0 cm toward the wall, another image of the candle is formed. Find (a) the two object distances that produce the specified images and (b) the focal length of the lens. (c) Characterize the second image.

72. Figure P36.72 shows a thin converging lens for which the radii of curvature are $R_1 = 9.00$ cm and $R_2 = − 11.0$ cm. The lens is in front of a concave spherical mirror with the radius of curvature $R = 8.00$ cm. (a) Assume its focal points F_1 and F_2 are 5.00 cm from the center of the lens. Determine its index of refraction. (b) The lens and mirror are 20.0 cm apart, and an object is placed 8.00 cm to the left of the lens. Determine the position of the final image and its magnification as seen by the eye in the figure. (c) Is the final image inverted or upright? Explain.

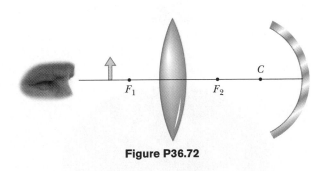

Figure P36.72

73. A compound microscope has an objective of focal length 0.300 cm and an eyepiece of focal length 2.50 cm. If an object is 3.40 mm from the objective, what is the magnification? (*Suggestion:* Use the lens equation for the objective.)

74. Two converging lenses having focal lengths of 10.0 cm and 20.0 cm are located 50.0 cm apart, as shown in

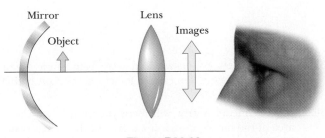

Figure P36.68

Figure P36.74. The final image is to be located between the lenses at the position indicated. (a) How far to the left of the first lens should the object be? (b) What is the overall magnification? (c) Is the final image upright or inverted?

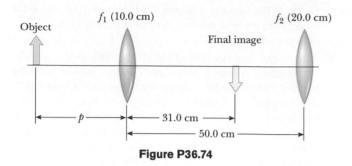

Figure P36.74

75. A cataract-impaired lens in an eye may be surgically removed and replaced by a manufactured lens. The focal length required for the new lens is determined by the lens-to-retina distance, which is measured by a sonar-like device, and by the requirement that the implant provide for correct distant vision. (a) Assuming the distance from lens to retina is 22.4 mm, calculate the power of the implanted lens in diopters. (b) Because no accommodation occurs and the implant allows for correct distant vision, a corrective lens for close work or reading must be used. Assume a reading distance of 33.0 cm and calculate the power of the lens in reading glasses.

76. A floating strawberry illusion is achieved with two parabolic mirrors, each having a focal length 7.50 cm, facing each other so that their centers are 7.50 cm apart (Fig.

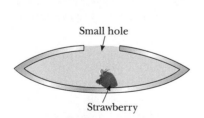

Figure P36.76

P36.76). If a strawberry is placed on the lower mirror, an image of the strawberry is formed at the small opening at the center of the top mirror. Show that the final image is formed at that location and describe its characteristics. (*Note:* A very startling effect is to shine a flashlight beam on this image. Even at a glancing angle, the incoming light beam is seemingly reflected from the image! Do you understand why?)

77. An object 2.00 cm high is placed 40.0 cm to the left of a converging lens having a focal length of 30.0 cm. A diverging lens with a focal length of −20.0 cm is placed 110 cm to the right of the converging lens. (a) Determine the position and magnification of the final image. (b) Is the image upright or inverted? (c) **What If?** Repeat parts (a) and (b) for the case where the second lens is a converging lens having a focal length of +20.0 cm.

78. Two lenses made of kinds of glass having different refractive indices n_1 and n_2 are cemented together to form what is called an *optical doublet*. Optical doublets are often used to correct chromatic aberrations in optical devices. The first lens of a doublet has one flat side and one concave side of radius of curvature R. The second lens has two convex sides of radius of curvature R. Show that the doublet can be modeled as a single thin lens with a focal length described by

$$\frac{1}{f} = \frac{2n_2 - n_1 - 1}{R}$$

Answers to Quick Quizzes

36.1 At C. A ray traced from the stone to the mirror and then to observer 2 looks like this:

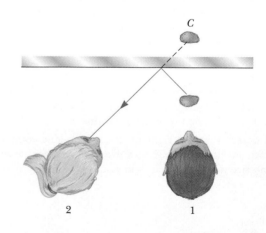

36.2 False. The water spots are 2 m away from you and your image is 4 m away. You cannot focus your eyes on both at the same time.

36.3 (b). A concave mirror will focus the light from a large area of the mirror onto a small area of the paper, resulting in a very high power input to the paper.

36.4 (b). A convex mirror always forms an image with a magnification less than one, so the mirror must be concave. In a concave mirror, only virtual images are upright. This particular photograph is of the Hubble Space Telescope primary mirror.

36.5 (d). When O is far away, the rays refract into the material of index n_2 and converge to form a real image as in Figure 36.18. For certain combinations of R and n_2 as O moves very close to the refracting surface, the incident angle of the rays increases so much that rays are no longer refracted back toward the principal axis. This results in a virtual image as shown below:

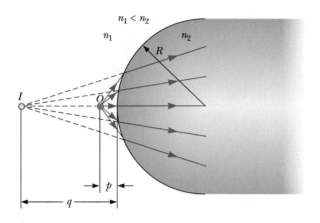

36.6 (a). No matter where O is, the rays refract into the air away from the normal and form a virtual image between O and the surface.

36.7 (b). Because the flat surfaces of the plane have infinite radii of curvature, Equation 36.15 indicates that the focal length is also infinite. Parallel rays striking the plane focus at infinity, which means that they remain parallel after passing through the glass.

36.8 (b). If there is a curve on the front surface, the refraction will differ at that surface when the mask is worn in air and water. In order for there to be no difference in refraction (for normal incidence), the front of the mask should be flat.

36.9 (a). Because the light reflecting from a mirror does not enter the material of the mirror, there is no opportunity for the dispersion of the material to cause chromatic aberration.

36.10 (a). If the object is brought closer to the lens, the image moves farther away from the lens, behind the plane of the film. In order to bring the image back up to the film, the lens is moved toward the object and away from the film.

36.11 (c). The Sun's rays must converge onto the paper. A far-sighted person wears converging lenses.

Chapter 37

Interference of Light Waves

▲ The colors in many of a hummingbird's feathers are not due to pigment. The iridescence that makes the brilliant colors that often appear on the throat and belly is due to an interference effect caused by structures in the feathers. The colors will vary with the viewing angle. (RO-MA/Index Stock Imagery)

In the preceding chapter, we used light rays to examine what happens when light passes through a lens or reflects from a mirror. This discussion completed our study of *geometric optics*. Here in Chapter 37 and in the next chapter, we are concerned with *wave optics* or *physical optics,* the study of interference, diffraction, and polarization of light. These phenomena cannot be adequately explained with the ray optics used in Chapters 35 and 36. We now learn how treating light as waves rather than as rays leads to a satisfying description of such phenomena.

37.1 Conditions for Interference

In Chapter 18, we found that the superposition of two mechanical waves can be constructive or destructive. In constructive interference, the amplitude of the resultant wave at a given position or time is greater than that of either individual wave, whereas in destructive interference, the resultant amplitude is less than that of either individual wave. Light waves also interfere with each other. Fundamentally, all interference associated with light waves arises when the electromagnetic fields that constitute the individual waves combine.

As with the hummingbird feathers shown in the opening photograph, the bright colors of peacock feathers are also due to interference. In both types of birds, structures in the feathers split and recombine visible light so that interference occurs for certain colors.

If two lightbulbs are placed side by side, no interference effects are observed because the light waves from one bulb are emitted independently of those from the other bulb. The emissions from the two lightbulbs do not maintain a constant phase relationship with each other over time. Light waves from an ordinary source such as a lightbulb undergo random phase changes in time intervals less than a nanosecond. Therefore, the conditions for constructive interference, destructive interference, or some intermediate state are maintained only for such short time intervals. Because the eye cannot follow such rapid changes, no interference effects are observed. Such light sources are said to be **incoherent.**

In order to observe interference in light waves, the following conditions must be met:

- The sources must be **coherent**—that is, **they must maintain a constant phase with respect to each other.**

- The sources should be **monochromatic**—that is, of a single wavelength.

Conditions for interference

As an example, single-frequency sound waves emitted by two side-by-side loudspeakers driven by a single amplifier can interfere with each other because the two speakers are coherent—that is, they respond to the amplifier in the same way at the same time.

37.2 Young's Double-Slit Experiment

A common method for producing two coherent light sources is to use a monochromatic source to illuminate a barrier containing two small openings (usually in the shape of slits). The light emerging from the two slits is coherent because a single

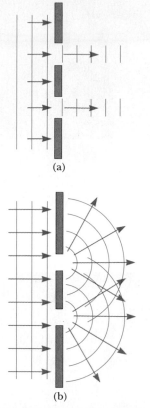

(a)

(b)

Figure 37.1 (a) If light waves did not spread out after passing through the slits, no interference would occur. (b) The light waves from the two slits overlap as they spread out, filling what we expect to be shadowed regions with light and producing interference fringes on a screen placed to the right of the slits.

▲ **PITFALL PREVENTION**

37.1 Interference Patterns Are Not Standing Waves

The interference pattern in Figure 37.2b shows bright and dark regions that appear similar to the antinodes and nodes of a standing-wave pattern on a string (Section 18.3). While both patterns depend on the principle of superposition, here are two major differences: (1) waves on a string propagate in only one dimension while the light-wave interference pattern exists in three dimensions; (2) the standing-wave pattern represents no net energy flow, while there is a net energy flow from the slits to the screen in an interference pattern.

At a beach in Tel Aviv, Israel, plane water waves pass through two openings in a breakwall. Notice the diffraction effect—the waves exit the openings with circular wave fronts, as in Figure 37.1b. Notice also how the beach has been shaped by the circular wave fronts.

source produces the original light beam and the two slits serve only to separate the original beam into two parts (which, after all, is what is done to the sound signal from the side-by-side loudspeakers at the end of the preceding section). Any random change in the light emitted by the source occurs in both beams at the same time, and as a result interference effects can be observed when the light from the two slits arrives at a viewing screen.

If the light traveled only in its original direction after passing through the slits, as shown in Figure 37.1a, the waves would not overlap and no interference pattern would be seen. Instead, as we have discussed in our treatment of Huygens's principle (Section 35.6), the waves spread out from the slits as shown in Figure 37.1b. In other words, the light deviates from a straight-line path and enters the region that would otherwise be shadowed. As noted in Section 35.3, this divergence of light from its initial line of travel is called **diffraction.**

Interference in light waves from two sources was first demonstrated by Thomas Young in 1801. A schematic diagram of the apparatus that Young used is shown in Figure 37.2a. Plane light waves arrive at a barrier that contains two parallel slits S_1 and S_2. These two slits serve as a pair of coherent light sources because waves emerging from them originate from the same wave front and therefore maintain a constant phase relationship. The light from S_1 and S_2 produces on a viewing screen a visible pattern of bright and dark parallel bands called **fringes** (Fig. 37.2b). When the light from S_1 and that from S_2 both arrive at a point on the screen such that constructive interference occurs at that location, a bright fringe appears. When the light from the two slits combines destructively at any location on the screen, a dark fringe results. Figure 37.3 is a photograph of an interference pattern produced by two coherent vibrating sources in a water tank.

Figure 37.4 shows some of the ways in which two waves can combine at the screen. In Figure 37.4a, the two waves, which leave the two slits in phase, strike the screen at the central point P. Because both waves travel the same distance, they arrive at P in phase. As a result, constructive interference occurs at this location, and a bright fringe is observed. In Figure 37.4b, the two waves also start in phase, but in this case the upper wave has to travel one wavelength farther than the lower

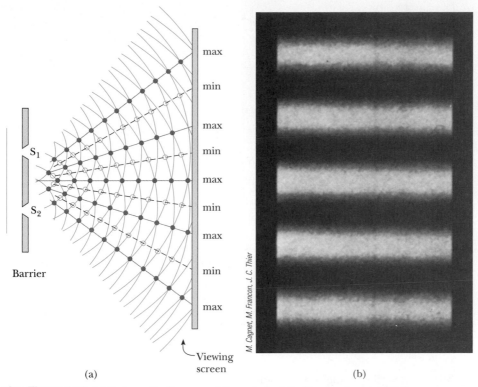

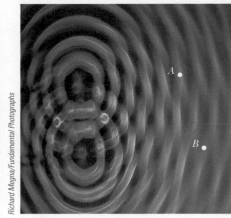

Figure 37.3 An interference pattern involving water waves is produced by two vibrating sources at the water's surface. The pattern is analogous to that observed in Young's double-slit experiment. Note the regions of constructive (*A*) and destructive (*B*) interference.

Active Figure 37.2 (a) Schematic diagram of Young's double-slit experiment. Slits S$_1$ and S$_2$ behave as coherent sources of light waves that produce an interference pattern on the viewing screen (drawing not to scale). (b) An enlargement of the center of a fringe pattern formed on the viewing screen.

At the Active Figures link at http://www.pse6.com, you can adjust the slit separation and the wavelength of the light to see the effect on the interference pattern.

wave to reach point *Q*. Because the upper wave falls behind the lower one by exactly one wavelength, they still arrive in phase at *Q*, and so a second bright fringe appears at this location. At point *R* in Figure 37.4c, however, between points *P* and *Q*, the upper wave has fallen half a wavelength behind the lower wave. This means that a trough of the lower wave overlaps a crest of the upper wave; this gives rise to destructive interference at point *R*. For this reason, a dark fringe is observed at this location.

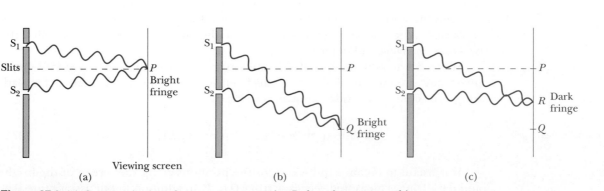

Figure 37.4 (a) Constructive interference occurs at point *P* when the waves combine. (b) Constructive interference also occurs at point *Q*. (c) Destructive interference occurs at *R* when the two waves combine because the upper wave falls half a wavelength behind the lower wave. (All figures not to scale.)

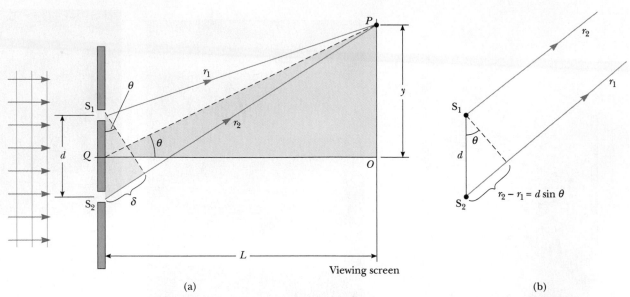

Figure 37.5 (a) Geometric construction for describing Young's double-slit experiment (not to scale). (b) When we assume that r_1 is parallel to r_2, the path difference between the two rays is $r_2 - r_1 = d \sin \theta$. For this approximation to be valid, it is essential that $L \gg d$.

We can describe Young's experiment quantitatively with the help of Figure 37.5. The viewing screen is located a perpendicular distance L from the barrier containing two slits, S_1 and S_2. These slits are separated by a distance d, and the source is monochromatic. To reach any arbitrary point P in the upper half of the screen, a wave from the lower slit must travel farther than a wave from the upper slit by a distance $d \sin \theta$. This distance is called the **path difference** δ (lowercase Greek delta). If we assume that r_1 and r_2 are parallel, which is approximately true if L is much greater than d, then δ is given by

Path difference

$$\delta = r_2 - r_1 = d \sin\theta \qquad (37.1)$$

The value of δ determines whether the two waves are in phase when they arrive at point P. If δ is either zero or some integer multiple of the wavelength, then the two waves are in phase at point P and constructive interference results. Therefore, the condition for bright fringes, or **constructive interference,** at point P is

Conditions for constructive interference

$$\delta = d \sin\theta_{\text{bright}} = m\lambda \qquad (m = 0, \pm 1, \pm 2, \ldots) \qquad (37.2)$$

The number m is called the **order number.** For constructive interference, the order number is the same as the number of wavelengths that represents the path difference between the waves from the two slits. The central bright fringe at $\theta = 0$ is called the *zeroth-order maximum.* The first maximum on either side, where $m = \pm 1$, is called the *first-order maximum,* and so forth.

When δ is an odd multiple of $\lambda/2$, the two waves arriving at point P are $180°$ out of phase and give rise to destructive interference. Therefore, the condition for dark fringes, or **destructive interference,** at point P is

Conditions for destructive interference

$$d \sin\theta_{\text{dark}} = (m + \tfrac{1}{2})\lambda \qquad (m = 0, \pm 1, \pm 2, \ldots) \qquad (37.3)$$

It is useful to obtain expressions for the positions along the screen of the bright and dark fringes measured vertically from O to P. In addition to our assumption that $L \gg d$, we assume $d \gg \lambda$. These can be valid assumptions because in practice L is often on the order of 1 m, d a fraction of a millimeter, and λ a fraction of a micrometer for visible light. Under these conditions, θ is small; thus, we can use the small angle approximation $\sin\theta \approx \tan\theta$. Then, from triangle OPQ in Figure 37.5a, we see that

$$y = L \tan\theta \approx L \sin\theta \qquad (37.4)$$

Solving Equation 37.2 for $\sin\theta$ and substituting the result into Equation 37.4, we see that the positions of the bright fringes measured from O are given by the expression

$$y_{\text{bright}} = \frac{\lambda L}{d} m \qquad (m = 0, \pm 1, \pm 2, \ldots) \qquad (37.5)$$

Using Equations 37.3 and 37.4, we find that the dark fringes are located at

$$y_{\text{dark}} = \frac{\lambda L}{d} (m + \tfrac{1}{2}) \qquad (m = 0, \pm 1, \pm 2, \ldots) \qquad (37.6)$$

As we demonstrate in Example 37.1, Young's double-slit experiment provides a method for measuring the wavelength of light. In fact, Young used this technique to do just that. Additionally, his experiment gave the wave model of light a great deal of credibility. It was inconceivable that particles of light coming through the slits could cancel each other in a way that would explain the dark fringes.

▲ **PITFALL PREVENTION**

37.2 It May Not Be True That θ Is Small

The approximation $\sin\theta \approx \tan\theta$ is true to three-digit precision only for angles less than about 4°. If you are considering fringes that are far removed from the central fringe, $\tan\theta = y/L$ is still true, but the small-angle approximation may not be valid. In this case, Equations 37.5 and 37.6 cannot be used. These problems can be solved, but the geometry is not as simple.

▲ **PITFALL PREVENTION**

37.3 It May Not Be True That $L \gg d$

Equations 37.2, 37.3, 37.5, and 37.6 were developed under the assumption that $L \gg d$. This is a very common situation, but you are likely to encounter some situations in which this assumption is not valid. In those cases, the geometric construction will be more complicated, but the general approach outlined here will be similar.

Quick Quiz 37.1 If you were to blow smoke into the space between the barrier and the viewing screen of Figure 37.5a, the smoke would show (a) no evidence of interference between the barrier and the screen (b) evidence of interference everywhere between the barrier and the screen.

Quick Quiz 37.2 In a two-slit interference pattern projected on a screen, the fringes are equally spaced on the screen (a) everywhere (b) only for large angles (c) only for small angles.

Quick Quiz 37.3 Which of the following will cause the fringes in a two-slit interference pattern to move farther apart? (a) decreasing the wavelength of the light (b) decreasing the screen distance L (c) decreasing the slit spacing d (d) immersing the entire apparatus in water.

Example 37.1 Measuring the Wavelength of a Light Source   `Interactive`

A viewing screen is separated from a double-slit source by 1.2 m. The distance between the two slits is 0.030 mm. The second-order bright fringe ($m = 2$) is 4.5 cm from the center line.

(A) Determine the wavelength of the light.

Solution We can use Equation 37.5, with $m = 2$, $y_{\text{bright}} = 4.5 \times 10^{-2}$ m, $L = 1.2$ m, and $d = 3.0 \times 10^{-5}$ m:

$$\lambda = \frac{y_{\text{bright}} d}{mL} = \frac{(4.5 \times 10^{-2} \text{ m})(3.0 \times 10^{-5} \text{ m})}{2(1.2 \text{ m})}$$

$$= 5.6 \times 10^{-7} \text{ m} = \boxed{560 \text{ nm}}$$

which is in the green range of visible light.

(B) Calculate the distance between adjacent bright fringes.

Solution From Equation 37.5 and the results of part (A), we obtain

$$y_{m+1} - y_m = \frac{\lambda L}{d}(m + 1) - \frac{\lambda L}{d} m$$

$$= \frac{\lambda L}{d} = \frac{(5.6 \times 10^{-7} \text{ m})(1.2 \text{ m})}{3.0 \times 10^{-5} \text{ m}}$$

$$= 2.2 \times 10^{-2} \text{ m} = \boxed{2.2 \text{ cm}}$$

Investigate the double-slit interference pattern at the Interactive Worked Example link at **http://www.pse6.com.**

Example 37.2   Separating Double-Slit Fringes of Two Wavelengths

A light source emits visible light of two wavelengths: $\lambda = 430$ nm and $\lambda' = 510$ nm. The source is used in a double-slit interference experiment in which $L = 1.50$ m and $d = 0.025\,0$ mm. Find the separation distance between the third-order bright fringes.

Solution Using Equation 37.5, with $m = 3$, we find that the fringe positions corresponding to these two wavelengths are

$$y_{bright} = \frac{\lambda L}{d} m = 3 \frac{\lambda L}{d} = 3 \frac{(430 \times 10^{-9}\,\text{m})(1.50\,\text{m})}{0.025\,0 \times 10^{-3}\,\text{m}}$$

$$= 7.74 \times 10^{-2}\,\text{m}$$

$$y'_{bright} = \frac{\lambda' L}{d} m = 3 \frac{\lambda' L}{d} = 3 \frac{(510 \times 10^{-9}\,\text{m})(1.50\,\text{m})}{0.025\,0 \times 10^{-3}\,\text{m}}$$

$$= 9.18 \times 10^{-2}\,\text{m}$$

Hence, the separation distance between the two fringes is

$$\Delta y = 9.18 \times 10^{-2}\,\text{m} - 7.74 \times 10^{-2}\,\text{m}$$

$$= 1.40 \times 10^{-2}\,\text{m} = \boxed{1.40\,\text{cm}}$$

What If? What if we examine the entire interference pattern due to the two wavelengths and look for overlapping fringes? Are there any locations on the screen where the bright fringes from the two wavelengths overlap exactly?

Answer We could find such a location by setting the location of any bright fringe due to λ equal to one due to λ',

using Equation 37.5:

$$\frac{\lambda L}{d} m = \frac{\lambda' L}{d} m'$$

$$\frac{\lambda}{\lambda'} = \frac{m'}{m}$$

Substituting the wavelengths, we have

$$\frac{m'}{m} = \frac{\lambda}{\lambda'} = \frac{430\,\text{nm}}{510\,\text{nm}} = \frac{43}{51}$$

This might suggest that the 51st bright fringe of the 430-nm light would overlap with the 43rd bright fringe of the 510-nm light. However, if we use Equation 37.5 to find the value of y for these fringes, we find

$$y = 51 \frac{(430 \times 10^{-9}\,\text{m})(1.5\,\text{m})}{0.025 \times 10^{-3}\,\text{m}} = 1.32\,\text{m} = y'$$

This value of y is comparable to L, so that the small-angle approximation used in Equation 37.4 is *not* valid. This suggests that we should not expect Equation 37.5 to give us the correct result. If you use the exact relationship $y = L \tan\theta$, you can show that the bright fringes do indeed overlap when the same condition, $m'/m = \lambda/\lambda'$, is met (see Problem 44). Thus, the 51st fringe of the 430-nm light does overlap with the 43rd fringe of the 510-nm light, but not at the location of 1.32 m. You are asked to find the correct location as part of Problem 44.

37.3   Intensity Distribution of the Double-Slit Interference Pattern

Note that the edges of the bright fringes in Figure 37.2b are not sharp—there is a gradual change from bright to dark. So far we have discussed the locations of only the centers of the bright and dark fringes on a distant screen. Let us now direct our attention to the intensity of the light at other points between the positions of maximum constructive and destructive interference. In other words, we now calculate the distribution of light intensity associated with the double-slit interference pattern.

Again, suppose that the two slits represent coherent sources of sinusoidal waves such that the two waves from the slits have the same angular frequency ω and a constant phase difference ϕ. The total magnitude of the electric field at point P on the screen in Figure 37.6 is the superposition of the two waves. Assuming that the two waves have the same amplitude E_0, we can write the magnitude of the electric field at point P due to each wave separately as

$$E_1 = E_0 \sin \omega t \quad \text{and} \quad E_2 = E_0 \sin(\omega t + \phi) \tag{37.7}$$

Although the waves are in phase at the slits, *their phase difference ϕ at P depends on the path difference* $\delta = r_2 - r_1 = d \sin\theta$. A path difference of λ (for constructive interference) corresponds to a phase difference of 2π rad. A path difference of δ is the same fraction of λ as the phase difference ϕ is of 2π. We can describe this mathematically

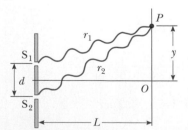

Figure 37.6 Construction for analyzing the double-slit interference pattern. A bright fringe, or intensity maximum, is observed at O.

with the ratio

$$\frac{\delta}{\lambda} = \frac{\phi}{2\pi}$$

which gives us

$$\phi = \frac{2\pi}{\lambda} \delta = \frac{2\pi}{\lambda} d \sin \theta \qquad (37.8)$$

Phase difference

This equation tells us precisely how the phase difference ϕ depends on the angle θ in Figure 37.5.

Using the superposition principle and Equation 37.7, we can obtain the magnitude of the resultant electric field at point P:

$$E_P = E_1 + E_2 = E_0[\sin \omega t + \sin(\omega t + \phi)] \qquad (37.9)$$

To simplify this expression, we use the trigonometric identity

$$\sin A + \sin B = 2 \sin\left(\frac{A + B}{2}\right) \cos\left(\frac{A - B}{2}\right)$$

Taking $A = \omega t + \phi$ and $B = \omega t$, we can write Equation 37.9 in the form

$$E_P = 2E_0 \cos\left(\frac{\phi}{2}\right) \sin\left(\omega t + \frac{\phi}{2}\right) \qquad (37.10)$$

This result indicates that the electric field at point P has the same frequency ω as the light at the slits, but that the amplitude of the field is multiplied by the factor $2 \cos(\phi/2)$. To check the consistency of this result, note that if $\phi = 0, 2\pi, 4\pi, \ldots$, then the magnitude of the electric field at point P is $2E_0$, corresponding to the condition for maximum constructive interference. These values of ϕ are consistent with Equation 37.2 for constructive interference. Likewise, if $\phi = \pi, 3\pi, 5\pi, \ldots$, then the magnitude of the electric field at point P is zero; this is consistent with Equation 37.3 for total destructive interference.

Finally, to obtain an expression for the light intensity at point P, recall from Section 34.3 that *the intensity of a wave is proportional to the square of the resultant electric field magnitude at that point* (Eq. 34.21). Using Equation 37.10, we can therefore express the light intensity at point P as

$$I \propto E_P^2 = 4E_0^2 \cos^2\left(\frac{\phi}{2}\right) \sin^2\left(\omega t + \frac{\phi}{2}\right)$$

Most light-detecting instruments measure time-averaged light intensity, and the time-averaged value of $\sin^2(\omega t + \phi/2)$ over one cycle is $\frac{1}{2}$. (See Figure 33.5.) Therefore, we can write the average light intensity at point P as

$$I = I_{\text{max}} \cos^2\left(\frac{\phi}{2}\right) \qquad (37.11)$$

where I_{max} is the maximum intensity on the screen and the expression represents the time average. Substituting the value for ϕ given by Equation 37.8 into this expression, we find that

$$I = I_{\text{max}} \cos^2\left(\frac{\pi d \sin \theta}{\lambda}\right) \qquad (37.12)$$

Alternatively, because $\sin\theta \approx y/L$ for small values of θ in Figure 37.5, we can write Equation 37.12 in the form

$$I \approx I_{\text{max}} \cos^2\left(\frac{\pi d}{\lambda L} y\right) \qquad (37.13)$$

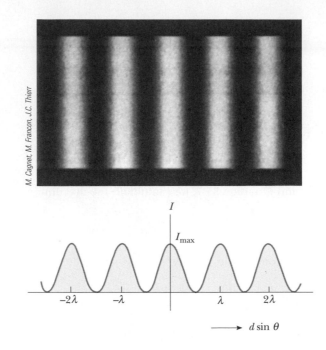

M. Cagnet, M. Francon, J.C. Thierr

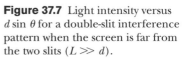

Figure 37.7 Light intensity versus $d \sin \theta$ for a double-slit interference pattern when the screen is far from the two slits ($L \gg d$).

Constructive interference, which produces light intensity maxima, occurs when the quantity $\pi \, dy/\lambda L$ is an integral multiple of π, corresponding to $y = (\lambda L/d)m$. This is consistent with Equation 37.5.

A plot of light intensity versus $d \sin \theta$ is given in Figure 37.7. The interference pattern consists of equally spaced fringes of equal intensity. Remember, however, that this result is valid only if the slit-to-screen distance L is much greater than the slit separation, and only for small values of θ.

Quick Quiz 37.4 At dark areas in an interference pattern, the light waves have canceled. Thus, there is zero intensity at these regions and, therefore, no energy is arriving. Consequently, when light waves interfere and form an interference pattern, (a) energy conservation is violated because energy disappears in the dark areas (b) energy transferred by the light is transformed to another type of energy in the dark areas (c) the total energy leaving the slits is distributed among light and dark areas and energy is conserved.

37.4 Phasor Addition of Waves

In the preceding section, we combined two waves algebraically to obtain the resultant wave amplitude at some point on a screen. Unfortunately, this analytical procedure becomes cumbersome when we must add several wave amplitudes. Because we shall eventually be interested in combining a large number of waves, we now describe a graphical procedure for this purpose.

Let us again consider a sinusoidal wave whose electric field component is given by

$$E_1 = E_0 \sin \omega t$$

where E_0 is the wave amplitude and ω is the angular frequency. We used phasors in Chapter 33 to analyze AC circuits, and again we find the use of phasors to be valuable

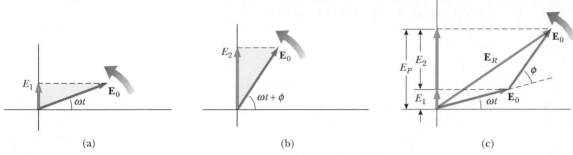

(a)   (b)   (c)

Figure 37.8 (a) Phasor diagram for the wave disturbance $E_1 = E_0 \sin \omega t$. The phasor is a vector of length E_0 rotating counterclockwise. (b) Phasor diagram for the wave $E_2 = E_0 \sin(\omega t + \phi)$. (c) The phasor $\mathbf{E}_R$ represents the combination of the waves in part (a) and (b).

in discussing wave interference. The sinusoidal wave we are discussing can be represented graphically by a phasor of magnitude E_0 rotating about the origin counterclockwise with an angular frequency ω, as in Figure 37.8a. Note that the phasor makes an angle ωt with the horizontal axis. The projection of the phasor on the vertical axis represents E_1, the magnitude of the wave disturbance at some time t. Hence, as the phasor rotates in a circle about the origin, the projection E_1 oscillates along the vertical axis.

Now consider a second sinusoidal wave whose electric field component is given by

$$E_2 = E_0 \sin(\omega t + \phi)$$

This wave has the same amplitude and frequency as E_1, but its phase is ϕ with respect to E_1. The phasor representing E_2 is shown in Figure 37.8b. We can obtain the resultant wave, which is the sum of E_1 and E_2, graphically by redrawing the phasors as shown in Figure 37.8c, in which the tail of the second phasor is placed at the tip of the first. As with vector addition, the resultant phasor $\mathbf{E}_R$ runs from the tail of the first phasor to the tip of the second. Furthermore, $\mathbf{E}_R$ rotates along with the two individual phasors at the same angular frequency ω. The projection of $\mathbf{E}_R$ along the vertical axis equals the sum of the projections of the two other phasors: $E_P = E_1 + E_2$.

It is convenient to construct the phasors at $t = 0$ as in Figure 37.9. From the geometry of one of the right triangles, we see that

$$\cos \alpha = \frac{E_R/2}{E_0}$$

which gives

$$E_R = 2E_0 \cos \alpha$$

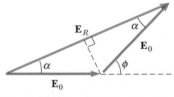

Figure 37.9 A reconstruction of the resultant phasor $\mathbf{E}_R$. From the geometry, note that $\alpha = \phi/2$.

Because the sum of the two opposite interior angles equals the exterior angle ϕ, we see that $\alpha = \phi/2$; thus,

$$E_R = 2E_0 \cos\left(\frac{\phi}{2}\right)$$

Hence, the projection of the phasor $\mathbf{E}_R$ along the vertical axis at any time t is

$$E_P = E_R \sin\left(\omega t + \frac{\phi}{2}\right) = 2E_0 \cos(\phi/2) \sin\left(\omega t + \frac{\phi}{2}\right)$$

This is consistent with the result obtained algebraically, Equation 37.10. The resultant phasor has an amplitude $2E_0 \cos(\phi/2)$ and makes an angle $\phi/2$ with the first phasor.

Furthermore, the average light intensity at point P, which varies as $E_P{}^2$, is proportional to $\cos^2(\phi/2)$, as described in Equation 37.11.

We can now describe how to obtain the resultant of several waves that have the same frequency:

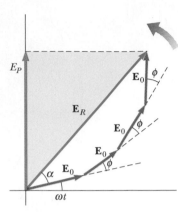

Figure 37.10 The phasor $\mathbf{E}_R$ is the resultant of four phasors of equal amplitude E_0. The phase of $\mathbf{E}_R$ with respect to the first phasor is α. The projection E_P on the vertical axis represents the combination of the four phasors.

- Represent the waves by phasors, as shown in Figure 37.10, remembering to maintain the proper phase relationship between one phasor and the next.

- The resultant phasor $\mathbf{E}_R$ is the vector sum of the individual phasors. At each instant, the projection of $\mathbf{E}_R$ along the vertical axis represents the time variation of the resultant wave. The phase angle α of the resultant wave is the angle between $\mathbf{E}_R$ and the first phasor. From Figure 37.10, drawn for four phasors, we see that the resultant wave is given by the expression $E_P = E_R \sin(\omega t + \alpha)$.

Phasor Diagrams for Two Coherent Sources

As an example of the phasor method, consider the interference pattern produced by two coherent sources. Figure 37.11 represents the phasor diagrams for various values of the phase difference ϕ and the corresponding values of the path difference δ, which are obtained from Equation 37.8. The light intensity at a point is a maximum when $\mathbf{E}_R$ is a maximum; this occurs at $\phi = 0, 2\pi, 4\pi, \ldots$. The light intensity at some point is zero when $\mathbf{E}_R$ is zero; this occurs at $\phi = \pi, 3\pi, 5\pi, \ldots$. These results are in complete agreement with the analytical procedure described in the preceding section.

Three-Slit Interference Pattern

Using phasor diagrams, let us analyze the interference pattern caused by three equally spaced slits. We can express the electric field components at a point P on the screen caused by waves from the individual slits as

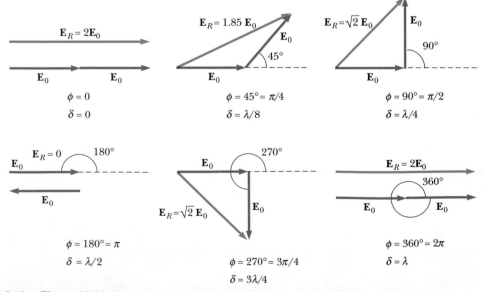

Active Figure 37.11 Phasor diagrams for a double-slit interference pattern. The resultant phasor $\mathbf{E}_R$ is a maximum when $\phi = 0, 2\pi, 4\pi, \ldots$ and is zero when $\phi = \pi, 3\pi, 5\pi, \ldots$.

$$E_1 = E_0 \sin \omega t$$

$$E_2 = E_0 \sin(\omega t + \phi)$$

$$E_3 = E_0 \sin(\omega t + 2\phi)$$

where ϕ is the phase difference between waves from adjacent slits. We can obtain the resultant magnitude of the electric field at point P from the phasor diagram in Figure 37.12.

The phasor diagrams for various values of ϕ are shown in Figure 37.13. Note that the resultant magnitude of the electric field at P has a maximum value of $3E_0$, a condition that occurs when $\phi = 0, \pm 2\pi, \pm 4\pi, \ldots$. These points are called *primary maxima*. Such primary maxima occur whenever the three phasors are aligned as shown in Figure 37.13a. We also find secondary maxima of amplitude E_0 occurring between the primary maxima at points where $\phi = \pm \pi, \pm 3\pi, \ldots$. For these points, the wave from one slit exactly cancels that from another slit (Fig. 37.13d). This means that only light from the third slit contributes to the resultant, which consequently has a total amplitude of E_0. Total destructive interference occurs whenever the three phasors form a closed triangle, as shown in Figure 37.13c. These points where $E_R = 0$ correspond to $\phi = \pm 2\pi/3, \pm 4\pi/3, \ldots$. You should be able to construct other phasor diagrams for values of ϕ greater than π.

Figure 37.14 shows multiple-slit interference patterns for a number of configurations. For three slits, note that the primary maxima are nine times more intense than the secondary maxima as measured by the height of the curve. This is because the intensity varies as E_R^2. For N slits, the intensity of the primary maxima is N^2 times greater than that due to a single slit. As the number of slits increases, the primary maxima increase in intensity and become narrower, while the secondary maxima decrease in intensity relative to the primary maxima. Figure 37.14 also shows that as the number of slits increases, the number of secondary maxima also increases. In fact, the number of secondary maxima is always $N - 2$ where N is the number of slits. In Section 38.4 (next chapter), we shall investigate the pattern for a very large number of slits in a device called a *diffraction grating*.

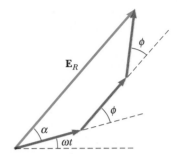

Figure 37.12 Phasor diagram for three equally spaced slits.

Quick Quiz 37.5 Using Figure 37.14 as a model, sketch the interference pattern from six slits.

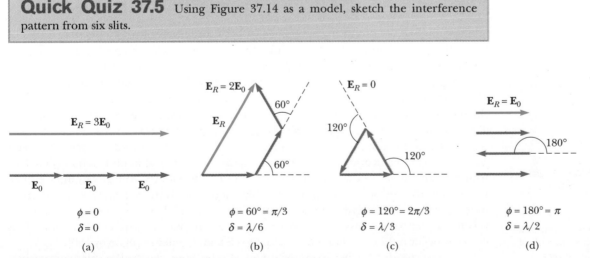

Active Figure 37.13 Phasor diagrams for three equally spaced slits at various values of ϕ. Note from (a) that there are primary maxima of amplitude $3E_0$ and from (d) that there are secondary maxima of amplitude E_0.

Choose any phase angle at the Active Figures link at http://www.pse6.com *and see the resultant phasor.*

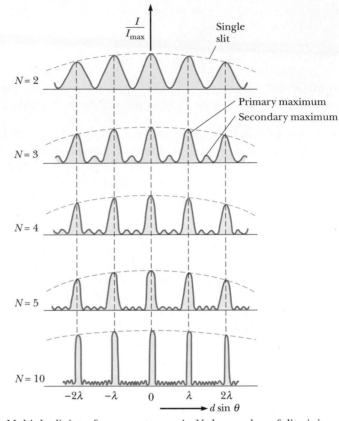

Figure 37.14 Multiple-slit interference patterns. As *N*, the number of slits, is increased, the primary maxima (the tallest peaks in each graph) become narrower but remain fixed in position and the number of secondary maxima increases. For any value of *N*, the decrease in intensity in maxima to the left and right of the central maximum, indicated by the blue dashed arcs, is due to *diffraction patterns* from the individual slits, which are discussed in Chapter 38.

37.5 Change of Phase Due to Reflection

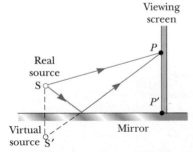

Figure 37.15 Lloyd's mirror. An interference pattern is produced at point *P* on the screen as a result of the combination of the direct ray (blue) and the reflected ray (brown). The reflected ray undergoes a phase change of 180°.

Young's method for producing two coherent light sources involves illuminating a pair of slits with a single source. Another simple, yet ingenious, arrangement for producing an interference pattern with a single light source is known as *Lloyd's mirror*[1] (Fig. 37.15). A point light source is placed at point S close to a mirror, and a viewing screen is positioned some distance away and perpendicular to the mirror. Light waves can reach point *P* on the screen either directly from S to *P* or by the path involving reflection from the mirror. The reflected ray can be treated as a ray originating from a virtual source at point S'. As a result, we can think of this arrangement as a double-slit source with the distance between points S and S' comparable to length *d* in Figure 37.5. Hence, at observation points far from the source (*L* ≫ *d*) we expect waves from points S and S' to form an interference pattern just like the one we see from two real coherent sources. An interference pattern is indeed observed. However, the positions of the dark and bright fringes are reversed relative to the pattern created by two real coherent sources (Young's experiment). This can only occur if the coherent sources at points S and S' differ in phase by 180°.

To illustrate this further, consider point *P'*, the point where the mirror intersects the screen. This point is equidistant from points S and S'. If path difference alone were responsible for the phase difference, we would see a bright fringe at point *P'* (because the path difference is zero for this point), corresponding to the central bright fringe of

---

[1] Developed in 1834 by Humphrey Lloyd (1800–1881), Professor of Natural and Experimental Philosophy, Trinity College, Dublin.

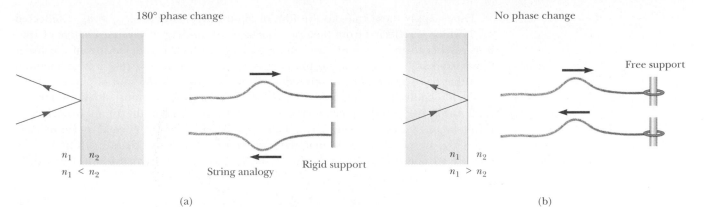

Figure 37.16 (a) For $n_1 < n_2$, a light ray traveling in medium 1 when reflected from the surface of medium 2 undergoes a 180° phase change. The same thing happens with a reflected pulse traveling along a string fixed at one end. (b) For $n_1 > n_2$, a light ray traveling in medium 1 undergoes no phase change when reflected from the surface of medium 2. The same is true of a reflected wave pulse on a string whose supported end is free to move.

the two-slit interference pattern. Instead, we observe a dark fringe at point P'. From this, we conclude that a 180° phase change must be produced by reflection from the mirror. In general, **an electromagnetic wave undergoes a phase change of 180° upon reflection from a medium that has a higher index of refraction than the one in which the wave is traveling.**

It is useful to draw an analogy between reflected light waves and the reflections of a transverse wave pulse on a stretched string (Section 16.4). The reflected pulse on a string undergoes a phase change of 180° when reflected from the boundary of a denser medium, but no phase change occurs when the pulse is reflected from the boundary of a less dense medium. Similarly, an electromagnetic wave undergoes a 180° phase change when reflected from a boundary leading to an optically denser medium (defined as a medium with a higher index of refraction), but no phase change occurs when the wave is reflected from a boundary leading to a less dense medium. These rules, summarized in Figure 37.16, can be deduced from Maxwell's equations, but the treatment is beyond the scope of this text.

37.6   Interference in Thin Films

Interference effects are commonly observed in thin films, such as thin layers of oil on water or the thin surface of a soap bubble. The varied colors observed when white light is incident on such films result from the interference of waves reflected from the two surfaces of the film.

Consider a film of uniform thickness t and index of refraction n, as shown in Figure 37.17. Let us assume that the light rays traveling in air are nearly normal to the two surfaces of the film. To determine whether the reflected rays interfere constructively or destructively, we first note the following facts:

• A wave traveling from a medium of index of refraction n_1 toward a medium of index of refraction n_2 undergoes a 180° phase change upon reflection when $n_2 > n_1$ and undergoes no phase change if $n_2 < n_1$.

• The wavelength of light λ_n in a medium whose index of refraction is n (see Section 35.5) is

$$\lambda_n = \frac{\lambda}{n} \tag{37.14}$$

where λ is the wavelength of the light in free space.

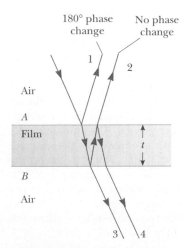

Figure 37.17 Interference in light reflected from a thin film is due to a combination of rays 1 and 2 reflected from the upper and lower surfaces of the film. Rays 3 and 4 lead to interference effects for light transmitted through the film.

Let us apply these rules to the film of Figure 37.17, where $n_{film} > n_{air}$. Reflected ray 1, which is reflected from the upper surface (A), undergoes a phase change of 180° with respect to the incident wave. Reflected ray 2, which is reflected from the lower film surface (B), undergoes no phase change because it is reflected from a medium (air) that has a lower index of refraction. Therefore, ray 1 is 180° out of phase with ray 2, which is equivalent to a path difference of $\lambda_n/2$. However, we must also consider that ray 2 travels an extra distance $2t$ before the waves recombine in the air above surface A. (Remember that we are considering light rays that are close to normal to the surface. If the rays are not close to normal, the path difference is larger than $2t$.) If $2t = \lambda_n/2$, then rays 1 and 2 recombine in phase, and the result is constructive interference. In general, the condition for *constructive* interference in thin films is[2]

$$2t = (m + \tfrac{1}{2})\lambda_n \qquad (m = 0, 1, 2, \ldots) \qquad (37.15)$$

This condition takes into account two factors: (1) the difference in path length for the two rays (the term $m\lambda_n$) and (2) the 180° phase change upon reflection (the term $\lambda_n/2$). Because $\lambda_n = \lambda/n$, we can write Equation 37.15 as

$$2nt = (m + \tfrac{1}{2})\lambda \qquad (m = 0, 1, 2, \ldots) \qquad (37.16)$$

> **Conditions for constructive interference in thin films**

If the extra distance $2t$ traveled by ray 2 corresponds to a multiple of λ_n, then the two waves combine out of phase, and the result is destructive interference. The general equation for *destructive* interference in thin films is

$$2nt = m\lambda \qquad (m = 0, 1, 2, \ldots) \qquad (37.17)$$

> **Conditions for destructive interference in thin films**

The foregoing conditions for constructive and destructive interference are valid when the medium above the top surface of the film is the same as the medium below the bottom surface or, if there are different media above and below the film, the index of refraction of both is less than n. If the film is placed between two different media, one with $n < n_{film}$ and the other with $n > n_{film}$, then the conditions for constructive and destructive interference are reversed. In this case, either there is a phase change of 180° for both ray 1 reflecting from surface A and ray 2 reflecting from surface B, or there is no phase change for either ray; hence, the net change in relative phase due to the reflections is zero.

Rays 3 and 4 in Figure 37.17 lead to interference effects in the light transmitted through the thin film. The analysis of these effects is similar to that of the reflected light. You are asked to explore the transmitted light in Problems 31, 36, and 37.

▲ **PITFALL PREVENTION**

37.4 Be Careful with Thin Films

Be sure to include *both* effects—path length and phase change—when analyzing an interference pattern resulting from a thin film. The possible phase change is a new feature that we did not need to consider for double-slit interference. Also think carefully about the material on either side of the film. You may have situations in which there is a 180° phase change at *both* surfaces or at *neither* surface, if there are different materials on either side of the film.

Quick Quiz 37.6 In a laboratory accident, you spill two liquids onto water, neither of which mixes with the water. They both form thin films on the water surface. When the films become very thin as they spread, you observe that one film becomes bright and the other dark in reflected light. The film that is dark (a) has an index of refraction higher than that of water (b) has an index of refraction lower than that of water (c) has an index of refraction equal to that of water (d) has an index of refraction lower than that of the bright film.

Quick Quiz 37.7 One microscope slide is placed on top of another with their left edges in contact and a human hair under the right edge of the upper slide. As a result, a wedge of air exists between the slides. An interference pattern results when monochromatic light is incident on the wedge. At the left edges of the slides, there is (a) a dark fringe (b) a bright fringe (c) impossible to determine.

---

[2]   The full interference effect in a thin film requires an analysis of an infinite number of reflections back and forth between the top and bottom surfaces of the film. We focus here only on a single reflection from the bottom of the film, which provides the largest contribution to the interference effect.

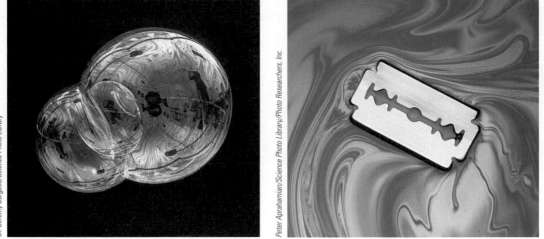

(*Left*) Interference in soap bubbles. The colors are due to interference between light rays reflected from the front and back surfaces of the thin film of soap making up the bubble. The color depends on the thickness of the film, ranging from black where the film is thinnest to magenta where it is thickest. (*Right*) A thin film of oil floating on water displays interference, as shown by the pattern of colors when white light is incident on the film. Variations in film thickness produce the interesting color pattern. The razor blade gives you an idea of the size of the colored bands.

Newton's Rings

Another method for observing interference in light waves is to place a plano-convex lens on top of a flat glass surface, as shown in Figure 37.18a. With this arrangement, the air film between the glass surfaces varies in thickness from zero at the point of contact to some value t at point P. If the radius of curvature R of the lens is much greater than the distance r, and if the system is viewed from above, a pattern of light and dark rings is observed, as shown in Figure 37.18b. These circular fringes, discovered by Newton, are called **Newton's rings.**

The interference effect is due to the combination of ray 1, reflected from the flat plate, with ray 2, reflected from the curved surface of the lens. Ray 1 undergoes a phase change of 180° upon reflection (because it is reflected from a medium of higher index of refraction), whereas ray 2 undergoes no phase change (because it is reflected from a medium of lower refractive index). Hence, the conditions for constructive and destructive interference are given by Equations 37.16 and 37.17, respectively, with $n = 1$ because the film is air.

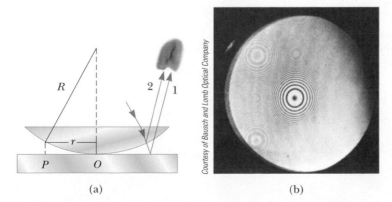

(a)   (b)

Figure 37.18 (a) The combination of rays reflected from the flat plate and the curved lens surface gives rise to an interference pattern known as Newton's rings. (b) Photograph of Newton's rings.

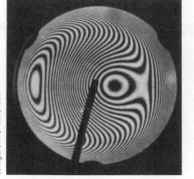

Figure 37.19 This asymmetrical interference pattern indicates imperfections in the lens of a Newton's-rings apparatus.

The contact point at O is dark, as seen in Figure 37.18b, because there is no path difference and the total phase change is due only to the 180° phase change upon reflection.

Using the geometry shown in Figure 37.18a, we can obtain expressions for the radii of the bright and dark bands in terms of the radius of curvature R and wavelength λ. For example, the dark rings have radii given by the expression $r \approx \sqrt{m\lambda R/n}$. The details are left as a problem for you to solve (see Problem 62). We can obtain the wavelength of the light causing the interference pattern by measuring the radii of the rings, provided R is known. Conversely, we can use a known wavelength to obtain R.

One important use of Newton's rings is in the testing of optical lenses. A circular pattern like that pictured in Figure 37.18b is obtained only when the lens is ground to a perfectly symmetric curvature. Variations from such symmetry might produce a pattern like that shown in Figure 37.19. These variations indicate how the lens must be reground and repolished to remove imperfections.

PROBLEM-SOLVING HINTS

Thin-Film Interference

You should keep the following ideas in mind when you work thin-film interference problems:

- Identify the thin film causing the interference.

- The type of interference that occurs is determined by the phase relationship between the portion of the wave reflected at the upper surface of the film and the portion reflected at the lower surface.

- Phase differences between the two portions of the wave have two causes: (1) differences in the distances traveled by the two portions and (2) phase changes that may occur upon reflection.

- When the distance traveled and phase changes upon reflection are both taken into account, the interference is constructive if the equivalent path difference between the two waves is an integral multiple of λ, and it is destructive if the path difference is $\lambda/2$, $3\lambda/2$, $5\lambda/2$, and so forth.

Example 37.3   Interference in a Soap Film

Calculate the minimum thickness of a soap-bubble film that results in constructive interference in the reflected light if the film is illuminated with light whose wavelength in free space is $\lambda = 600$ nm.

Solution The minimum film thickness for constructive interference in the reflected light corresponds to $m = 0$ in Equation 37.16. This gives $2nt = \lambda/2$, or

$$t = \frac{\lambda}{4n} = \frac{600 \text{ nm}}{4(1.33)} = \boxed{113 \text{ nm}}$$

What If? What if the film is twice as thick? Does this situation produce constructive interference?

Answer Using Equation 37.16, we can solve for the thicknesses at which constructive interference will occur:

$$t = \left(m + \tfrac{1}{2}\right) \frac{\lambda}{2n} = (2m + 1) \frac{\lambda}{4n} \qquad (m = 0, 1, 2, \ldots)$$

The allowed values of m show that constructive interference will occur for *odd* multiples of the thickness corresponding to $m = 0$, $t = 113$ nm. Thus, constructive interference will *not* occur for a film that is twice as thick.

Example 37.4   Nonreflective Coatings for Solar Cells

Solar cells—devices that generate electricity when exposed to sunlight—are often coated with a transparent, thin film of silicon monoxide (SiO, $n = 1.45$) to minimize reflective losses from the surface. Suppose that a silicon solar cell ($n = 3.5$) is coated with a thin film of silicon monoxide for this purpose (Fig. 37.20). Determine the minimum film thickness that

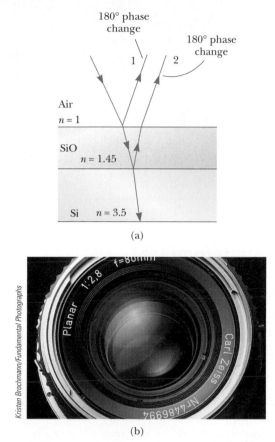

(a)

(b)

Figure 37.20 (Example 37.4) (a) Reflective losses from a silicon solar cell are minimized by coating the surface of the cell with a thin film of silicon monoxide. (b) The reflected light from a coated camera lens often has a reddish-violet appearance.

produces the least reflection at a wavelength of 550 nm, near the center of the visible spectrum.

Solution Figure 37.20a helps us conceptualize the path of the rays in the SiO film that result in interference in the reflected light. Based on the geometry of the SiO layer, we categorize this as a thin-film interference problem. To analyze the problem, note that the reflected light is a minimum when rays 1 and 2 in Figure 37.20a meet the condition of destructive interference. In this situation, *both* rays undergo a 180° phase change upon reflection—ray 1 from the upper SiO surface and ray 2 from the lower SiO surface. The net change in phase due to reflection is therefore zero, and the condition for a reflection minimum requires a path difference of $\lambda_n/2$, where λ_n is the wavelength of the light in SiO. Hence $2t = \lambda/2n$, where λ is the wavelength in air and n is the index of refraction of SiO. The required thickness is

$$t = \frac{\lambda}{4n} = \frac{550 \text{ nm}}{4(1.45)} = \boxed{94.8 \text{ nm}}$$

To finalize the problem, we can investigate the losses in typical solar cells. A typical uncoated solar cell has reflective losses as high as 30%; a SiO coating can reduce this value to about 10%. This significant decrease in reflective losses increases the cell's efficiency because less reflection means that more sunlight enters the silicon to create charge carriers in the cell. No coating can ever be made perfectly nonreflecting because the required thickness is wavelength-dependent and the incident light covers a wide range of wavelengths.

Glass lenses used in cameras and other optical instruments are usually coated with a transparent thin film to reduce or eliminate unwanted reflection and enhance the transmission of light through the lenses. The camera lens in Figure 37.20b has several coatings (of different thicknesses) to minimize reflection of light waves having wavelengths near the center of the visible spectrum. As a result, the little light that is reflected by the lens has a greater proportion of the far ends of the spectrum and often appears reddish-violet.

Investigate the interference for various film properties at the Interactive Worked Example link at http://www.pse6.com.

Example 37.5   Interference in a Wedge-Shaped Film

A thin, wedge-shaped film of index of refraction n is illuminated with monochromatic light of wavelength λ, as illustrated in Figure 37.21a. Describe the interference pattern observed for this case.

Solution The interference pattern, because it is created by a thin film of variable thickness surrounded by air, is a series of alternating bright and dark parallel fringes. A dark fringe corresponding to destructive interference appears at point O, the apex, because here the upper reflected ray undergoes a 180° phase change while the lower one undergoes no phase change.

According to Equation 37.17, other dark minima appear when $2nt = m\lambda$; thus, $t_1 = \lambda/2n$, $t_2 = \lambda/n$, $t_3 = 3\lambda/2n$, and so on. Similarly, the bright maxima appear at locations where t satisfies Equation 37.16, $2nt = (m + \frac{1}{2})\lambda$, corresponding to thicknesses of $\lambda/4n$, $3\lambda/4n$, $5\lambda/4n$, and so on.

If white light is used, bands of different colors are observed at different points, corresponding to the different wavelengths of light (see Fig. 37.21b). This is why we see different colors in soap bubbles and other films of varying thickness.

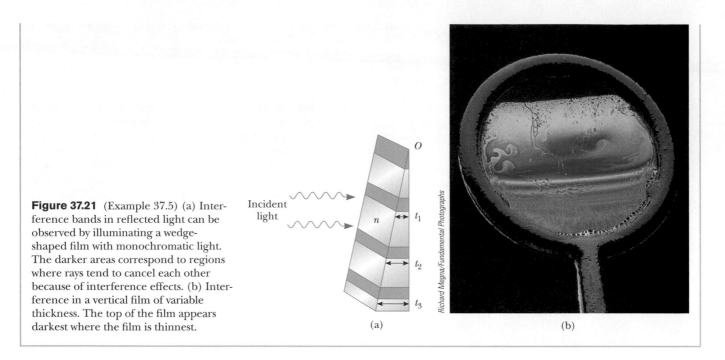

Figure 37.21 (Example 37.5) (a) Interference bands in reflected light can be observed by illuminating a wedge-shaped film with monochromatic light. The darker areas correspond to regions where rays tend to cancel each other because of interference effects. (b) Interference in a vertical film of variable thickness. The top of the film appears darkest where the film is thinnest.

Richard Megna/Fundamental Photographs

(a)

(b)

37.7 The Michelson Interferometer

The **interferometer,** invented by the American physicist A. A. Michelson (1852–1931), splits a light beam into two parts and then recombines the parts to form an interference pattern. The device can be used to measure wavelengths or other lengths with great precision because a large and precisely measurable displacement of one of the mirrors is related to an exactly countable number of wavelengths of light.

A schematic diagram of the interferometer is shown in Figure 37.22. A ray of light from a monochromatic source is split into two rays by mirror M_0, which is inclined at 45° to the incident light beam. Mirror M_0, called a *beam splitter*, transmits half the light incident on it and reflects the rest. One ray is reflected from M_0 vertically upward toward mirror M_1, and the second ray is transmitted horizontally through M_0 toward mirror M_2. Hence, the two rays travel separate paths L_1 and L_2. After reflecting from M_1 and M_2, the two rays eventually recombine at M_0 to produce an interference pattern, which can be viewed through a telescope.

The interference condition for the two rays is determined by their path length differences. When the two mirrors are exactly perpendicular to each other, the interference pattern is a target pattern of bright and dark circular fringes, similar to Newton's rings. As M_1 is moved, the fringe pattern collapses or expands, depending on the direction in which M_1 is moved. For example, if a dark circle appears at the center of the target pattern (corresponding to destructive interference) and M_1 is then moved a distance $\lambda/4$ toward M_0, the path difference changes by $\lambda/2$. What was a dark circle at the center now becomes a bright circle. As M_1 is moved an additional distance $\lambda/4$ toward M_0, the bright circle becomes a dark circle again. Thus, the fringe pattern shifts by one-half fringe each time M_1 is moved a distance $\lambda/4$. The wavelength of light is then measured by counting the number of fringe shifts for a given displacement of M_1. If the wavelength is accurately known, mirror displacements can be measured to within a fraction of the wavelength.

We will see an important historical use of the Michelson interferometer in our discussion of relativity in Chapter 39. Modern uses include the following two applications.

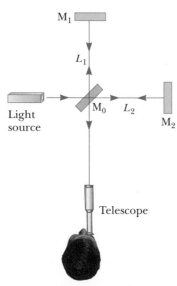

Active Figure 37.22 Diagram of the Michelson interferometer. A single ray of light is split into two rays by mirror M_0, which is called a beam splitter. The path difference between the two rays is varied with the adjustable mirror M_1. As M_1 is moved, an interference pattern changes in the field of view.

At the Active Figures link at http://www.pse6.com, move the mirror to see the effect on the interference pattern and use the interferometer to measure the wavelength of light.

Fourier Transform Infrared Spectroscopy (FTIR)

Spectroscopy is the study of the wavelength distribution of radiation from a sample that can be used to identify the characteristics of atoms or molecules in the sample. Infrared spectroscopy is particularly important to organic chemists in analyzing organic molecules. Traditional spectroscopy involves the use of an optical element, such as a prism (Section 35.7) or a diffraction grating (Section 38.4), which spreads out various wavelengths in a complex optical signal from the sample into different angles. In this way, the various wavelengths of radiation and their intensities in the signal can be determined. These types of devices are limited in their resolution and effectiveness because they must be scanned through the various angular deviations of the radiation.

The technique of *Fourier Transform Infrared Spectroscopy* (FTIR) is used to create a higher-resolution spectrum in a time interval of one second that may have required 30 minutes with a standard spectrometer. In this technique, the radiation from a sample enters a Michelson interferometer. The movable mirror is swept through the zero-path-difference condition and the intensity of radiation at the viewing position is recorded. The result is a complex set of data relating light intensity as a function of mirror position, called an *interferogram*. Because there is a relationship between mirror position and light intensity for a given wavelength, the interferogram contains information about all wavelengths in the signal.

In Section 18.8, we discussed Fourier analysis of a waveform. The waveform is a function that contains information about all of the individual frequency components that make up the waveform.[3] Equation 18.16 shows how the waveform is generated from the individual frequency components. Similarly, the interferogram can be analyzed by computer, in a process called a *Fourier transform*, to provide all of the wavelength components. This is the same information generated by traditional spectroscopy, but the resolution of FTIR is much higher.

Laser Interferometer Gravitational-Wave Observatory (LIGO)

Einstein's general theory of relativity (Section 39.10) predicts the existence of *gravitational waves*. These waves propagate from the site of any gravitational disturbance, which could be periodic and predictable, such as the rotation of a double star around a center of mass, or unpredictable, such as the supernova explosion of a massive star.

In Einstein's theory, gravitation is equivalent to a distortion of space. Thus, a gravitational disturbance causes an additional distortion that propagates through space in a manner similar to mechanical or electromagnetic waves. When gravitational waves from a disturbance pass by the Earth, they create a distortion of the local space. The LIGO apparatus is designed to detect this distortion. The apparatus employs a Michelson interferometer that uses laser beams with an effective path length of several kilometers. At the end of an arm of the interferometer, a mirror is mounted on a massive pendulum. When a gravitational wave passes by, the pendulum and the attached mirror move, and the interference pattern due to the laser beams from the two arms changes.

Two sites have been developed in the United States for interferometers in order to allow coincidence studies of gravitational waves. These sites are located in Richland, Washington, and Livingston, Louisiana. Figure 37.23 shows the Washington site. The two arms of the Michelson interferometer are evident in the photograph. Test runs are being performed as of the printing of this book. Cooperation with other gravitational wave detectors, such as VIRGO in Cascina, Italy, will allow detailed studies of gravitational waves.

[3] In acoustics, it is common to talk about the components of a complex signal in terms of frequency. In optics, it is more common to identify the components by wavelength.

LIGO Hanford Observatory

Figure 37.23 The Laser Interferometer Gravitational-Wave Observatory (LIGO) near Richland, Washington. Note the two perpendicular arms of the Michelson interferometer.

SUMMARY

Take a practice test for this chapter by clicking on the Practice Test link at http://www.pse6.com.

Interference in light waves occurs whenever two or more waves overlap at a given point. An interference pattern is observed if (1) the sources are coherent and (2) the sources have identical wavelengths.

In Young's double-slit experiment, two slits S_1 and S_2 separated by a distance d are illuminated by a single-wavelength light source. An interference pattern consisting of bright and dark fringes is observed on a viewing screen. The condition for bright fringes **(constructive interference)** is

$$\delta = d \sin\theta_{\text{bright}} = m\lambda \qquad (m = 0, \pm 1, \pm 2, \ldots) \qquad (37.2)$$

The condition for dark fringes **(destructive interference)** is

$$d \sin\theta_{\text{dark}} = (m + \tfrac{1}{2})\lambda \qquad (m = 0, \pm 1, \pm 2, \ldots) \qquad (37.3)$$

The number m is called the **order number** of the fringe.

The **intensity** at a point in the double-slit interference pattern is

$$I = I_{\max} \cos^2\left(\frac{\pi d \sin\theta}{\lambda}\right) \qquad (37.12)$$

where $I_{\max}$ is the maximum intensity on the screen and the expression represents the time average.

A wave traveling from a medium of index of refraction n_1 toward a medium of index of refraction n_2 undergoes a 180° phase change upon reflection when $n_2 > n_1$ and undergoes no phase change when $n_2 < n_1$.

The condition for constructive interference in a film of thickness t and index of refraction n surrounded by air is

$$2nt = (m + \tfrac{1}{2})\lambda \qquad (m = 0, 1, 2, \ldots) \qquad (37.16)$$

where λ is the wavelength of the light in free space.

Similarly, the condition for destructive interference in a thin film surrounded by air is

$$2nt = m\lambda \qquad (m = 0, 1, 2, \ldots) \qquad (37.17)$$

QUESTIONS

1. What is the necessary condition on the path length difference between two waves that interfere (a) constructively and (b) destructively?

2. Explain why two flashlights held close together do not produce an interference pattern on a distant screen.

3. If Young's double-slit experiment were performed under water, how would the observed interference pattern be affected?

4. In Young's double-slit experiment, why do we use monochromatic light? If white light is used, how would the pattern change?

5. A simple way to observe an interference pattern is to look at a distant light source through a stretched handkerchief or an opened umbrella. Explain how this works.

6. A certain oil film on water appears brightest at the outer regions, where it is thinnest. From this information, what can you say about the index of refraction of oil relative to that of water?

7. As a soap bubble evaporates, it appears black just before it breaks. Explain this phenomenon in terms of the phase changes that occur on reflection from the two surfaces of the soap film.

8. If we are to observe interference in a thin film, why must the film not be very thick (with thickness only on the order of a few wavelengths)?

9. A lens with outer radius of curvature R and index of refraction n rests on a flat glass plate. The combination is illuminated with white light from above and observed from above. Is there a dark spot or a light spot at the center of the lens? What does it mean if the observed rings are noncircular?

10. Why is the lens on a good-quality camera coated with a thin film?

11. Why is it so much easier to perform interference experiments with a laser than with an ordinary light source?

12. Suppose that reflected white light is used to observe a thin transparent coating on glass as the coating material is gradually deposited by evaporation in a vacuum. Describe color changes that might occur during the process of building up the thickness of the coating.

13. In our discussion of thin-film interference, we looked at light *reflecting* from a thin film. **What If?** Consider one light ray, the direct ray, which transmits through the film without reflecting. Consider a second ray, the reflected ray, that transmits through the first surface, reflects from the second, reflects again from the first, and then transmits out into the air, parallel to the direct ray. For normal incidence, how thick must the film be, in terms of the wavelength of light, for the outgoing rays to interfere destructively? Is it the same thickness as for reflected destructive interference?

14. Suppose you are watching television by connection to an antenna rather than a cable system. If an airplane flies near your location, you may notice wavering ghost images in the television picture. What might cause this?

PROBLEMS

1, 2, 3 = straightforward, intermediate, challenging ☐ = full solution available in the *Student Solutions Manual and Study Guide*

🌐 = coached solution with hints available at http://www.pse6.com 💻 = computer useful in solving problem

▨ = paired numerical and symbolic problems

Section 37.1 Conditions for Interference
Section 37.2 Young's Double-Slit Experiment

> *Note:* Problems 8, 9, 10, and 12 in Chapter 18 can be assigned with these sections.

1. A laser beam ($\lambda = 632.8$ nm) is incident on two slits 0.200 mm apart. How far apart are the bright interference fringes on a screen 5.00 m away from the double slits?

2. A Young's interference experiment is performed with monochromatic light. The separation between the slits is 0.500 mm, and the interference pattern on a screen 3.30 m away shows the first side maximum 3.40 mm from the center of the pattern. What is the wavelength?

3. 🌐 Two radio antennas separated by 300 m as shown in Figure P37.3 simultaneously broadcast identical signals at

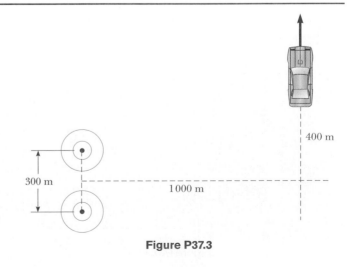

Figure P37.3

the same wavelength. A radio in a car traveling due north receives the signals. (a) If the car is at the position of the second maximum, what is the wavelength of the signals? (b) How much farther must the car travel to encounter the next minimum in reception? (*Note:* Do not use the small-angle approximation in this problem.)

4. In a location where the speed of sound is 354 m/s, a 2 000-Hz sound wave impinges on two slits 30.0 cm apart. (a) At what angle is the first maximum located? (b) **What If?** If the sound wave is replaced by 3.00-cm microwaves, what slit separation gives the same angle for the first maximum? (c) **What If?** If the slit separation is 1.00 μm, what frequency of light gives the same first maximum angle?

5. ![www] Young's double-slit experiment is performed with 589-nm light and a distance of 2.00 m between the slits and the screen. The tenth interference minimum is observed 7.26 mm from the central maximum. Determine the spacing of the slits.

6. The two speakers of a boom box are 35.0 cm apart. A single oscillator makes the speakers vibrate in phase at a frequency of 2.00 kHz. At what angles, measured from the perpendicular bisector of the line joining the speakers, would a distant observer hear maximum sound intensity? Minimum sound intensity? (Take the speed of sound as 340 m/s.)

7. Two narrow, parallel slits separated by 0.250 mm are illuminated by green light ($\lambda = 546.1$ nm). The interference pattern is observed on a screen 1.20 m away from the plane of the slits. Calculate the distance (a) from the central maximum to the first bright region on either side of the central maximum and (b) between the first and second dark bands.

8. Light with wavelength 442 nm passes through a double-slit system that has a slit separation $d = 0.400$ mm. Determine how far away a screen must be placed in order that a dark fringe appear directly opposite both slits, with just one bright fringe between them.

9. A riverside warehouse has two open doors as shown in Figure P37.9. Its walls are lined with sound-absorbing material. A boat on the river sounds its horn. To person A the sound is loud and clear. To person B the sound is barely audible. The principal wavelength of the sound waves is 3.00 m. Assuming person B is at the position of the first minimum, determine the distance between the doors, center to center.

10. Two slits are separated by 0.320 mm. A beam of 500-nm light strikes the slits, producing an interference pattern. Determine the number of maxima observed in the angular range $-30.0° < \theta < 30.0°$.

11. Young's double-slit experiment underlies the *Instrument Landing System* used to guide aircraft to safe landings when the visibility is poor. Although real systems are more complicated than the example described here, they operate on the same principles. A pilot is trying to align her plane with a runway, as suggested in Figure P37.11a. Two radio antennas A_1 and A_2 are positioned adjacent to the runway, separated by 40.0 m. The antennas broadcast unmodulated coherent radio waves at 30.0 MHz. (a) Find the wavelength of the waves. The pilot "locks onto" the strong signal radiated along an interference maximum, and steers the plane to keep the received signal strong. If she has found the central maximum, the plane will have just the right heading to land when it reaches the runway. (b) **What If?** Suppose instead that the plane is flying along the first side maximum (Fig. P37.11b). How far to the side of the runway centerline will the plane be when it is 2.00 km from the antennas? (c) It is possible to tell the pilot she is on the wrong maximum by sending out two signals from each antenna and equipping the aircraft with a two-channel receiver. The ratio of the two frequencies must not be the ratio of small integers (such as 3/4). Explain how this two-frequency system would work, and why it would not necessarily work if the frequencies were related by an integer ratio.

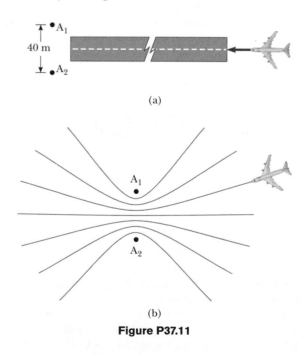

(a)

(b)

Figure P37.11

12. A student holds a laser that emits light of wavelength 633 nm. The beam passes though a pair of slits separated by 0.300 mm, in a glass plate attached to the front of the laser. The beam then falls perpendicularly on a screen, creating an interference pattern on it. The student begins to walk directly toward the screen at 3.00 m/s. The central maximum on the screen is stationary. Find the speed of the first-order maxima on the screen.

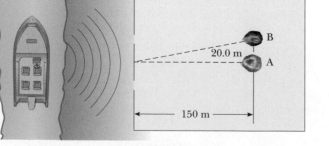

Figure P37.9

13. In Figure 37.5 let $L = 1.20$ m and $d = 0.120$ mm and assume that the slit system is illuminated with monochromatic 500-nm light. Calculate the phase difference between the two wave fronts arriving at P when (a) $\theta = 0.500°$ and (b) $y = 5.00$ mm. (c) What is the value of θ for which the phase difference is 0.333 rad? (d) What is the value of θ for which the path difference is $\lambda/4$?

14. Coherent light rays of wavelength λ strike a pair of slits separated by distance d at an angle θ_1 as shown in Figure P37.14. Assume an interference maximum is formed at an angle θ_2 a great distance from the slits. Show that $d(\sin\theta_2 - \sin\theta_1) = m\lambda$, where m is an integer.

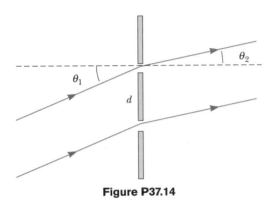

Figure P37.14

15. In a double-slit arrangement of Figure 37.5, $d = 0.150$ mm, $L = 140$ cm, $\lambda = 643$ nm, and $y = 1.80$ cm. (a) What is the path difference δ for the rays from the two slits arriving at P? (b) Express this path difference in terms of λ. (c) Does P correspond to a maximum, a minimum, or an intermediate condition?

Section 37.3 Intensity Distribution of the Double-Slit Interference Pattern

16. The intensity on the screen at a certain point in a double-slit interference pattern is 64.0% of the maximum value. (a) What minimum phase difference (in radians) between sources produces this result? (b) Express this phase difference as a path difference for 486.1-nm light.

17. In Figure 37.5, let $L = 120$ cm and $d = 0.250$ cm. The slits are illuminated with coherent 600-nm light. Calculate the distance y above the central maximum for which the average intensity on the screen is 75.0% of the maximum.

18. Two slits are separated by 0.180 mm. An interference pattern is formed on a screen 80.0 cm away by 656.3-nm light. Calculate the fraction of the maximum intensity 0.600 cm above the central maximum.

19. Two narrow parallel slits separated by 0.850 mm are illuminated by 600-nm light, and the viewing screen is 2.80 m away from the slits. (a) What is the phase difference between the two interfering waves on a screen at a point 2.50 mm from the central bright fringe? (b) What is the ratio of the intensity at this point to the intensity at the center of a bright fringe?

20. Monochromatic coherent light of amplitude E_0 and angular frequency ω passes through three parallel slits each separated by a distance d from its neighbor. (a) Show that the time-averaged intensity as a function of the angle θ is

$$I(\theta) = I_{max}\left[1 + 2\cos\left(\frac{2\pi d \sin\theta}{\lambda}\right)\right]^2$$

(b) Determine the ratio of the intensities of the primary and secondary maxima.

Section 37.4 Phasor Addition of Waves

Note: Problems 4, 5, and 6 in Chapter 18 can be assigned with this section.

21. Marie Cornu, a physicist at the Polytechnic Institute in Paris, invented phasors in about 1880. This problem helps you to see their utility. Find the amplitude and phase constant of the sum of two waves represented by the expressions

$$E_1 = (12.0 \text{ kN/C}) \sin(15x - 4.5t)$$

and

$$E_2 = (12.0 \text{ kN/C}) \sin(15x - 4.5t + 70°)$$

(a) by using a trigonometric identity (as from Appendix B), and (b) by representing the waves by phasors. (c) Find the amplitude and phase constant of the sum of the three waves represented by

$$E_1 = (12.0 \text{ kN/C}) \sin(15x - 4.5t + 70°),$$

$$E_2 = (15.5 \text{ kN/C}) \sin(15x - 4.5t - 80°),$$

and

$$E_3 = (17.0 \text{ kN/C}) \sin(15x - 4.5t + 160°)$$

22. The electric fields from three coherent sources are described by $E_1 = E_0 \sin\omega t$, $E_2 = E_0 \sin(\omega t + \phi)$, and $E_3 = E_0 \sin(\omega t + 2\phi)$. Let the resultant field be represented by $E_P = E_R \sin(\omega t + \alpha)$. Use phasors to find E_R and α when (a) $\phi = 20.0°$, (b) $\phi = 60.0°$, and (c) $\phi = 120°$. (d) Repeat when $\phi = (3\pi/2)$ rad.

23. Determine the resultant of the two waves given by $E_1 = 6.0 \sin(100\pi t)$ and $E_2 = 8.0 \sin(100\pi t + \pi/2)$.

24. Suppose the slit openings in a Young's double-slit experiment have different sizes so that the electric fields and intensities from each slit are different. With $E_1 = E_{01}\sin(\omega t)$ and $E_2 = E_{02}\sin(\omega t + \phi)$, show that the resultant electric field is $E = E_0 \sin(\omega t + \theta)$, where

$$E_0 = \sqrt{E_{01}^2 + E_{02}^2 + 2E_{01}E_{02}\cos\phi}$$

and

$$\sin\theta = \frac{E_{02}\sin\phi}{E_0}$$

25. Use phasors to find the resultant (magnitude and phase angle) of two fields represented by $E_1 = 12 \sin\omega t$ and $E_2 = 18 \sin(\omega t + 60°)$. (Note that in this case the amplitudes of the two fields are unequal.)

26. Two coherent waves are described by

$$E_1 = E_0 \sin\left(\frac{2\pi x_1}{\lambda} - 2\pi ft + \frac{\pi}{6}\right)$$

$$E_2 = E_0 \sin\left(\frac{2\pi x_2}{\lambda} - 2\pi ft + \frac{\pi}{8}\right)$$

Determine the relationship between x_1 and x_2 that produces constructive interference when the two waves are superposed.

27. When illuminated, four equally spaced parallel slits act as multiple coherent sources, each differing in phase from the adjacent one by an angle ϕ. Use a phasor diagram to determine the smallest value of ϕ for which the resultant of the four waves (assumed to be of equal amplitude) is zero.

28. Sketch a phasor diagram to illustrate the resultant of $E_1 = E_{01} \sin \omega t$ and $E_2 = E_{02} \sin(\omega t + \phi)$, where $E_{02} = 1.50 E_{01}$ and $\pi/6 \le \phi \le \pi/3$. Use the sketch and the law of cosines to show that, for two coherent waves, the resultant intensity can be written in the form $I_R = I_1 + I_2 + 2\sqrt{I_1 I_2} \cos \phi$.

29. Consider N coherent sources described as follows: $E_1 = E_0 \sin(\omega t + \phi)$, $E_2 = E_0 \sin(\omega t + 2\phi)$, $E_3 = E_0 \sin(\omega t + 3\phi)$, . . . , $E_N = E_0 \sin(\omega t + N\phi)$. Find the minimum value of ϕ for which $E_R = E_1 + E_2 + E_3 + \cdots + E_N$ is zero.

Section 37.5 Change of Phase Due to Reflection
Section 37.6 Interference in Thin Films

30. A soap bubble ($n = 1.33$) is floating in air. If the thickness of the bubble wall is 115 nm, what is the wavelength of the light that is most strongly reflected?

31. An oil film ($n = 1.45$) floating on water is illuminated by white light at normal incidence. The film is 280 nm thick. Find (a) the color of the light in the visible spectrum most strongly reflected and (b) the color of the light in the spectrum most strongly transmitted. Explain your reasoning.

32. A thin film of oil ($n = 1.25$) is located on a smooth wet pavement. When viewed perpendicular to the pavement, the film reflects most strongly red light at 640 nm and reflects no blue light at 512 nm. How thick is the oil film?

33. A possible means for making an airplane invisible to radar is to coat the plane with an antireflective polymer. If radar waves have a wavelength of 3.00 cm and the index of refraction of the polymer is $n = 1.50$, how thick would you make the coating?

34. A material having an index of refraction of 1.30 is used as an antireflective coating on a piece of glass ($n = 1.50$). What should be the minimum thickness of this film in order to minimize reflection of 500-nm light?

35. A film of MgF_2 ($n = 1.38$) having thickness 1.00×10^{-5} cm is used to coat a camera lens. Are any wavelengths in the visible spectrum intensified in the reflected light?

36. Astronomers observe the chromosphere of the Sun with a filter that passes the red hydrogen spectral line of wavelength 656.3 nm, called the H_α line. The filter consists of a transparent dielectric of thickness d held between two partially aluminized glass plates. The filter is held at a constant temperature. (a) Find the minimum value of d that produces maximum transmission of perpendicular H_α light, if the dielectric has an index of refraction of 1.378. (b) **What If?** If the temperature of the filter increases above the normal value, what happens to the transmitted wavelength? (Its index of refraction does not change significantly.) (c) The dielectric will also pass what near-visible wavelength? One of the glass plates is colored red to absorb this light.

37. A beam of 580-nm light passes through two closely spaced glass plates, as shown in Figure P37.37. For what minimum nonzero value of the plate separation d is the transmitted light bright?

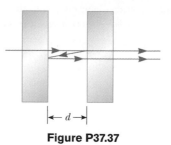

Figure P37.37

38. When a liquid is introduced into the air space between the lens and the plate in a Newton's-rings apparatus, the diameter of the tenth ring changes from 1.50 to 1.31 cm. Find the index of refraction of the liquid.

39. An air wedge is formed between two glass plates separated at one edge by a very fine wire, as shown in Figure P37.39. When the wedge is illuminated from above by 600-nm light and viewed from above, 30 dark fringes are observed. Calculate the radius of the wire.

Figure P37.39 Problems 39 and 40.

40. Two glass plates 10.0 cm long are in contact at one end and separated at the other end by a thread 0.050 0 mm in diameter (Fig. P37.39). Light containing the two wavelengths 400 nm and 600 nm is incident perpendicularly and viewed by reflection. At what distance from the contact point is the next dark fringe?

Section 37.7 The Michelson Interferometer

41. Mirror M_1 in Figure 37.22 is displaced a distance ΔL. During this displacement, 250 fringe reversals (formation of successive dark or bright bands) are counted. The light being used has a wavelength of 632.8 nm. Calculate the displacement ΔL.

42. Monochromatic light is beamed into a Michelson interferometer. The movable mirror is displaced 0.382 mm, causing the interferometer pattern to reproduce itself 1 700 times. Determine the wavelength of the light. What color is it?

43. One leg of a Michelson interferometer contains an evacuated cylinder of length L, having glass plates on each end.

A gas is slowly leaked into the cylinder until a pressure of 1 atm is reached. If N bright fringes pass on the screen when light of wavelength λ is used, what is the index of refraction of the gas?

Additional Problems

44. In the **What If?** section of Example 37.2, it was claimed that overlapping fringes in a two-slit interference pattern for two different wavelengths obey the following relationship even for large values of the angle θ:

$$\frac{\lambda}{\lambda'} = \frac{m'}{m}$$

(a) Prove this assertion. (b) Using the data in Example 37.2, find the value of y on the screen at which the fringes from the two wavelengths first coincide.

45. One radio transmitter A operating at 60.0 MHz is 10.0 m from another similar transmitter B that is 180° out of phase with A. How far must an observer move from A toward B along the line connecting A and B to reach the nearest point where the two beams are in phase?

46. **Review problem.** This problem extends the result of Problem 12 in Chapter 18. Figure P37.46 shows two adjacent vibrating balls dipping into a tank of water. At distant points they produce an interference pattern of water waves, as shown in Figure 37.3. Let λ represent the wavelength of the ripples. Show that the two sources produce a standing wave along the line segment, of length d, between them. In terms of λ and d, find the number of nodes and the number of antinodes in the standing wave. Find the number of zones of constructive and of destructive interference in the interference pattern far away from the sources. Each line of destructive interference springs from a node in the standing wave and each line of constructive interference springs from an antinode.

Courtesy of Central Scientific Company

Figure P37.46

47. Raise your hand and hold it flat. Think of the space between your index finger and your middle finger as one slit, and think of the space between middle finger and ring finger as a second slit. (a) Consider the interference resulting from sending coherent visible light perpendicularly through this pair of openings. Compute an order-of-magnitude estimate for the angle between adjacent zones of constructive interference. (b) To make the angles in the interference pattern easy to measure with a plastic protractor, you should use an electromagnetic wave with frequency of what order of magnitude? How is this wave classified on the electromagnetic spectrum?

48. In a Young's double-slit experiment using light of wavelength λ, a thin piece of Plexiglas having index of refraction n covers one of the slits. If the center point on the screen is a dark spot instead of a bright spot, what is the minimum thickness of the Plexiglas?

49. **Review problem.** A flat piece of glass is held stationary and horizontal above the flat top end of a 10.0-cm-long vertical metal rod that has its lower end rigidly fixed. The thin film of air between the rod and glass is observed to be bright by reflected light when it is illuminated by light of wavelength 500 nm. As the temperature is slowly increased by 25.0°C, the film changes from bright to dark and back to bright 200 times. What is the coefficient of linear expansion of the metal?

50. A certain crude oil has an index of refraction of 1.25. A ship dumps 1.00 m^3 of this oil into the ocean, and the oil spreads into a thin uniform slick. If the film produces a first-order maximum of light of wavelength 500 nm normally incident on it, how much surface area of the ocean does the oil slick cover? Assume that the index of refraction of the ocean water is 1.34.

51. Astronomers observe a 60.0-MHz radio source both directly and by reflection from the sea. If the receiving dish is 20.0 m above sea level, what is the angle of the radio source above the horizon at first maximum?

52. Interference effects are produced at point P on a screen as a result of direct rays from a 500-nm source and reflected rays from the mirror, as shown in Figure P37.52. Assume the source is 100 m to the left of the screen and 1.00 cm above the mirror. Find the distance y to the first dark band above the mirror.

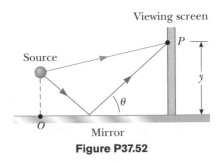

Figure P37.52

53. The waves from a radio station can reach a home receiver by two paths. One is a straight-line path from transmitter to home, a distance of 30.0 km. The second path is by reflection from the ionosphere (a layer of ionized air molecules high in the atmosphere). Assume this reflection takes place at a point midway between receiver and transmitter and that the wavelength broadcast by the radio station is 350 m. Find the minimum height of the ionospheric layer that could produce destructive interference between the direct and reflected beams. (Assume that no phase change occurs on reflection.)

54. Many cells are transparent and colorless. Structures of great interest in biology and medicine can be practically invisible to ordinary microscopy. An *interference microscope* reveals a difference in index of refraction as a shift in interference fringes, to indicate the size and shape of cell structures. The idea is exemplified in the following problem: An air wedge is formed between two glass plates in contact along one edge and slightly separated at the opposite edge. When the plates are illuminated with monochromatic light from above, the reflected light has 85 dark fringes. Calculate the number of dark fringes that appear if water ($n = 1.33$) replaces the air between the plates.

55. Measurements are made of the intensity distribution in a Young's interference pattern (see Fig. 37.7). At a particular value of y, it is found that $I/I_{max} = 0.810$ when 600-nm light is used. What wavelength of light should be used to reduce the relative intensity at the same location to 64.0% of the maximum intensity?

56. Our discussion of the techniques for determining constructive and destructive interference by reflection from a thin film in air has been confined to rays striking the film at nearly normal incidence. **What If?** Assume that a ray is incident at an angle of 30.0° (relative to the normal) on a film with index of refraction 1.38. Calculate the minimum thickness for constructive interference of sodium light with a wavelength of 590 nm.

57. The condition for constructive interference by reflection from a thin film in air as developed in Section 37.6 assumes nearly normal incidence. **What If?** Show that if the light is incident on the film at a nonzero angle ϕ_1 (relative to the normal), then the condition for constructive interference is $2nt \cos \theta_2 = (m + \frac{1}{2})\lambda$, where θ_2 is the angle of refraction.

58. (a) Both sides of a uniform film that has index of refraction n and thickness d are in contact with air. For normal incidence of light, an intensity minimum is observed in the reflected light at λ_2 and an intensity maximum is observed at λ_1, where $\lambda_1 > \lambda_2$. Assuming that no intensity minima are observed between λ_1 and λ_2, show that the integer m in Equations 37.16 and 37.17 is given by $m = \lambda_1/2(\lambda_1 - \lambda_2)$. (b) Determine the thickness of the film, assuming $n = 1.40$, $\lambda_1 = 500$ nm, and $\lambda_2 = 370$ nm.

59. Figure P37.59 shows a radio-wave transmitter and a receiver separated by a distance d and both a distance h above the ground. The receiver can receive signals both directly from

the transmitter and indirectly from signals that reflect from the ground. Assume that the ground is level between the transmitter and receiver and that a 180° phase shift occurs upon reflection. Determine the longest wavelengths that interfere (a) constructively and (b) destructively.

60. A piece of transparent material having an index of refraction n is cut into the shape of a wedge as shown in Figure P37.60. The angle of the wedge is small. Monochromatic light of wavelength λ is normally incident from above, and viewed from above. Let h represent the height of the wedge and ℓ its width. Show that bright fringes occur at the positions $x = \lambda \ell (m + \frac{1}{2})/2hn$ and dark fringes occur at the positions $x = \lambda \ell m/2hn$, where $m = 0, 1, 2, \ldots$ and x is measured as shown.

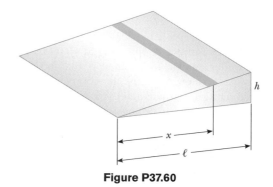

Figure P37.60

61. Consider the double-slit arrangement shown in Figure P37.61, where the slit separation is d and the slit to screen distance is L. A sheet of transparent plastic having an index of refraction n and thickness t is placed over the upper slit. As a result, the central maximum of the interference pattern moves upward a distance y'. Find y'.

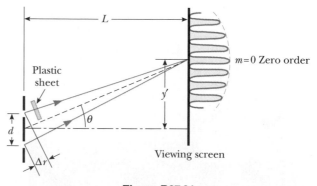

Figure P37.61

62. A plano-convex lens has index of refraction n. The curved side of the lens has radius of curvature R and rests on a flat glass surface of the same index of refraction, with a film of index n_{film} between them, as shown in Fig. 37.18a. The lens is illuminated from above by light of wavelength λ. Show that the dark Newton's rings have radii given approximately by

$$r \approx \sqrt{\frac{m\lambda R}{n_{film}}}$$

where m is an integer and r is much less than R.

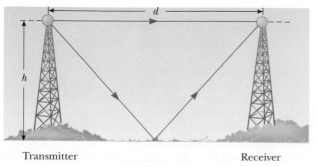

Transmitter   Receiver

Figure P37.59

63. In a Newton's-rings experiment, a plano-convex glass ($n = 1.52$) lens having diameter 10.0 cm is placed on a flat plate as shown in Figure 37.18a. When 650-nm light is incident normally, 55 bright rings are observed with the last one right on the edge of the lens. (a) What is the radius of curvature of the convex surface of the lens? (b) What is the focal length of the lens?

64. A plano-concave lens having index of refraction 1.50 is placed on a flat glass plate, as shown in Figure P37.64. Its curved surface, with radius of curvature 8.00 m, is on the bottom. The lens is illuminated from above with yellow sodium light of wavelength 589 nm, and a series of concentric bright and dark rings is observed by reflection. The interference pattern has a dark spot at the center, surrounded by 50 dark rings, of which the largest is at the outer edge of the lens. (a) What is the thickness of the air layer at the center of the interference pattern? (b) Calculate the radius of the outermost dark ring. (c) Find the focal length of the lens.

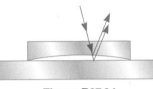

Figure P37.64

65. A plano-convex lens having a radius of curvature of $r = 4.00$ m is placed on a concave glass surface whose radius of curvature is $R = 12.0$ m, as shown in Figure P37.65. Determine the radius of the 100th bright ring, assuming 500-nm light is incident normal to the flat surface of the lens.

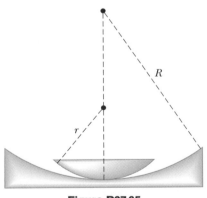

Figure P37.65

66. Use phasor addition to find the resultant amplitude and phase constant when the following three harmonic functions are combined: $E_1 = \sin(\omega t + \pi/6)$, $E_2 = 3.0 \sin(\omega t + 7\pi/2)$, and $E_3 = 6.0 \sin(\omega t + 4\pi/3)$.

67. A soap film ($n = 1.33$) is contained within a rectangular wire frame. The frame is held vertically so that the film drains downward and forms a wedge with flat faces. The thickness of the film at the top is essentially zero. The film is viewed in reflected white light with near-normal incidence, and the first violet ($\lambda = 420$ nm) interference band is observed 3.00 cm from the top edge of the film.

(a) Locate the first red ($\lambda = 680$ nm) interference band. (b) Determine the film thickness at the positions of the violet and red bands. (c) What is the wedge angle of the film?

68. Compact disc (CD) and digital video disc (DVD) players use interference to generate a strong signal from a tiny bump. The depth of a pit is chosen to be one quarter of the wavelength of the laser light used to read the disc. Then light reflected from the pit and light reflected from the adjoining flat differ in path length traveled by one-half wavelength, to interfere destructively at the detector. As the disc rotates, the light intensity drops significantly every time light is reflected from near a pit edge. The space between the leading and trailing edges of a pit determines the time between the fluctuations. The series of time intervals is decoded into a series of zeros and ones that carries the stored information. Assume that infrared light with a wavelength of 780 nm in vacuum is used in a CD player. The disc is coated with plastic having an index of refraction of 1.50. What should be the depth of each pit? A DVD player uses light of a shorter wavelength, and the pit dimensions are correspondingly smaller. This is one factor resulting in greater storage capacity on a DVD compared to a CD.

69. Interference fringes are produced using Lloyd's mirror and a 606-nm source as shown in Figure 37.15. Fringes 1.20 mm apart are formed on a screen 2.00 m from the real source S. Find the vertical distance h of the source above the reflecting surface.

70. Monochromatic light of wavelength 620 nm passes through a very narrow slit S and then strikes a screen in which are two parallel slits, S_1 and S_2, as in Figure P37.70. Slit S_1 is directly in line with S and at a distance of $L = 1.20$ m away from S, whereas S_2 is displaced a distance d to one side. The light is detected at point P on a second screen, equidistant from S_1 and S_2. When either one of the slits S_1 and S_2 is open, equal light intensities are measured at point P. When both are open, the intensity is three times larger. Find the minimum possible value for the slit separation d.

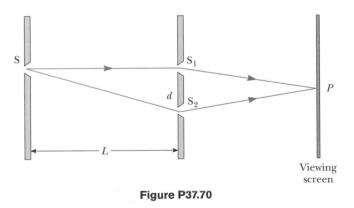

Figure P37.70

71. Slit 1 of a double slit is wider than slit 2, so that the light from 1 has an amplitude 3.00 times that of the light from 2. Show that for this situation, Equation 37.11 is replaced by the equation $I = (4I_{max}/9)(1 + 3 \cos^2 \phi/2)$.

When plane light waves pass through a small aperture in an opaque barrier, the aperture acts as if it were a point source of light, with waves entering the shadow region behind the barrier. This phenomenon, known as diffraction, can be described only with a wave model for light, as discussed in Section 35.3. In this chapter, we investigate the features of the *diffraction pattern* that occurs when the light from the aperture is allowed to fall upon a screen.

In Chapter 34, we learned that electromagnetic waves are transverse. That is, the electric and magnetic field vectors associated with electromagnetic waves are perpendicular to the direction of wave propagation. In this chapter, we show that under certain conditions these transverse waves with electric field vectors in all possible transverse directions can be *polarized* in various ways. This means that only certain directions of the electric field vectors are present in the polarized wave.

38.1 Introduction to Diffraction Patterns

In Section 35.3 we discussed the fact that light of wavelength comparable to or larger than the width of a slit spreads out in all forward directions upon passing through the slit. We call this phenomenon *diffraction*. This behavior indicates that light, once it has passed through a narrow slit, spreads beyond the narrow path defined by the slit into regions that would be in shadow if light traveled in straight lines. Other waves, such as sound waves and water waves, also have this property of spreading when passing through apertures or by sharp edges.

We might expect that the light passing through a small opening would simply result in a broad region of light on a screen, due to the spreading of the light as it passes through the opening. We find something more interesting, however. A **diffraction pattern** consisting of light and dark areas is observed, somewhat similar to the interference patterns discussed earlier. For example, when a narrow slit is placed between a distant light source (or a laser beam) and a screen, the light produces a diffraction pattern like that in Figure 38.1. The pattern consists of a broad, intense central band (called the **central maximum**), flanked by a series of narrower, less intense additional bands (called **side maxima** or **secondary maxima**) and a series of intervening dark bands (or **minima**). Figure 38.2 shows a diffraction pattern associated with light passing by the edge of an object. Again we see bright and dark fringes, which is reminiscent of an interference pattern.

Figure 38.3 shows a diffraction pattern associated with the shadow of a penny. A bright spot occurs at the center, and circular fringes extend outward from the shadow's edge. We can explain the central bright spot only by using the wave theory of light, which predicts constructive interference at this point. From the viewpoint of geometric optics (in which light is viewed as rays traveling in straight lines), we expect the center of the shadow to be dark because that part of the viewing screen is completely shielded by the penny.

It is interesting to point out an historical incident that occurred shortly before the central bright spot was first observed. One of the supporters of geometric optics,

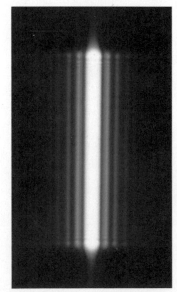

Figure 38.1 The diffraction pattern that appears on a screen when light passes through a narrow vertical slit. The pattern consists of a broad central fringe and a series of less intense and narrower side fringes.

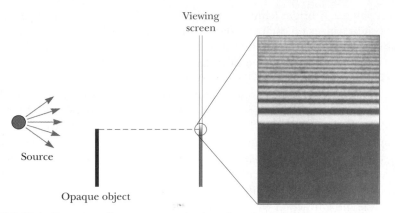

Figure 38.2 Light from a small source passes by the edge of an opaque object and continues on to a screen. A diffraction pattern consisting of bright and dark fringes appears on the screen in the region above the edge of the object.

Figure 38.3 Diffraction pattern created by the illumination of a penny, with the penny positioned midway between screen and light source. Note the bright spot at the center.

Simeon Poisson, argued that if Augustin Fresnel's wave theory of light were valid, then a central bright spot should be observed in the shadow of a circular object illuminated by a point source of light. To Poisson's astonishment, the spot was observed by Dominique Arago shortly thereafter. Thus, Poisson's prediction reinforced the wave theory rather than disproving it.

38.2 Diffraction Patterns from Narrow Slits

Let us consider a common situation, that of light passing through a narrow opening modeled as a slit, and projected onto a screen. To simplify our analysis, we assume that the observing screen is far from the slit, so that the rays reaching the screen are approximately parallel. This can also be achieved experimentally by using a converging lens to focus the parallel rays on a nearby screen. In this model, the pattern on the screen is called a **Fraunhofer diffraction pattern.**[1]

Figure 38.4a shows light entering a single slit from the left and diffracting as it propagates toward a screen. Figure 38.4b is a photograph of a single-slit Fraunhofer

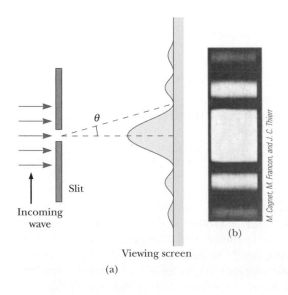

(b)

Active Figure 38.4 (a) Fraunhofer diffraction pattern of a single slit. The pattern consists of a central bright fringe flanked by much weaker maxima alternating with dark fringes. (Drawing not to scale.) (b) Photograph of a single-slit Fraunhofer diffraction pattern.

▲ **PITFALL PREVENTION**

38.1 Diffraction vs. Diffraction Pattern

Diffraction refers to the general behavior of waves spreading out as they pass through a slit. We used diffraction in explaining the existence of an interference pattern in Chapter 37. A *diffraction pattern* is actually a misnomer but is deeply entrenched in the language of physics. The diffraction pattern seen on a screen when a single slit is illuminated is really another interference pattern. The interference is between parts of the incident light illuminating different regions of the slit.

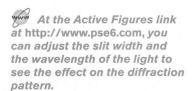

At the Active Figures link at http://www.pse6.com, you can adjust the slit width and the wavelength of the light to see the effect on the diffraction pattern.

---

[1]   If the screen is brought close to the slit (and no lens is used), the pattern is a *Fresnel* diffraction pattern. The Fresnel pattern is more difficult to analyze, so we shall restrict our discussion to Fraunhofer diffraction.

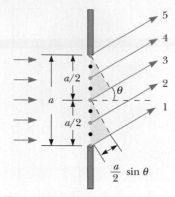

Figure 38.5 Paths of light rays that encounter a narrow slit of width a and diffract toward a screen in the direction described by angle θ. Each portion of the slit acts as a point source of light waves. The path difference between rays 1 and 3, rays 2 and 4, or rays 3 and 5 is $(a/2) \sin \theta$. (Drawing not to scale.)

▲ **PITFALL PREVENTION**

38.2   Similar Equation Warning!

Equation 38.1 has exactly the same form as Equation 37.2, with d, the slit separation, used in Equation 37.2 and a, the slit width, in Equation 38.1. However, Equation 37.2 describes the *bright* regions in a two-slit interference pattern while Equation 38.1 describes the *dark* regions in a single-slit diffraction pattern. Furthermore, $m = 0$ does not represent a dark fringe in the diffraction pattern.

Condition for destructive interference for a single slit

diffraction pattern. A bright fringe is observed along the axis at $\theta = 0$, with alternating dark and bright fringes on each side of the central bright fringe.

Until now, we have assumed that slits are point sources of light. In this section, we abandon that assumption and see how the finite width of slits is the basis for understanding Fraunhofer diffraction. We can deduce some important features of this phenomenon by examining waves coming from various portions of the slit, as shown in Figure 38.5. According to Huygens's principle, **each portion of the slit acts as a source of light waves.** Hence, light from one portion of the slit can interfere with light from another portion, and the resultant light intensity on a viewing screen depends on the direction θ. Based on this analysis, we recognize that a diffraction pattern is actually an interference pattern, in which the different sources of light are different portions of the single slit!

To analyze the diffraction pattern, it is convenient to divide the slit into two halves, as shown in Figure 38.5. Keeping in mind that all the waves are in phase as they leave the slit, consider rays 1 and 3. As these two rays travel toward a viewing screen far to the right of the figure, ray 1 travels farther than ray 3 by an amount equal to the path difference $(a/2)\sin\theta$, where a is the width of the slit. Similarly, the path difference between rays 2 and 4 is also $(a/2) \sin \theta$, as is that between rays 3 and 5. If this path difference is exactly half a wavelength (corresponding to a phase difference of 180°), then the two waves cancel each other and destructive interference results. If this is true for two such rays, then it is true for any two rays that originate at points separated by half the slit width because the phase difference between two such points is 180°. Therefore, waves from the upper half of the slit interfere destructively with waves from the lower half when

$$\frac{a}{2} \sin \theta = \pm \frac{\lambda}{2}$$

or when

$$\sin \theta = \pm \frac{\lambda}{a}$$

If we divide the slit into four equal parts and use similar reasoning, we find that the viewing screen is also dark when

$$\sin \theta = \pm \frac{2\lambda}{a}$$

Likewise, we can divide the slit into six equal parts and show that darkness occurs on the screen when

$$\sin \theta = \pm \frac{3\lambda}{a}$$

Therefore, the general condition for destructive interference is

$$\sin \theta_{\text{dark}} = m \frac{\lambda}{a} \qquad m = \pm 1, \pm 2, \pm 3, \ldots \qquad (38.1)$$

This equation gives the values of θ_{dark} for which the diffraction pattern has zero light intensity—that is, when a dark fringe is formed. However, it tells us nothing about the variation in light intensity along the screen. The general features of the intensity distribution are shown in Figure 38.6. A broad central bright fringe is observed; this fringe is flanked by much weaker bright fringes alternating with dark fringes. The various dark fringes occur at the values of θ_{dark} that satisfy Equation 38.1. Each bright-fringe peak lies approximately halfway between its bordering dark-fringe minima. Note that the central bright maximum is twice as wide as the secondary maxima.

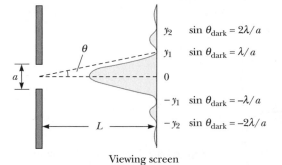

Figure 38.6 Intensity distribution for a Fraunhofer diffraction pattern from a single slit of width a. The positions of two minima on each side of the central maximum are labeled. (Drawing not to scale.)

Quick Quiz 38.1 Suppose the slit width in Figure 38.6 is made half as wide. The central bright fringe (a) becomes wider (b) remains the same (c) becomes narrower.

Quick Quiz 38.2 If a classroom door is open slightly, you can hear sounds coming from the hallway. Yet you cannot see what is happening in the hallway. Why is there this difference? (a) Light waves do not diffract through the single slit of the open doorway. (b) Sound waves can pass through the walls, but light waves cannot. (c) The open door is a small slit for sound waves, but a large slit for light waves. (d) The open door is a large slit for sound waves, but a small slit for light waves.

Example 38.1   Where Are the Dark Fringes?   `Interactive`

Light of wavelength 580 nm is incident on a slit having a width of 0.300 mm. The viewing screen is 2.00 m from the slit. Find the positions of the first dark fringes and the width of the central bright fringe.

Solution The problem statement cues us to conceptualize a single-slit diffraction pattern similar to that in Figure 38.6. We categorize this as a straightforward application of our discussion of single-slit diffraction patterns. To analyze the problem, note that the two dark fringes that flank the central bright fringe correspond to $m = \pm 1$ in Equation 38.1. Hence, we find that

$$\sin \theta_{\text{dark}} = \pm \frac{\lambda}{a} = \pm \frac{5.80 \times 10^{-7}\,\text{m}}{0.300 \times 10^{-3}\,\text{m}} = \pm 1.933 \times 10^{-3}$$

From the triangle in Figure 38.6, note that $\tan \theta_{\text{dark}} = y_1/L$. Because θ_{dark} is very small, we can use the approximation $\sin \theta_{\text{dark}} \approx \tan \theta_{\text{dark}}$; thus, $\sin \theta_{\text{dark}} \approx y_1/L$. Therefore, the positions of the first minima measured from the central axis are given by

$$y_1 \approx L \sin \theta_{\text{dark}} = (2.00\,\text{m})(\pm 1.933 \times 10^{-3})$$
$$= \boxed{\pm 3.87 \times 10^{-3}\,\text{m}}$$

The positive and negative signs correspond to the dark fringes on either side of the central bright fringe. Hence, the width of the central bright fringe is equal to $2|y_1| = 7.74 \times 10^{-3}\,\text{m} = \boxed{7.74\,\text{mm}}$. To finalize this problem,

note that this value is much greater than the width of the slit. We finalize further by exploring what happens if we change the slit width.

What If? What if the slit width is increased by an order of magnitude to 3.00 mm? What happens to the diffraction pattern?

Answer Based on Equation 38.1, we expect that the angles at which the dark bands appear will decrease as a increases. Thus, the diffraction pattern narrows. For $a = 3.00$ mm, the sines of the angles θ_{dark} for the $m = \pm 1$ dark fringes are

$$\sin \theta_{\text{dark}} = \pm \frac{\lambda}{a} = \pm \frac{5.80 \times 10^{-7}\,\text{m}}{3.00 \times 10^{-3}\,\text{m}} = \pm 1.933 \times 10^{-4}$$

The positions of the first minima measured from the central axis are given by

$$y_1 \approx L \sin \theta_{\text{dark}} = (2.00\,\text{m})(\pm 1.933 \times 10^{-4})$$
$$= \pm 3.87 \times 10^{-4}\,\text{m}$$

and the width of the central bright fringe is equal to $2|y_1| = 7.74 \times 10^{-4}\,\text{m} = 0.774$ mm. Notice that this is *smaller* than the width of the slit.

In general, for large values of a, the various maxima and minima are so closely spaced that only a large central bright area resembling the geometric image of the slit is observed. This is very important in the performance of optical instruments such as telescopes.

Investigate the single-slit diffraction pattern at the Interactive Worked Example link at **http://www.pse6.com.**

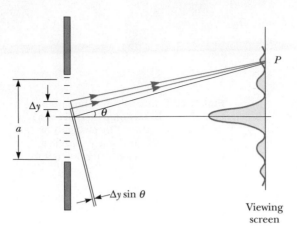

Figure 38.7 Fraunhofer diffraction pattern for a single slit. The light intensity at a distant screen is the resultant of all the incremental electric field magnitudes from zones of width Δy.

Intensity of Single-Slit Diffraction Patterns

We can use phasors to determine the light intensity distribution for a single-slit diffraction pattern. Imagine a slit divided into a large number of small zones, each of width Δy as shown in Figure 38.7. Each zone acts as a source of coherent radiation, and each contributes an incremental electric field of magnitude ΔE at some point on the screen. We obtain the total electric field magnitude E at a point on the screen by summing the contributions from all the zones. The light intensity at this point is proportional to the square of the magnitude of the electric field (Section 37.3).

The incremental electric field magnitudes between adjacent zones are out of phase with one another by an amount $\Delta \beta$, where the phase difference $\Delta \beta$ is related to the path difference $\Delta y \sin \theta$ between adjacent zones by an expression given by an argument similar to that leading to Equation 37.8:

$$\Delta \beta = \frac{2\pi}{\lambda} \Delta y \sin \theta \tag{38.2}$$

To find the magnitude of the total electric field on the screen at any angle θ, we sum the incremental magnitudes ΔE due to each zone. For small values of θ, we can assume that all the ΔE values are the same. It is convenient to use phasor diagrams for various angles, as in Figure 38.8. When $\theta = 0$, all phasors are aligned as in Figure 38.8a because all the waves from the various zones are in phase. In this case, the total electric field at the center of the screen is $E_0 = N \Delta E$, where N is the number of zones. The resultant magnitude E_R at some small angle θ is shown in Figure 38.8b, where each phasor differs in phase from an adjacent one by an amount $\Delta \beta$. In this case, E_R is the

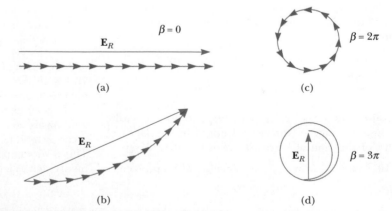

Figure 38.8 Phasor diagrams for obtaining the various maxima and minima of a single-slit diffraction pattern.

vector sum of the incremental magnitudes and hence is given by the length of the chord. Therefore, $E_R < E_0$. The total phase difference β between waves from the top and bottom portions of the slit is

$$\beta = N\,\Delta\beta = \frac{2\pi}{\lambda}\,N\,\Delta y\sin\theta = \frac{2\pi}{\lambda}\,a\sin\theta \qquad (38.3)$$

where $a = N\,\Delta y$ is the width of the slit.

As θ increases, the chain of phasors eventually forms the closed path shown in Figure 38.8c. At this point, the vector sum is zero, and so $E_R = 0$, corresponding to the first minimum on the screen. Noting that $\beta = N\,\Delta\beta = 2\pi$ in this situation, we see from Equation 38.3 that

$$2\pi = \frac{2\pi}{\lambda}\,a\sin\theta_{\text{dark}}$$

$$\sin\theta_{\text{dark}} = \frac{\lambda}{a}$$

That is, the first minimum in the diffraction pattern occurs where $\sin\theta_{\text{dark}} = \lambda/a$; this is in agreement with Equation 38.1.

At larger values of θ, the spiral chain of phasors tightens. For example, Figure 38.8d represents the situation corresponding to the second maximum, which occurs when $\beta = 360° + 180° = 540°$ (3π rad). The second minimum (two complete circles, not shown) corresponds to $\beta = 720°$ (4π rad), which satisfies the condition $\sin\theta_{\text{dark}} = 2\lambda/a$.

We can obtain the total electric-field magnitude E_R and light intensity I at any point on the screen in Figure 38.7 by considering the limiting case in which Δy becomes infinitesimal (dy) and N approaches ∞. In this limit, the phasor chains in Figure 38.8 become the curve of Figure 38.9. The arc length of the curve is E_0 because it is the sum of the magnitudes of the phasors (which is the total electric field magnitude at the center of the screen). From this figure, we see that at some angle θ, the resultant electric field magnitude E_R on the screen is equal to the chord length. From the triangle containing the angle $\beta/2$, we see that

$$\sin\frac{\beta}{2} = \frac{E_R/2}{R}$$

where R is the radius of curvature. But the arc length E_0 is equal to the product $R\beta$, where β is measured in radians. Combining this information with the previous expression gives

$$E_R = 2R\sin\frac{\beta}{2} = 2\left(\frac{E_0}{\beta}\right)\sin\frac{\beta}{2} = E_0\left[\frac{\sin(\beta/2)}{\beta/2}\right]$$

Because the resultant light intensity I at a point on the screen is proportional to the square of the magnitude E_R, we find that

$$I = I_{\text{max}}\left[\frac{\sin(\beta/2)}{\beta/2}\right]^2 \qquad (38.4)$$

where I_{max} is the intensity at $\theta = 0$ (the central maximum). Substituting the expression for β (Eq. 38.3) into Equation 38.4, we have

$$I = I_{\text{max}}\left[\frac{\sin(\pi a\sin\theta/\lambda)}{\pi a\sin\theta/\lambda}\right]^2 \qquad (38.5)$$

From this result, we see that *minima* occur when

$$\frac{\pi a\sin\theta_{\text{dark}}}{\lambda} = m\pi$$

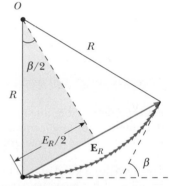

Figure 38.9 Phasor diagram for a large number of coherent sources. All the ends of the phasors lie on the circular arc of radius R. The resultant electric field magnitude E_R equals the length of the chord.

Intensity of a single-slit Fraunhofer diffraction pattern

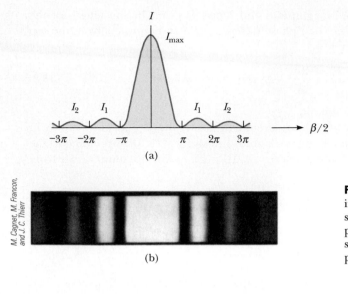

M. Cagnet, M. Francon, and J. C. Thierr

Figure 38.10 (a) A plot of light intensity I versus $\beta/2$ for the single-slit Fraunhofer diffraction pattern. (b) Photograph of a single-slit Fraunhofer diffraction pattern.

or

Condition for intensity minima for a single slit

$$\sin \theta_{\text{dark}} = m \frac{\lambda}{a} \qquad m = \pm 1, \pm 2, \pm 3, \ldots$$

in agreement with Equation 38.1.

Figure 38.10a represents a plot of Equation 38.4, and Figure 38.10b is a photograph of a single-slit Fraunhofer diffraction pattern. Note that most of the light intensity is concentrated in the central bright fringe.

Example 38.2 Relative Intensities of the Maxima

Find the ratio of the intensities of the secondary maxima to the intensity of the central maximum for the single-slit Fraunhofer diffraction pattern.

Solution To a good approximation, the secondary maxima lie midway between the zero points. From Figure 38.10a, we see that this corresponds to $\beta/2$ values of $3\pi/2$, $5\pi/2$, $7\pi/2$, ... Substituting these values into Equation 38.4 gives for the first two ratios

$$\frac{I_1}{I_{\text{max}}} = \left[\frac{\sin(3\pi/2)}{(3\pi/2)} \right]^2 = \frac{1}{9\pi^2/4} = \boxed{0.045}$$

$$\frac{I_2}{I_{\text{max}}} = \left[\frac{\sin(5\pi/2)}{5\pi/2} \right]^2 = \frac{1}{25\pi^2/4} = \boxed{0.016}$$

That is, the first secondary maxima (the ones adjacent to the central maximum) have an intensity of 4.5% that of the central maximum, and the next secondary maxima have an intensity of 1.6% that of the central maximum.

Intensity of Two-Slit Diffraction Patterns

When more than one slit is present, we must consider not only diffraction patterns due to the individual slits but also the interference patterns due to the waves coming from different slits. Notice the curved dashed lines in Figure 37.14, which indicate a decrease in intensity of the interference maxima as θ increases. This decrease is due to a diffraction pattern. To determine the effects of both two-slit interference and a single-slit diffraction pattern from each slit, we combine Equations 37.12 and 38.5:

$$I = I_{\text{max}} \cos^2\left(\frac{\pi d \sin \theta}{\lambda} \right) \left[\frac{\sin(\pi a \sin \theta/\lambda)}{\pi a \sin \theta/\lambda} \right]^2 \tag{38.6}$$

Although this expression looks complicated, it merely represents the single-slit diffraction pattern (the factor in square brackets) acting as an "envelope" for a two-slit

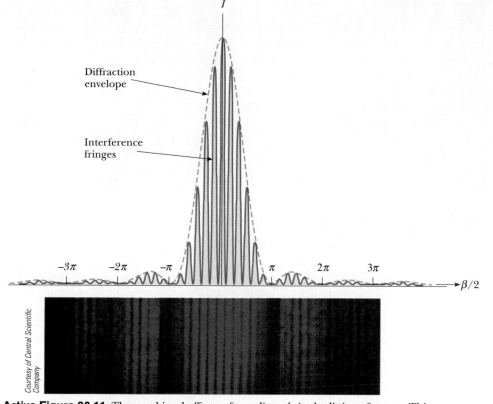

Active Figure 38.11 The combined effects of two-slit and single-slit interference. This is the pattern produced when 650-nm light waves pass through two 3.0-μm slits that are 18 μm apart. Notice how the diffraction pattern acts as an "envelope" and controls the intensity of the regularly spaced interference maxima.

At the Active Figures link at http://www.pse6.com, you can adjust the slit width, slit separation, and the wavelength of the light to see the effect on the interference pattern.

interference pattern (the cosine-squared factor), as shown in Figure 38.11. The broken blue curve in Figure 38.11 represents the factor in square brackets in Equation 38.6. The cosine-squared factor by itself would give a series of peaks all with the same height as the highest peak of the red-brown curve in Figure 38.11. Because of the effect of the square-bracket factor, however, these peaks vary in height as shown.

Equation 37.2 indicates the conditions for interference maxima as $d\sin\theta = m\lambda$, where d is the distance between the two slits. Equation 38.1 specifies that the first diffraction minimum occurs when $a\sin\theta = \lambda$, where a is the slit width. Dividing Equation 37.2 by Equation 38.1 (with $m = 1$) allows us to determine which interference maximum coincides with the first diffraction minimum:

$$\frac{d\sin\theta}{a\sin\theta} = \frac{m\lambda}{\lambda}$$

$$\frac{d}{a} = m \tag{38.7}$$

In Figure 38.11, $d/a = 18\ \mu m/3.0\ \mu m = 6$. Therefore, the sixth interference maximum (if we count the central maximum as $m = 0$) is aligned with the first diffraction minimum and cannot be seen.

Quick Quiz 38.3 Using Figure 38.11 as a starting point, make a sketch of the combined diffraction and interference pattern for 650-nm light waves striking two 3.0-μm slits located 9.0 μm apart.

Quick Quiz 38.4 Consider the central peak in the diffraction envelope in Figure 38.11. Suppose the wavelength of the light is changed to 450 nm. What happens to this central peak? (a) The width of the peak decreases and the number of interference fringes it encloses decreases. (b) The width of the peak decreases and the number of interference fringes it encloses increases. (c) The width of the peak decreases and the number of interference fringes it encloses remains the same. (d) The width of the peak increases and the number of interference fringes it encloses decreases. (e) The width of the peak increases and the number of interference fringes it encloses increases. (f) The width of the peak increases and the number of interference fringes it encloses remains the same.

38.3 Resolution of Single-Slit and Circular Apertures

The ability of optical systems to distinguish between closely spaced objects is limited because of the wave nature of light. To understand this difficulty, consider Figure 38.12, which shows two light sources far from a narrow slit of width a. The sources can be two noncoherent point sources S_1 and S_2—for example, they could be two distant stars. If no interference occurred between light passing through different parts of the slit, two distinct bright spots (or images) would be observed on the viewing screen. However, because of such interference, each source is imaged as a bright central region flanked by weaker bright and dark fringes—a diffraction pattern. What is observed on the screen is the sum of two diffraction patterns: one from S_1, and the other from S_2.

If the two sources are far enough apart to keep their central maxima from overlapping as in Figure 38.12a, their images can be distinguished and are said to be *resolved*. If the sources are close together, however, as in Figure 38.12b, the two central maxima overlap, and the images are not resolved. To determine whether two images are resolved, the following condition is often used:

When the central maximum of one image falls on the first minimum of another image, the images are said to be just resolved. This limiting condition of resolution is known as **Rayleigh's criterion.**

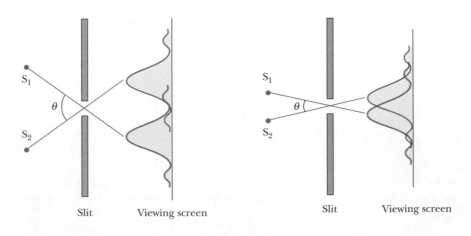

(a)   (b)

Figure 38.12 Two point sources far from a narrow slit each produce a diffraction pattern. (a) The angle subtended by the sources at the slit is large enough for the diffraction patterns to be distinguishable. (b) The angle subtended by the sources is so small that their diffraction patterns overlap, and the images are not well resolved. (Note that the angles are greatly exaggerated. The drawing is not to scale.)

From Rayleigh's criterion, we can determine the minimum angular separation $\theta_{\min}$ subtended by the sources at the slit in Figure 38.12 for which the images are just resolved. Equation 38.1 indicates that the first minimum in a single-slit diffraction pattern occurs at the angle for which

$$\sin\theta = \frac{\lambda}{a}$$

where a is the width of the slit. According to Rayleigh's criterion, this expression gives the smallest angular separation for which the two images are resolved. Because $\lambda \ll a$ in most situations, $\sin\theta$ is small, and we can use the approximation $\sin\theta \approx \theta$. Therefore, the limiting angle of resolution for a slit of width a is

$$\theta_{\min} = \frac{\lambda}{a} \qquad (38.8)$$

where $\theta_{\min}$ is expressed in radians. Hence, the angle subtended by the two sources at the slit must be greater than λ/a if the images are to be resolved.

Many optical systems use circular apertures rather than slits. The diffraction pattern of a circular aperture, as shown in the lower half of Figure 38.13, consists of a central circular bright disk surrounded by progressively fainter bright and dark rings. Figure 38.13 shows diffraction patterns for three situations in which light from two point sources passes through a circular aperture. When the sources are far apart, their images are well resolved (Fig. 38.13a). When the angular separation of the sources satisfies Rayleigh's criterion, the images are just resolved (Fig. 38.13b). Finally, when the sources are close together, the images are said to be unresolved (Fig. 38.13c).

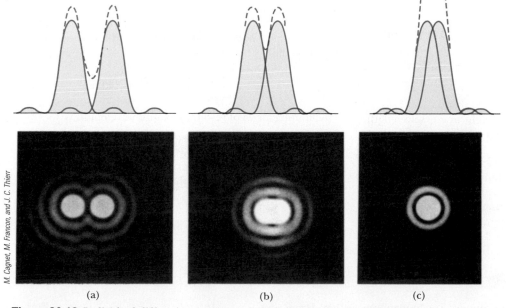

M. Cagnet, M. Francon, and J. C. Thierr

(a)   (b)   (c)

Figure 38.13 Individual diffraction patterns of two point sources (solid curves) and the resultant patterns (dashed curves) for various angular separations of the sources. In each case, the dashed curve is the sum of the two solid curves. (a) The sources are far apart, and the patterns are well resolved. (b) The sources are closer together such that the angular separation just satisfies Rayleigh's criterion, and the patterns are just resolved. (c) The sources are so close together that the patterns are not resolved.

Analysis shows that the limiting angle of resolution of the circular aperture is

$$\theta_{\min} = 1.22 \frac{\lambda}{D} \tag{38.9}$$

where D is the diameter of the aperture. Note that this expression is similar to Equation 38.8 except for the factor 1.22, which arises from a mathematical analysis of diffraction from the circular aperture.

Quick Quiz 38.5 Cat's eyes have pupils that can be modeled as vertical slits. At night, would cats be more successful in resolving (a) headlights on a distant car, or (b) vertically-separated lights on the mast of a distant boat?

Quick Quiz 38.6 Suppose you are observing a binary star with a telescope and are having difficulty resolving the two stars. You decide to use a colored filter to maximize the resolution. (A filter of a given color transmits only that color of light.) What color filter should you choose? (a) blue (b) green (c) yellow (d) red.

Example 38.3 Limiting Resolution of a Microscope

Light of wavelength 589 nm is used to view an object under a microscope. If the aperture of the objective has a diameter of 0.900 cm,

(A) what is the limiting angle of resolution?

Solution Using Equation 38.9, we find that the limiting angle of resolution is

$$\theta_{\min} = 1.22 \left(\frac{589 \times 10^{-9} \text{ m}}{0.900 \times 10^{-2} \text{ m}} \right) = \boxed{7.98 \times 10^{-5} \text{ rad}}$$

This means that any two points on the object subtending an angle smaller than this at the objective cannot be distinguished in the image.

(B) If it were possible to use visible light of any wavelength, what would be the maximum limit of resolution for this microscope?

Solution To obtain the smallest limiting angle, we have to use the shortest wavelength available in the visible spectrum. Violet light (400 nm) gives a limiting angle of resolution of

$$\theta_{\min} = 1.22 \left(\frac{400 \times 10^{-9} \text{ m}}{0.900 \times 10^{-2} \text{ m}} \right) = \boxed{5.42 \times 10^{-5} \text{ rad}}$$

What If? Suppose that water ($n = 1.33$) fills the space between the object and the objective. What effect does this have on resolving power when 589-nm light is used?

Answer Because light travels more slowly in water, we know that the wavelength of the light in water is smaller than that in vacuum. Based on Equation 38.9, we expect the limiting angle of resolution to be smaller. To find the new value of the limiting angle of resolution, we first calculate the wavelength of the 589-nm light in water using Equation 35.7:

$$\lambda_{\text{water}} = \frac{\lambda_{\text{air}}}{n_{\text{water}}} = \frac{589 \text{ nm}}{1.33} = 443 \text{ nm}$$

The limiting angle of resolution at this wavelength is

$$\theta_{\min} = 1.22 \left(\frac{443 \times 10^{-9} \text{ m}}{0.900 \times 10^{-2} \text{ m}} \right) = \boxed{6.00 \times 10^{-5} \text{ rad}}$$

which is indeed smaller than that calculated in part (A).

Example 38.4 Resolution of the Eye

Estimate the limiting angle of resolution for the human eye, assuming its resolution is limited only by diffraction.

Solution Let us choose a wavelength of 500 nm, near the center of the visible spectrum. Although pupil diameter varies from person to person, we estimate a daytime diameter of 2 mm. We use Equation 38.9, taking $\lambda = 500$ nm

and $D = 2$ mm:

$$\theta_{\min} = 1.22 \frac{\lambda}{D} = 1.22 \left(\frac{5.00 \times 10^{-7} \text{ m}}{2 \times 10^{-3} \text{ m}} \right)$$

$$\approx 3 \times 10^{-4} \text{ rad} \approx \boxed{1 \text{ min of arc}}$$

We can use this result to determine the minimum separation distance d between two point sources that the eye can distinguish if they are a distance L from the observer (Fig. 38.14). Because θ_{min} is small, we see that

$$\sin \theta_{min} \approx \theta_{min} \approx \frac{d}{L}$$

$$d = L\theta_{min}$$

For example, if the point sources are 25 cm from the eye (the near point), then

$$d = (25\ \text{cm})(3 \times 10^{-4}\ \text{rad}) = 8 \times 10^{-3}\ \text{cm}$$

This is approximately equal to the thickness of a human hair.

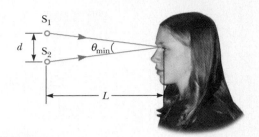

Figure 38.14 (Example 38.4) Two point sources separated by a distance d as observed by the eye.

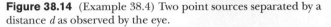

Example 38.5   Resolution of a Telescope

The Keck telescope at Mauna Kea, Hawaii, has an effective diameter of 10 m. What is its limiting angle of resolution for 600-nm light?

Solution Because $D = 10$ m and $\lambda = 6.00 \times 10^{-7}$ m, Equation 38.9 gives

$$\theta_{min} = 1.22\ \frac{\lambda}{D} = 1.22 \left(\frac{6.00 \times 10^{-7}\ \text{m}}{10\ \text{m}} \right)$$

$$= 7.3 \times 10^{-8}\ \text{rad} \approx \boxed{0.015\ \text{s of arc}}$$

Any two stars that subtend an angle greater than or equal to this value are resolved (if atmospheric conditions are ideal).

The Keck telescope can never reach its diffraction limit because the limiting angle of resolution is always set by atmospheric blurring at optical wavelengths. This seeing limit is usually about 1 s of arc and is never smaller than about 0.1 s of arc. (This is one of the reasons for the superiority of photographs from the Hubble Space Telescope, which views celestial objects from an orbital position above the atmosphere.)

What If? What if we consider radio telescopes? These are much larger in diameter than optical telescopes, but do they have angular resolutions that are better than optical telescopes? For example, the radio telescope at Arecibo, Puerto Rico, has a diameter of 305 m and is designed to detect radio waves of 0.75-m wavelength. How does its resolution compare to that of the Keck telescope?

Answer The increase in diameter might suggest that radio telescopes would have better resolution, but Equation 38.9 shows that θ_{min} depends on *both* diameter and wavelength. Calculating the minimum angle of resolution for the radio telescope, we find

$$\theta_{min} = 1.22\ \frac{\lambda}{D} = 1.22 \left(\frac{0.75\ \text{m}}{305\ \text{m}} \right)$$

$$= 3.0 \times 10^{-3}\ \text{rad} \approx 10\ \text{min of arc}$$

Notice that this limiting angle of resolution is measured in *minutes* of arc rather than the *seconds* of arc for the optical telescope. Thus, the change in wavelength more than compensates for the increase in diameter, and the limiting angle of resolution for the Arecibo radio telescope is more than 40 000 times larger (that is, *worse*) than the Keck minimum.

As an example of the effects of atmospheric blurring mentioned in Example 38.5, consider telescopic images of Pluto and its moon Charon. Figure 38.15a shows the image taken in 1978 that represents the discovery of Charon. In this photograph taken from an Earth-based telescope, atmospheric turbulence causes the image of Charon to appear only as a bump on the edge of Pluto. In comparison, Figure 38.15b shows a photograph taken with the Hubble Space Telescope. Without the problems of atmospheric turbulence, Pluto and its moon are clearly resolved.

38.4   The Diffraction Grating

The **diffraction grating,** a useful device for analyzing light sources, consists of a large number of equally spaced parallel slits. A *transmission grating* can be made by cutting parallel grooves on a glass plate with a precision ruling machine. The spaces between the grooves are transparent to the light and hence act as separate slits. A *reflection grating* can

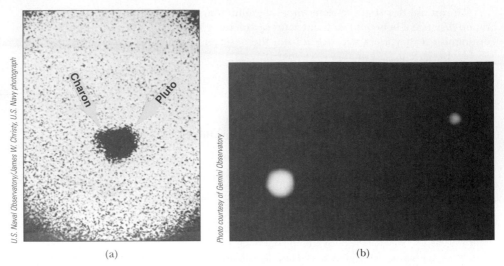

U.S. Naval Observatory/James W. Christy, U.S. Navy photograph

Charon

Pluto

(a)

Photo courtesy of Gemini Observatory

(b)

Figure 38.15 (a) The photograph on which Charon, the moon of Pluto, was discovered in 1978. From an Earth-based telescope, atmospheric blurring results in Charon appearing only as a subtle bump on the edge of Pluto. (b) A Hubble Space Telescope photo of Pluto and Charon, clearly resolving the two objects.

be made by cutting parallel grooves on the surface of a reflective material. The reflection of light from the spaces between the grooves is specular, and the reflection from the grooves cut into the material is diffuse. Thus, the spaces between the grooves act as parallel sources of reflected light, like the slits in a transmission grating. Current technology can produce gratings that have very small slit spacings. For example, a typical grating ruled with 5 000 grooves/cm has a slit spacing $d = (1/5\,000)$ cm $= 2.00 \times 10^{-4}$ cm.

A section of a diffraction grating is illustrated in Figure 38.16. A plane wave is incident from the left, normal to the plane of the grating. The pattern observed on the

▲ **PITFALL PREVENTION**

38.3 A Diffraction Grating Is an Interference Grating

As with *diffraction pattern*, *diffraction grating* is a misnomer, but is deeply entrenched in the language of physics. The diffraction grating depends on diffraction in the same way as the double slit—spreading the light so that light from different slits can interfere. It would be more correct to call it an *interference grating*, but *diffraction grating* is the name in use.

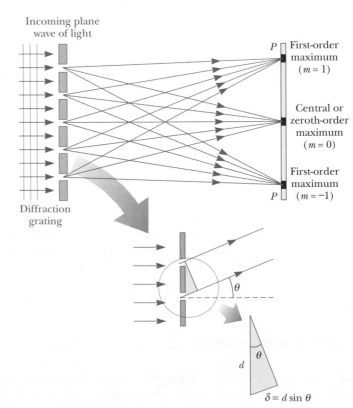

Incoming plane wave of light

P — First-order maximum ($m = 1$)

Central or zeroth-order maximum ($m = 0$)

First-order maximum ($m = -1$)

P

Diffraction grating

θ

d

θ

$\delta = d \sin \theta$

Figure 38.16 Side view of a diffraction grating. The slit separation is d, and the path difference between adjacent slits is $d \sin \theta$.

screen (far to the right of Figure 38.16) is the result of the combined effects of interference and diffraction. Each slit produces diffraction, and the diffracted beams interfere with one another to produce the final pattern.

The waves from all slits are in phase as they leave the slits. However, for some arbitrary direction θ measured from the horizontal, the waves must travel different path lengths before reaching the screen. From Figure 38.16, note that the path difference δ between rays from any two adjacent slits is equal to $d \sin \theta$. If this path difference equals one wavelength or some integral multiple of a wavelength, then waves from all slits are in phase at the screen and a bright fringe is observed. Therefore, the condition for *maxima* in the interference pattern at the angle θ_{bright} is

$$d \sin \theta_{bright} = m\lambda \qquad m = 0, \pm 1, \pm 2, \pm 3, \ldots \qquad (38.10)$$

Condition for interference maxima for a grating

We can use this expression to calculate the wavelength if we know the grating spacing d and the angle θ_{bright}. If the incident radiation contains several wavelengths, the mth-order maximum for each wavelength occurs at a specific angle. All wavelengths are seen at $\theta = 0$, corresponding to $m = 0$, the zeroth-order maximum. The first-order maximum ($m = 1$) is observed at an angle that satisfies the relationship $\sin \theta_{bright} = \lambda/d$; the second-order maximum ($m = 2$) is observed at a larger angle θ_{bright}, and so on.

The intensity distribution for a diffraction grating obtained with the use of a monochromatic source is shown in Figure 38.17. Note the sharpness of the principal maxima and the broadness of the dark areas. This is in contrast to the broad bright fringes characteristic of the two-slit interference pattern (see Fig. 37.7). You should also review Figure 37.14, which shows that the width of the intensity maxima decreases as the number of slits increases. Because the principal maxima are so sharp, they are much brighter than two-slit interference maxima.

A schematic drawing of a simple apparatus used to measure angles in a diffraction pattern is shown in Figure 38.18. This apparatus is a *diffraction grating spectrometer*. The light to be analyzed passes through a slit, and a collimated beam of light is incident on the grating. The diffracted light leaves the grating at angles that satisfy Equation 38.10, and a telescope is used to view the image of the slit. The wavelength can be determined by measuring the precise angles at which the images of the slit appear for the various orders.

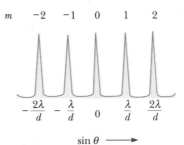

Active Figure 38.17 Intensity versus $\sin \theta$ for a diffraction grating. The zeroth-, first-, and second-order maxima are shown.

At the Active Figures link at http://www.pse6.com, you can choose the number of slits to be illuminated to see the effect on the interference pattern.

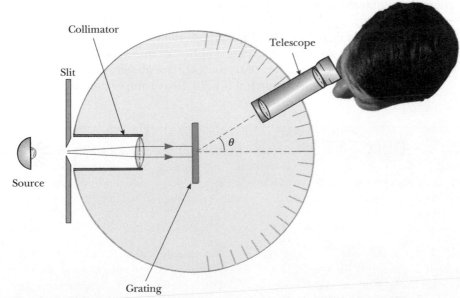

Active Figure 38.18 Diagram of a diffraction grating spectrometer. The collimated beam incident on the grating is spread into its various wavelength components with constructive interference for a particular wavelength occurring at the angles θ_{bright} that satisfy the equation $d \sin \theta_{bright} = m\lambda$, where $m = 0, 1, 2, \ldots$.

Use the spectrometer at the Active Figures link at http://www.pse6.com to observe constructive interference for various wavelengths.

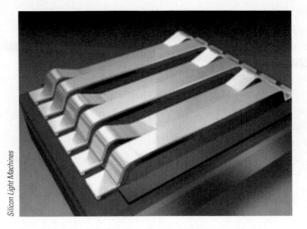

Silicon Light Machines

Figure 38.19 A small portion of a grating light valve. The alternating reflective ribbons at different levels act as a diffraction grating, offering very-high-speed control of the direction of light toward a digital display device.

The spectrometer is a useful tool in *atomic spectroscopy*, in which the light from an atom is analyzed to find the wavelength components. These wavelength components can be used to identify the atom. We will investigate atomic spectra in Chapter 42 of the extended version of this text.

Another application of diffraction gratings is in the recently developed *grating light valve* (GLV), which may compete in the near future in video projection with the digital micromirror devices (DMDs) discussed in Section 35.4. The grating light valve consists of a silicon microchip fitted with an array of parallel silicon nitride ribbons coated with a thin layer of aluminum (Fig. 38.19). Each ribbon is about 20 μm long and about 5 μm wide and is separated from the silicon substrate by an air gap on the order of 100 nm. With no voltage applied, all ribbons are at the same level. In this situation, the array of ribbons acts as a flat surface, specularly reflecting incident light.

When a voltage is applied between a ribbon and the electrode on the silicon substrate, an electric force pulls the ribbon downward, closer to the substrate. Alternate ribbons can be pulled down, while those in between remain in the higher configuration. As a result, the array of ribbons acts as a diffraction grating, such that the constructive interference for a particular wavelength of light can be directed toward a screen or other optical display system. By using three such devices, one each for red, blue, and green light, full-color display is possible.

The GLV tends to be simpler to fabricate and higher in resolution than comparable DMD devices. On the other hand, DMD devices have already made an entry into the market. It will be interesting to watch this technology competition in future years.

Quick Quiz 38.7 If laser light is reflected from a phonograph record or a compact disc, a diffraction pattern appears. This is due to the fact that both devices contain parallel tracks of information that act as a reflection diffraction grating. Which device, (a) record or (b) compact disc, results in diffraction maxima that are farther apart in angle?

Quick Quiz 38.8 Ultraviolet light of wavelength 350 nm is incident on a diffraction grating with slit spacing d and forms an interference pattern on a screen a distance L away. The angular positions θ_{bright} of the interference maxima are large. The locations of the bright fringes are marked on the screen. Now red light of wavelength 700 nm is used with a diffraction grating to form another diffraction pattern on the screen. The bright fringes of this pattern will be located at the marks on the screen if

(a) the screen is moved to a distance $2L$ from the grating (b) the screen is moved to a distance $L/2$ from the grating (c) the grating is replaced with one of slit spacing $2d$ (d) the grating is replaced with one of slit spacing $d/2$ (e) nothing is changed.

Conceptual Example 38.6   A Compact Disc Is a Diffraction Grating

Light reflected from the surface of a compact disc is multicolored, as shown in Figure 38.20. The colors and their intensities depend on the orientation of the disc relative to the eye and relative to the light source. Explain how this works.

Solution The surface of a compact disc has a spiral grooved track (with adjacent grooves having a separation on the order of 1 μm). Thus, the surface acts as a reflection grating. The light reflecting from the regions between these closely spaced grooves interferes constructively only in certain directions that depend on the wavelength and on the direction of the incident light. Any section of the disc serves as a diffraction grating for white light, sending different colors in different directions. The different colors you see when viewing one section change as the light source, the disc, or you move to change the angles of incidence or diffraction.

Figure 38.20 (Conceptual Example 38.6) A compact disc observed under white light. The colors observed in the reflected light and their intensities depend on the orientation of the disc relative to the eye and relative to the light source.

Example 38.7   The Orders of a Diffraction Grating   Interactive

Monochromatic light from a helium–neon laser (λ = 632.8 nm) is incident normally on a diffraction grating containing 6 000 grooves per centimeter. Find the angles at which the first- and second-order maxima are observed.

Solution First, we must calculate the slit separation, which is equal to the inverse of the number of grooves per centimeter:

$$d = \frac{1}{6\,000}\text{ cm} = 1.667 \times 10^{-4}\text{ cm} = 1\,667\text{ nm}$$

For the first-order maximum ($m = 1$), we obtain

$$\sin \theta_1 = \frac{\lambda}{d} = \frac{632.8\text{ nm}}{1\,667\text{ nm}} = 0.379\,6$$

$$\theta_1 = \boxed{22.31°}$$

For the second-order maximum ($m = 2$), we find

$$\sin \theta_2 = \frac{2\lambda}{d} = \frac{2(632.8\text{ nm})}{1\,667\text{ nm}} = 0.759\,2$$

$$\theta_2 = \boxed{49.39°}$$

What If? What if we look for the third-order maximum? Do we find it?

Answer For $m = 3$, we find $\sin \theta_3 = 1.139$. Because $\sin\theta$ cannot exceed unity, this does not represent a realistic solution. Hence, only zeroth-, first-, and second-order maxima are observed for this situation.

Investigate the interference pattern from a diffraction grating at the Interactive Worked Example link at **http://www.pse6.com.**

Resolving Power of the Diffraction Grating

The diffraction grating is useful for measuring wavelengths accurately. Like the prism, the diffraction grating can be used to separate white light into its wavelength components. Of the two devices, a grating with very small slit separation is more precise if one wants to distinguish two closely spaced wavelengths.

For two nearly equal wavelengths λ_1 and λ_2 between which a diffraction grating can just barely distinguish, the **resolving power** R of the grating is defined as

Resolving power

$$R \equiv \frac{\lambda}{\lambda_2 - \lambda_1} = \frac{\lambda}{\Delta\lambda} \qquad (38.11)$$

where $\lambda = (\lambda_1 + \lambda_2)/2$ and $\Delta\lambda = \lambda_2 - \lambda_1$. Thus, a grating that has a high resolving power can distinguish small differences in wavelength. If N slits of the grating are illuminated, it can be shown that the resolving power in the mth-order diffraction is

Resolving power of a grating

$$R = Nm \qquad (38.12)$$

Thus, resolving power increases with increasing order number and with increasing number of illuminated slits.

Note that $R = 0$ for $m = 0$; this signifies that all wavelengths are indistinguishable for the zeroth-order maximum. However, consider the second-order diffraction pattern ($m = 2$) of a grating that has 5 000 rulings illuminated by the light source. The resolving power of such a grating in second order is $R = 5\,000 \times 2 = 10\,000$. Therefore, for a mean wavelength of, for example, 600 nm, the minimum wavelength separation between two spectral lines that can be just resolved is $\Delta\lambda = \lambda/R = 6.00 \times 10^{-2}$ nm. For the third-order principal maximum, $R = 15\,000$ and $\Delta\lambda = 4.00 \times 10^{-2}$ nm, and so on.

Example 38.8   Resolving Sodium Spectral Lines

When a gaseous element is raised to a very high temperature, the atoms emit radiation having discrete wavelengths. The set of wavelengths for a given element is called its *atomic spectrum* (Chapter 42). Two strong components in the atomic spectrum of sodium have wavelengths of 589.00 nm and 589.59 nm.

(A) What resolving power must a grating have if these wavelengths are to be distinguished?

Solution Using Equation 38.11,

$$R = \frac{\lambda}{\Delta\lambda} = \frac{589.30 \text{ nm}}{589.59 \text{ nm} - 589.00 \text{ nm}} = \frac{589.30}{0.59} = \boxed{999}$$

(B) To resolve these lines in the second-order spectrum, how many slits of the grating must be illuminated?

Solution From Equation 38.12 and the result to part (A), we find that

$$N = \frac{R}{m} = \frac{999}{2} = \boxed{500 \text{ slits}}$$

Application   Holography

One interesting application of diffraction gratings is **holography,** the production of three-dimensional images of objects. The physics of holography was developed by Dennis Gabor in 1948, and resulted in the Nobel Prize in physics for Gabor in 1971. The requirement of coherent light for holography, however, delayed the realization of holographic images from Gabor's work until the development of lasers in the 1960s. Figure 38.21 shows a hologram and the three-dimensional character of its image.

Figure 38.22 shows how a hologram is made. Light from the laser is split into two parts by a half-silvered mirror at *B*. One part of the beam reflects off the object to be photographed and strikes an ordinary photographic film. The other half of the beam is diverged by lens L_2, reflects from mirrors M_1 and M_2, and finally strikes the film. The two beams overlap to form an extremely complicated interference pattern on the film. Such an interference pattern can be produced only if the phase relationship of the two waves is constant throughout the exposure of the film. This condition is met by illuminating the scene with light coming through a pinhole or with coherent laser radiation. The hologram records not only the intensity of the light scattered from the object (as in a conventional photograph), but also the phase difference between the reference beam and the beam scattered from the object. Because of this phase difference, an interference pattern is formed that produces an image in which all three-dimensional information available from the perspective of any point on the hologram is preserved.

In a normal photographic image, a lens is used to focus the image so that each point on the object corresponds to a single point on the film. Notice that there is no lens used in Figure 38.22 to focus the light onto the film. Thus, light from each point on the object reaches *all* points on the film. As a result, each region of the photographic film on which the hologram is recorded contains information about all illuminated points on the object. This leads to a remarkable

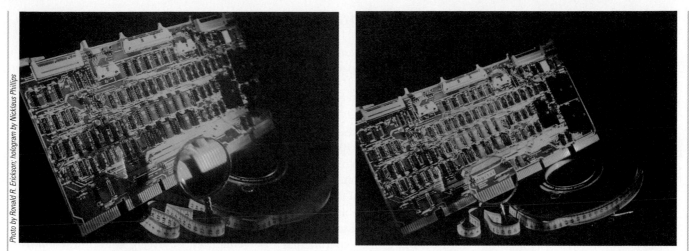

Photo by Ronald R. Erickson; hologram by Nicklaus Phillips

Figure 38.21 In this hologram, a circuit board is shown from two different views. Notice the difference in the appearance of the measuring tape and the view through the magnifying lens.

result—if a small section of the hologram is cut from the film, the complete image can be formed from the small piece! (The quality of the image is reduced, but the entire image is present.)

A hologram is best viewed by allowing coherent light to pass through the developed film as one looks back along the direction from which the beam comes. The interference pattern on the film acts as a diffraction grating. Figure 38.23 shows two rays of light striking the film and passing through. For each ray, the $m = 0$ and $m = \pm 1$ rays in the diffraction pattern are shown emerging from the right side of the film. The $m = +1$ rays converge to

form a real image of the scene, which is not the image that is normally viewed. By extending the light rays corresponding to $m = -1$ back behind the film, we see that there is a virtual image located there, with light coming from it in exactly the same way that light came from the actual object when the film was exposed. This is the image that we see by looking through the holographic film.

Holograms are finding a number of applications. You may have a hologram on your credit card. This is a special type of hologram called a *rainbow hologram,* designed to be viewed in reflected white light.

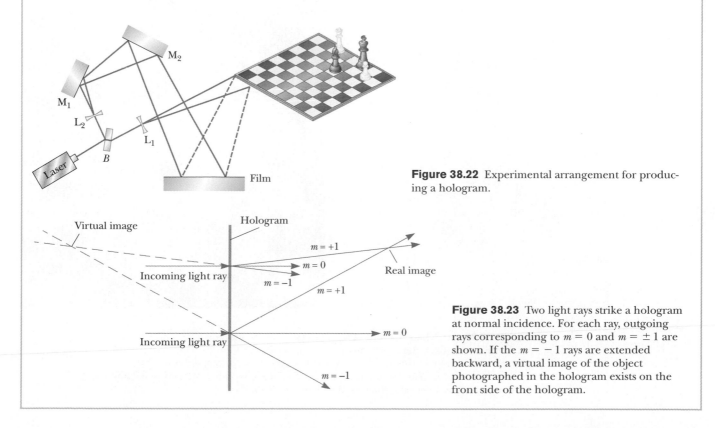

Figure 38.22 Experimental arrangement for producing a hologram.

Figure 38.23 Two light rays strike a hologram at normal incidence. For each ray, outgoing rays corresponding to $m = 0$ and $m = \pm 1$ are shown. If the $m = -1$ rays are extended backward, a virtual image of the object photographed in the hologram exists on the front side of the hologram.

38.5 Diffraction of X-Rays by Crystals

In principle, the wavelength of any electromagnetic wave can be determined if a grating of the proper spacing (on the order of λ) is available. X-rays, discovered by Wilhelm Roentgen (1845–1923) in 1895, are electromagnetic waves of very short wavelength (on the order of 0.1 nm). It would be impossible to construct a grating having such a small spacing by the cutting process described at the beginning of Section 38.4. However, the atomic spacing in a solid is known to be about 0.1 nm. In 1913, Max von Laue (1879–1960) suggested that the regular array of atoms in a crystal could act as a three-dimensional diffraction grating for x-rays. Subsequent experiments confirmed this prediction. The diffraction patterns from crystals are complex because of the three-dimensional nature of crystal structure. Nevertheless, x-ray diffraction has proved to be an invaluable technique for elucidating these structures and for understanding the structure of matter.

Figure 38.24 is one experimental arrangement for observing x-ray diffraction from a crystal. A collimated beam of monochromatic x-rays is incident on a crystal. The diffracted beams are very intense in certain directions, corresponding to constructive interference from waves reflected from layers of atoms in the crystal. The diffracted beams, which can be detected by a photographic film, form an array of spots known as a *Laue pattern*, as in Figure 38.25a. One can deduce the crystalline structure by analyzing the positions and intensities of the various spots in the pattern. Fig. 38.25b shows a Laue pattern from a crystalline enzyme, using a wide range of wavelengths so that a swirling pattern results.

The arrangement of atoms in a crystal of sodium chloride (NaCl) is shown in Figure 38.26. Each unit cell (the geometric solid that repeats throughout the crystal) is a cube having an edge length a. A careful examination of the NaCl structure shows that the ions lie in discrete planes (the shaded areas in Fig. 38.26). Now suppose that an incident x-ray beam makes an angle θ with one of the planes, as in Figure 38.27. The beam can be reflected from both the upper plane and the lower one. However,

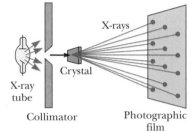

Figure 38.24 Schematic diagram of the technique used to observe the diffraction of x-rays by a crystal. The array of spots formed on the film is called a Laue pattern.

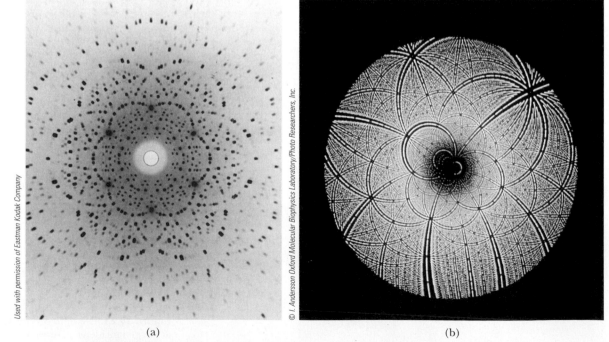

(a) (b)

Figure 38.25 (a) A Laue pattern of a single crystal of the mineral beryl (beryllium aluminum silicate). Each dot represents a point of constructive interference. (b) A Laue pattern of the enzyme Rubisco, produced with a wide-band x-ray spectrum. This enzyme is present in plants and takes part in the process of photosynthesis. The Laue pattern is used to determine the crystal structure of Rubisco.

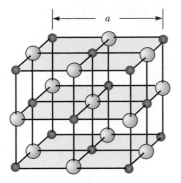

Figure 38.26 Crystalline structure of sodium chloride (NaCl). The blue spheres represent Cl⁻ ions, and the red spheres represent Na⁺ ions. The length of the cube edge is $a = 0.562\ 737$ nm.

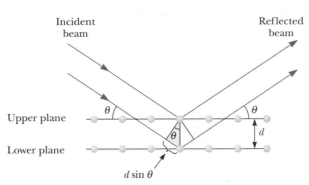

Figure 38.27 A two-dimensional description of the reflection of an x-ray beam from two parallel crystalline planes separated by a distance d. The beam reflected from the lower plane travels farther than the one reflected from the upper plane by a distance $2d \sin \theta$.

the beam reflected from the lower plane travels farther than the beam reflected from the upper plane. The effective path difference is $2d \sin \theta$. The two beams reinforce each other (constructive interference) when this path difference equals some integer multiple of λ. The same is true for reflection from the entire family of parallel planes. Hence, the condition for *constructive* interference (maxima in the reflected beam) is

$$2d \sin \theta = m\lambda \qquad m = 1, 2, 3, \ldots \qquad (38.13)$$

This condition is known as **Bragg's law,** after W. L. Bragg (1890–1971), who first derived the relationship. If the wavelength and diffraction angle are measured, Equation 38.13 can be used to calculate the spacing between atomic planes.

38.6   Polarization of Light Waves

In Chapter 34 we described the transverse nature of light and all other electromagnetic waves. Polarization, discussed in this section, is firm evidence of this transverse nature.

An ordinary beam of light consists of a large number of waves emitted by the atoms of the light source. Each atom produces a wave having some particular orientation of the electric field vector **E**, corresponding to the direction of atomic vibration. The *direction of polarization* of each individual wave is defined to be the direction in which the electric field is vibrating. In Figure 38.28, this direction happens to lie along the y axis. However, an individual electromagnetic wave could have its **E** vector in the yz plane, making any possible angle with the y axis. Because all directions of vibration from a wave source are possible, the resultant electromagnetic wave is a superposition of waves vibrating in many different directions. The result is an **unpolarized** light beam, represented in Figure 38.29a. The direction of wave propagation in this figure is perpendicular to the page. The arrows show a few possible directions of the electric field vectors for the individual waves making up the resultant beam. At any given point and at some instant of time, all these individual electric field vectors add to give one resultant electric field vector.

As noted in Section 34.2, a wave is said to be **linearly polarized** if the resultant electric field **E** vibrates in the same direction *at all times* at a particular point, as shown in Figure 38.29b. (Sometimes, such a wave is described as *plane-polarized*, or simply *polarized*.) The plane formed by **E** and the direction of propagation is called the *plane*

▲ **PITFALL PREVENTION**

38.4   Different Angles

Notice in Figure 38.27 that the angle θ is measured from the reflecting surface, rather than from the normal, as in the case of the law of reflection in Chapter 35. With slits and diffraction gratings, we also measured the angle θ from the normal to the array of slits. Because of historical tradition, the angle is measured differently in Bragg diffraction, so interpret Equation 38.13 with care.

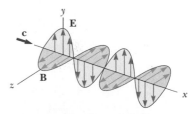

Figure 38.28 Schematic diagram of an electromagnetic wave propagating at velocity **c** in the x direction. The electric field vibrates in the xy plane, and the magnetic field vibrates in the xz plane.

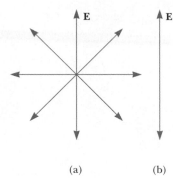

(a)   (b)

Figure 38.29 (a) A representation of an unpolarized light beam viewed along the direction of propagation (perpendicular to the page). The transverse electric field can vibrate in any direction in the plane of the page with equal probability. (b) A linearly polarized light beam with the electric field vibrating in the vertical direction.

of polarization of the wave. If the wave in Figure 38.28 represents the resultant of all individual waves, the plane of polarization is the *xy* plane.

It is possible to obtain a linearly polarized beam from an unpolarized beam by removing all waves from the beam except those whose electric field vectors oscillate in a single plane. We now discuss four processes for producing polarized light from unpolarized light.

Polarization by Selective Absorption

The most common technique for producing polarized light is to use a material that transmits waves whose electric fields vibrate in a plane parallel to a certain direction and that absorbs waves whose electric fields vibrate in all other directions.

In 1938, E. H. Land (1909–1991) discovered a material, which he called *polaroid*, that polarizes light through selective absorption by oriented molecules. This material is fabricated in thin sheets of long-chain hydrocarbons. The sheets are stretched during manufacture so that the long-chain molecules align. After a sheet is dipped into a solution containing iodine, the molecules become good electrical conductors. However, conduction takes place primarily along the hydrocarbon chains because electrons can move easily only along the chains. As a result, the molecules readily absorb light whose electric field vector is parallel to their length and allow light through whose electric field vector is perpendicular to their length.

It is common to refer to the direction perpendicular to the molecular chains as the *transmission axis*. In an ideal polarizer, all light with **E** parallel to the transmission axis is transmitted, and all light with **E** perpendicular to the transmission axis is absorbed.

Figure 38.30 represents an unpolarized light beam incident on a first polarizing sheet, called the *polarizer*. Because the transmission axis is oriented vertically in the figure, the light transmitted through this sheet is polarized vertically. A second polarizing sheet, called the *analyzer*, intercepts the beam. In Figure 38.30, the analyzer transmission axis is set at an angle θ to the polarizer axis. We call the electric field vector of the first transmitted beam $\mathbf{E}_0$. The component of $\mathbf{E}_0$ perpendicular to the analyzer axis is completely absorbed. The component of $\mathbf{E}_0$ parallel to the analyzer axis, which is allowed through by the analyzer, is $E_0 \cos \theta$. Because the intensity of the transmitted beam varies as the square of its magnitude, we conclude that the intensity of the (polarized) beam transmitted through the analyzer varies as

Malus's law

$$I = I_{\max} \cos^2 \theta \qquad (38.14)$$

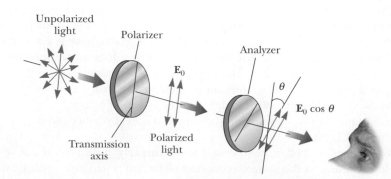

Active Figure 38.30 Two polarizing sheets whose transmission axes make an angle θ with each other. Only a fraction of the polarized light incident on the analyzer is transmitted through it.

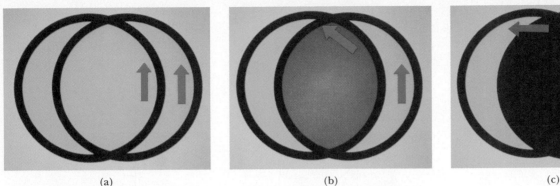

(a)   (b)   (c)

Figure 38.31 The intensity of light transmitted through two polarizers depends on the relative orientation of their transmission axes. (a) The transmitted light has maximum intensity when the transmission axes are aligned with each other. (b) The transmitted light has lesser intensity when the transmission axes are at an angle of 45° with each other. (c) The transmitted light intensity is a minimum when the transmission axes are perpendicular to each other.

where I_{max} is the intensity of the polarized beam incident on the analyzer. This expression, known as **Malus's law,**[2] applies to any two polarizing materials whose transmission axes are at an angle θ to each other. From this expression, we see that the intensity of the transmitted beam is maximum when the transmission axes are parallel ($\theta = 0$ or 180°) and that it is zero (complete absorption by the analyzer) when the transmission axes are perpendicular to each other. This variation in transmitted intensity through a pair of polarizing sheets is illustrated in Figure 38.31.

Polarization by Reflection

When an unpolarized light beam is reflected from a surface, the reflected light may be completely polarized, partially polarized, or unpolarized, depending on the angle of incidence. If the angle of incidence is 0°, the reflected beam is unpolarized. For other angles of incidence, the reflected light is polarized to some extent, and for one particular angle of incidence, the reflected light is completely polarized. Let us now investigate reflection at that special angle.

Suppose that an unpolarized light beam is incident on a surface, as in Figure 38.32a. Each individual electric field vector can be resolved into two components: one parallel to the surface (and perpendicular to the page in Fig. 38.32, represented by the dots), and the other (represented by the brown arrows) perpendicular both to the first component and to the direction of propagation. Thus, the polarization of the entire beam can be described by two electric field components in these directions. It is found that the parallel component reflects more strongly than the perpendicular component, and this results in a partially polarized reflected beam. Furthermore, the refracted beam is also partially polarized.

Now suppose that the angle of incidence θ_1 is varied until the angle between the reflected and refracted beams is 90°, as in Figure 38.32b. At this particular angle of incidence, the reflected beam is completely polarized (with its electric field vector parallel to the surface), and the refracted beam is still only partially polarized. The angle of incidence at which this polarization occurs is called the **polarizing angle** θ_p.

---

[2]   Named after its discoverer, E. L. Malus (1775–1812). Malus discovered that reflected light was polarized by viewing it through a calcite ($CaCO_3$) crystal.

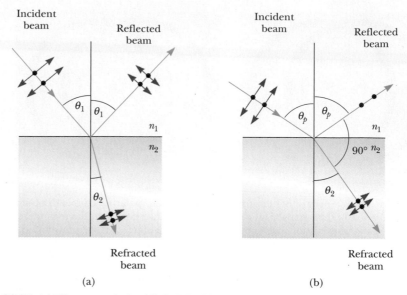

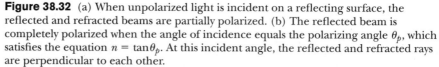

(a)   (b)

Figure 38.32 (a) When unpolarized light is incident on a reflecting surface, the reflected and refracted beams are partially polarized. (b) The reflected beam is completely polarized when the angle of incidence equals the polarizing angle θ_p, which satisfies the equation $n = \tan\theta_p$. At this incident angle, the reflected and refracted rays are perpendicular to each other.

We can obtain an expression relating the polarizing angle to the index of refraction of the reflecting substance by using Figure 38.32b. From this figure, we see that $\theta_p + 90° + \theta_2 = 180°$; thus $\theta_2 = 90° - \theta_p$. Using Snell's law of refraction (Eq. 35.8) and taking $n_1 = 1.00$ for air and $n_2 = n$, we have

$$n = \frac{\sin\theta_1}{\sin\theta_2} = \frac{\sin\theta_p}{\sin\theta_2}$$

Because $\sin\theta_2 = \sin(90° - \theta_p) = \cos\theta_p$, we can write this expression for n as $n = \sin\theta_p/\cos\theta_p$, which means that

Brewster's law

$$n = \tan\theta_p \tag{38.15}$$

This expression is called **Brewster's law,** and the polarizing angle θ_p is sometimes called **Brewster's angle,** after its discoverer, David Brewster (1781–1868). Because n varies with wavelength for a given substance, Brewster's angle is also a function of wavelength.

We can understand polarization by reflection by imagining that the electric field in the incident light sets electrons at the surface of the material in Figure 38.32b into oscillation. The component directions of oscillation are (1) parallel to the arrows shown on the refracted beam of light and (2) perpendicular to the page. The oscillating electrons act as antennas radiating light with a polarization parallel to the direction of oscillation. For the oscillations in direction (1), there is no radiation in the perpendicular direction, which is along the reflected ray (see the $\theta = 90°$ direction in Figure 34.11). For oscillations in direction (2), the electrons radiate light with a polarization perpendicular to the page (the $\theta = 0$ direction in Figure 34.11). Thus, the light reflected from the surface at this angle is completely polarized parallel to the surface.

Polarization by reflection is a common phenomenon. Sunlight reflected from water, glass, and snow is partially polarized. If the surface is horizontal, the electric field vector of the reflected light has a strong horizontal component. Sunglasses made of polarizing material reduce the glare of reflected light. The transmission axes of the lenses are oriented vertically so that they absorb the strong horizontal component of the reflected light. If you rotate sunglasses through 90 degrees, they are not as effective at blocking the glare from shiny horizontal surfaces.

Polarization by Double Refraction

Solids can be classified on the basis of internal structure. Those in which the atoms are arranged in a specific order are called *crystalline;* the NaCl structure of Figure 38.26 is just one example of a crystalline solid. Those solids in which the atoms are distributed randomly are called *amorphous*. When light travels through an amorphous material, such as glass, it travels with a speed that is the same in all directions. That is, glass has a single index of refraction. In certain crystalline materials, however, such as calcite and quartz, the speed of light is not the same in all directions. Such materials are characterized by two indices of refraction. Hence, they are often referred to as **double-refracting** or **birefringent** materials.

Upon entering a calcite crystal, unpolarized light splits into two plane-polarized rays that travel with different velocities, corresponding to two angles of refraction, as shown in Figure 38.33. The two rays are polarized in two mutually perpendicular directions, as indicated by the dots and arrows. One ray, called the **ordinary (O) ray,** is characterized by an index of refraction n_O that is the same in all directions. This means that if one could place a point source of light inside the crystal, as in Figure 38.34, the ordinary waves would spread out from the source as spheres.

The second plane-polarized ray, called the **extraordinary (E) ray,** travels with different speeds in different directions and hence is characterized by an index of refraction n_E that varies with the direction of propagation. Consider again the point source within a birefringent material, as in Figure 38.34. The source sends out an extraordinary wave having wave fronts that are elliptical in cross section. Note from Figure 38.34 that there is one direction, called the **optic axis,** along which the ordinary and extraordinary rays have the same speed, corresponding to the direction for which $n_O = n_E$. The difference in speed for the two rays is a maximum in the direction perpendicular to the optic axis. For example, in calcite, $n_O = 1.658$ at a wavelength of 589.3 nm, and n_E varies from 1.658 along the optic axis to 1.486 perpendicular to the optic axis. Values for n_O and n_E for various double-refracting crystals are given in Table 38.1.

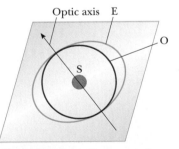

Figure 38.34 A point source S inside a double-refracting crystal produces a spherical wave front corresponding to the ordinary ray and an elliptical wave front corresponding to the extraordinary ray. The two waves propagate with the same velocity along the optic axis.

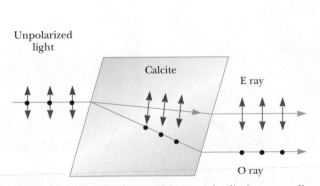

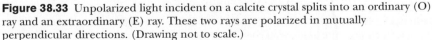

Figure 38.33 Unpolarized light incident on a calcite crystal splits into an ordinary (O) ray and an extraordinary (E) ray. These two rays are polarized in mutually perpendicular directions. (Drawing not to scale.)

Table 38.1

Indices of Refraction for Some Double-Refracting Crystals at a Wavelength of 589.3 nm			
Crystal	n_O	n_E	n_O/n_E
Calcite (CaCO$_3$)	1.658	1.486	1.116
Quartz (SiO$_2$)	1.544	1.553	0.994
Sodium nitrate (NaNO$_3$)	1.587	1.336	1.188
Sodium sulfite (NaSO$_3$)	1.565	1.515	1.033
Zinc chloride (ZnCl$_2$)	1.687	1.713	0.985
Zinc sulfide (ZnS)	2.356	2.378	0.991

Figure 38.35 A calcite crystal produces a double image because it is a birefringent (double-refracting) material.

If we place a piece of calcite on a sheet of paper and then look through the crystal at any writing on the paper, we see two images, as shown in Figure 38.35. As can be seen from Figure 38.33, these two images correspond to one formed by the ordinary ray and one formed by the extraordinary ray. If the two images are viewed through a sheet of rotating polarizing glass, they alternately appear and disappear because the ordinary and extraordinary rays are plane-polarized along mutually perpendicular directions.

Some materials, such as glass and plastic, become birefringent when stressed. Suppose that an unstressed piece of plastic is placed between a polarizer and an analyzer so that light passes from polarizer to plastic to analyzer. When the plastic is unstressed and the analyzer axis is perpendicular to the polarizer axis, none of the polarized light passes through the analyzer. In other words, the unstressed plastic has no effect on the light passing through it. If the plastic is stressed, however, regions of greatest stress become birefringent and the polarization of the light passing through the plastic changes. Hence, a series of bright and dark bands is observed in the transmitted light, with the bright bands corresponding to regions of greatest stress.

Engineers often use this technique, called *optical stress analysis*, in designing structures ranging from bridges to small tools. They build a plastic model and analyze it under different load conditions to determine regions of potential weakness and failure under stress. Some examples of plastic models under stress are shown in Figure 38.36.

Polarization by Scattering

When light is incident on any material, the electrons in the material can absorb and reradiate part of the light. Such absorption and reradiation of light by electrons in the gas molecules that make up air is what causes sunlight reaching an observer on the Earth to be partially polarized. You can observe this effect—called **scattering**—by looking

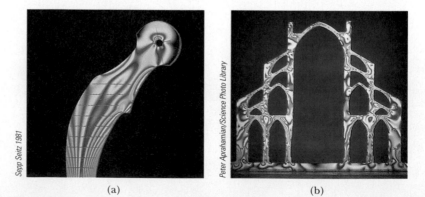

(a)   (b)

Figure 38.36 (a) Strain distribution in a plastic model of a hip replacement used in a medical research laboratory. The pattern is produced when the plastic model is viewed between a polarizer and analyzer oriented perpendicular to each other. (b) A plastic model of an arch structure under load conditions observed between perpendicular polarizers. Such patterns are useful in the optimal design of architectural components.

directly up at the sky through a pair of sunglasses whose lenses are made of polarizing material. Less light passes through at certain orientations of the lenses than at others.

Figure 38.37 illustrates how sunlight becomes polarized when it is scattered. The phenomenon is similar to that creating completely polarized light upon reflection from a surface at Brewster's angle. An unpolarized beam of sunlight traveling in the horizontal direction (parallel to the ground) strikes a molecule of one of the gases that make up air, setting the electrons of the molecule into vibration. These vibrating charges act like the vibrating charges in an antenna. The horizontal component of the electric field vector in the incident wave results in a horizontal component of the vibration of the charges, and the vertical component of the vector results in a vertical component of vibration. If the observer in Figure 38.37 is looking straight up (perpendicular to the original direction of propagation of the light), the vertical oscillations of the charges send no radiation toward the observer. Thus, the observer sees light that is completely polarized in the horizontal direction, as indicated by the brown arrows. If the observer looks in other directions, the light is partially polarized in the horizontal direction.

Some phenomena involving the scattering of light in the atmosphere can be understood as follows. When light of various wavelengths λ is incident on gas molecules of diameter d, where $d \ll \lambda$, the relative intensity of the scattered light varies as $1/\lambda^4$. The condition $d \ll \lambda$ is satisfied for scattering from oxygen (O_2) and nitrogen (N_2) molecules in the atmosphere, whose diameters are about 0.2 nm. Hence, short wavelengths (blue light) are scattered more efficiently than long wavelengths (red light). Therefore, when sunlight is scattered by gas molecules in the air, the short-wavelength radiation (blue) is scattered more intensely than the long-wavelength radiation (red).

When you look up into the sky in a direction that is not toward the Sun, you see the scattered light, which is predominantly blue; hence, you see a blue sky. If you look toward the west at sunset (or toward the east at sunrise), you are looking in a direction toward the Sun and are seeing light that has passed through a large distance of air. Most of the blue light has been scattered by the air between you and the Sun. The light that survives this trip through the air to you has had much of its blue component scattered and is thus heavily weighted toward the red end of the spectrum; as a result, you see the red and orange colors of sunset.

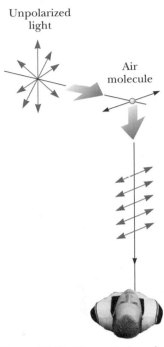

Figure 38.37 The scattering of unpolarized sunlight by air molecules. The scattered light traveling perpendicular to the incident light is plane-polarized because the vertical vibrations of the charges in the air molecule send no light in this direction.

Gary Friedman/Los Angeles Times

On the right side of this photograph is a view from the side of the freeway (cars and a truck are visible at the left) of a rocket launch from Vandenburg Air Force Base, California. The trail left by the rocket shows the effects of scattering of light by air molecules. The lower portion of the trail appears red, due to the scattering of wavelengths at the violet end of the spectrum as the light from the Sun travels through a large portion of the atmosphere to light up the trail. The upper portion of the trail is illuminated by light that has traveled through much less atmosphere and appears white.

Optical Activity

Many important applications of polarized light involve materials that display **optical activity.** A material is said to be optically active if it rotates the plane of polarization of any light transmitted through the material. The angle through which the light is rotated by a specific material depends on the length of the path through the material and on concentration if the material is in solution. One optically active material is a solution of the common sugar dextrose. A standard method for determining the concentration of sugar solutions is to measure the rotation produced by a fixed length of the solution.

Molecular asymmetry determines whether a material is optically active. For example, some proteins are optically active because of their spiral shape.

The liquid crystal displays found in most calculators have their optical activity changed by the application of electric potential across different parts of the display. Try using a pair of polarizing sunglasses to investigate the polarization used in the display of your calculator.

Quick Quiz 38.9 A polarizer for microwaves can be made as a grid of parallel metal wires about a centimeter apart. Is the electric field vector for microwaves transmitted through this polarizer (a) parallel or (b) perpendicular to the metal wires?

Quick Quiz 38.10 You are walking down a long hallway that has many light fixtures in the ceiling and a very shiny, newly waxed floor. In the floor, you see reflections of every light fixture. Now you put on sunglasses that are polarized. Some of the reflections of the light fixtures can no longer be seen (Try this!) The reflections that disappear are those (a) nearest to you (b) farthest from you (c) at an intermediate distance from you.

SUMMARY

Take a practice test for this chapter by clicking on the Practice Test link at http://www.pse6.com.

Diffraction is the deviation of light from a straight-line path when the light passes through an aperture or around an obstacle. Diffraction is due to the wave nature of light.

The **Fraunhofer diffraction pattern** produced by a single slit of width a on a distant screen consists of a central bright fringe and alternating bright and dark fringes of much lower intensities. The angles θ_{dark} at which the diffraction pattern has zero intensity, corresponding to destructive interference, are given by

$$\sin \theta_{\text{dark}} = m \frac{\lambda}{a} \qquad m = \pm 1, \pm 2, \pm 3, \ldots \tag{38.1}$$

The intensity I of a single-slit diffraction pattern as a function of angle θ is given by the expression

$$I = I_{\text{max}} \left[\frac{\sin (\beta/2)}{\beta/2} \right]^2 \tag{38.4}$$

where $\beta = (2\pi a \sin \theta)/\lambda$ and I_{max} is the intensity at $\theta = 0$.

Rayleigh's criterion, which is a limiting condition of resolution, states that two images formed by an aperture are just distinguishable if the central maximum of the diffraction pattern for one image falls on the first minimum of the diffraction pattern for the other image. The limiting angle of resolution for a slit of width a is $\theta_{\text{min}} = \lambda/a$, and the limiting angle of resolution for a circular aperture of diameter D is $\theta_{\text{min}} = 1.22\lambda/D$.

A **diffraction grating** consists of a large number of equally spaced, identical slits. The condition for intensity maxima in the interference pattern of a diffraction grating for normal incidence is

$$d \sin\theta_{\text{bright}} = m\lambda \qquad m = 0, \pm 1, \pm 2, \pm 3, \ldots \qquad (38.10)$$

where d is the spacing between adjacent slits and m is the order number of the diffraction pattern. The resolving power of a diffraction grating in the mth order of the diffraction pattern is

$$R = Nm \qquad (38.12)$$

where N is the number of lines in the grating that are illuminated.

When polarized light of intensity I_{max} is emitted by a polarizer and then incident on an analyzer, the light transmitted through the analyzer has an intensity equal to $I_{\text{max}} \cos^2\theta$, where θ is the angle between the polarizer and analyzer transmission axes.

In general, reflected light is partially polarized. However, reflected light is completely polarized when the angle of incidence is such that the angle between the reflected and refracted beams is 90°. This angle of incidence, called the **polarizing angle** θ_p, satisfies **Brewster's law:**

$$n = \tan\theta_p \qquad (38.15)$$

where n is the index of refraction of the reflecting medium.

QUESTIONS

1. Why can you hear around corners, but not see around corners?

2. Holding your hand at arm's length, you can readily block sunlight from reaching your eyes. Why can you not block sound from reaching your ears this way?

3. Observe the shadow of your book when it is held a few inches above a table with a small lamp several feet above the book. Why is the shadow somewhat fuzzy at the edges?

4. Knowing that radio waves travel at the speed of light and that a typical AM radio frequency is 1 000 kHz while an FM radio frequency might be 100 MHz, estimate the wavelengths of typical AM and FM radio signals. Use this information to explain why AM radio stations can fade out when you drive your car through a short tunnel or underpass, when FM radio stations do not.

5. Describe the change in width of the central maximum of the single-slit diffraction pattern as the width of the slit is made narrower.

6. John William Strutt, Lord Rayleigh (1842–1919), is known as the last person to understand all of physics and all of mathematics. He invented an improved foghorn. To warn ships of a coastline, a foghorn should radiate sound in a wide horizontal sheet over the ocean's surface. It should not waste energy by broadcasting sound upward. It should not emit sound downward, because the water in front of the foghorn would reflect that sound upward. Rayleigh's foghorn trumpet is shown in Figure Q38.6. Is it installed in the correct orientation? Decide whether the long dimension of the rectangular opening should be horizontal or vertical, and argue for your decision.

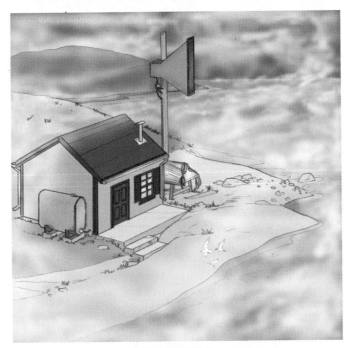

Figure Q38.6

7. Featured in the motion picture *M*A*S*H* (20th Century Fox, Aspen Productions, 1970) is a loudspeaker mounted on an exterior wall of an Army barracks. It has an approximately rectangular aperture. Its design can be thought of as based on Lord Rayleigh's foghorn trumpet, described in Question 6. Borrow or rent a copy of the movie, sketch the orientation of the loudspeaker, decide whether it is installed in the correct orientation, and argue for your decision.

8. Assuming that the headlights of a car are point sources, estimate the maximum distance from an observer to the car at which the headlights are distinguishable from each other.

9. A laser beam is incident at a shallow angle on a machinist's ruler that has a finely calibrated scale. The engraved rulings on the scale give rise to a diffraction pattern on a screen. Discuss how you can use this technique to obtain a measure of the wavelength of the laser light.

10. When you receive a chest x-ray at a hospital, the rays pass through a series of parallel ribs in your chest. Do the ribs act as a diffraction grating for x-rays?

11. Certain sunglasses use a polarizing material to reduce the intensity of light reflected from shiny surfaces. What orientation of polarization should the material have to be most effective?

12. During the "day" on the Moon (when the Sun is visible), you see a black sky and the stars can be clearly seen. During the day on the Earth, you see a blue sky with no stars. Account for this difference.

13. You can make the path of a light beam visible by placing dust in the air (perhaps by clapping two blackboard erasers in the path of the light beam). Explain why you can see the beam under these circumstances. In general, when is light visible?

14. Is light from the sky polarized? Why is it that clouds seen through Polaroid glasses stand out in bold contrast to the sky?

15. If a coin is glued to a glass sheet and this arrangement is held in front of a laser beam, the projected shadow has diffraction rings around its edge and a bright spot in the center. How is this possible?

16. How could the index of refraction of a flat piece of dark obsidian glass be determined?

17. A laser produces a beam a few millimeters wide, with uniform intensity across its width. A hair is stretched vertically across the front of the laser to cross the beam. How is the diffraction pattern it produces on a distant screen related to that of a vertical slit equal in width to the hair? How could you determine the width of the hair from measurements of its diffraction pattern?

18. A radio station serves listeners in a city to the northeast of its broadcast site. It broadcasts from three adjacent towers on a mountain ridge, along a line running east and west. Show that by introducing time delays among the signals the individual towers radiate, the station can maximize net intensity in the direction toward the city (and in the opposite direction) and minimize the signal transmitted in other directions. The towers together are said to form a *phased array*.

PROBLEMS

1, 2, 3 = straightforward, intermediate, challenging ☐ = full solution available in the *Student Solutions Manual and Study Guide*

🌐 = coached solution with hints available at http://www.pse6.com 🖥 = computer useful in solving problem

▨ = paired numerical and symbolic problems

Section 38.2 Diffraction Patterns from Narrow Slits

1. Helium–neon laser light ($\lambda = 632.8$ nm) is sent through a 0.300-mm-wide single slit. What is the width of the central maximum on a screen 1.00 m from the slit?

2. A beam of green light is diffracted by a slit of width 0.550 mm. The diffraction pattern forms on a wall 2.06 m beyond the slit. The distance between the positions of zero intensity on both sides of the central bright fringe is 4.10 mm. Calculate the wavelength of the laser light.

3. 🌐 A screen is placed 50.0 cm from a single slit, which is illuminated with 690-nm light. If the distance between the first and third minima in the diffraction pattern is 3.00 mm, what is the width of the slit?

4. Coherent microwaves of wavelength 5.00 cm enter a long, narrow window in a building otherwise essentially opaque to the microwaves. If the window is 36.0 cm wide, what is the distance from the central maximum to the first-order minimum along a wall 6.50 m from the window?

5. Sound with a frequency 650 Hz from a distant source passes through a doorway 1.10 m wide in a sound-absorbing wall. Find the number and approximate directions of the diffraction-maximum beams radiated into the space beyond.

6. Light of wavelength 587.5 nm illuminates a single slit 0.750 mm in width. (a) At what distance from the slit should a screen be located if the first minimum in the diffraction pattern is to be 0.850 mm from the center of the principal maximum? (b) What is the width of the central maximum?

7. A beam of laser light of wavelength 632.8 nm has a circular cross section 2.00 mm in diameter. A rectangular aperture is to be placed in the center of the beam so that, when the light falls perpendicularly on a wall 4.50 m away, the central maximum fills a rectangle 110 mm wide and 6.00 mm high. The dimensions are measured between the minima bracketing the central maximum. Find the required width and height of the aperture.

8. **What If?** Assume the light in Figure 38.5 strikes the single slit at an angle β from the perpendicular direction. Show that Equation 38.1, the condition for destructive interference, must be modified to read

$$\sin \theta_{dark} = m\left(\frac{\lambda}{a}\right) - \sin \beta$$

9. A diffraction pattern is formed on a screen 120 cm away from a 0.400-mm-wide slit. Monochromatic 546.1-nm light is used. Calculate the fractional intensity I/I_{max} at a point on the screen 4.10 mm from the center of the principal maximum.

10. Coherent light of wavelength 501.5 nm is sent through two parallel slits in a large flat wall. Each slit is 0.700 μm wide. Their centers are 2.80 μm apart. The light then falls on a semicylindrical screen, with its axis at the midline between the slits. (a) Predict the direction of each interference maximum on the screen, as an angle away from the bisector of the line joining the slits. (b) Describe the pattern of light on the screen, specifying the number of bright fringes and the location of each. (c) Find the intensity of light on the screen at the center of each bright fringe, expressed as a fraction of the light intensity I_{max} at the center of the pattern.

Section 38.3   Resolution of Single-Slit and Circular Apertures

11. The pupil of a cat's eye narrows to a vertical slit of width 0.500 mm in daylight. What is the angular resolution for horizontally separated mice? Assume that the average wavelength of the light is 500 nm.

12. Find the radius a star image forms on the retina of the eye if the aperture diameter (the pupil) at night is 0.700 cm and the length of the eye is 3.00 cm. Assume the representative wavelength of starlight in the eye is 500 nm.

13. www A helium–neon laser emits light that has a wavelength of 632.8 nm. The circular aperture through which the beam emerges has a diameter of 0.500 cm. Estimate the diameter of the beam 10.0 km from the laser.

14. You are vacationing in a Wonderland populated by friendly elves and a cannibalistic Cyclops that devours physics students. The elves and the Cyclops look precisely alike (everyone wears loose jeans and sweatshirts) except that each elf has two eyes, about 10.0 cm apart, and the Cyclops—you guessed it—has only one eye of about the same size as an elf's. The elves and the Cyclops are constantly at war with each other, so they rarely sleep and all have red eyes, predominantly reflecting light with a wavelength of 660 nm. From what maximum distance can you distinguish between a friendly elf and the predatory Cyclops? The air in Wonderland is always clear. Dilated with fear, your pupils have a diameter of 7.00 mm.

15. Narrow, parallel, glowing gas-filled tubes in a variety of colors form block letters to spell out the name of a night club. Adjacent tubes are all 2.80 cm apart. The tubes forming one letter are filled with neon and radiate predominantly red light with a wavelength of 640 nm. For another letter, the tubes emit predominantly violet light at 440 nm. The pupil of a dark-adapted viewer's eye is 5.20 mm in diameter. If she is in a certain range of distances away, the viewer can resolve the separate tubes of one color but not the other. Which color is easier to resolve? The viewer's distance must be in what range for her to resolve the tubes of only one color?

16. On the night of April 18, 1775, a signal was sent from the steeple of Old North Church in Boston to Paul Revere, who was 1.80 mi away: "One if by land, two if by sea." At what minimum separation did the sexton have to set the lanterns for Revere to receive the correct message about the approaching British? Assume that the patriot's pupils had a diameter of 4.00 mm at night and that the lantern light had a predominant wavelength of 580 nm.

17. The Impressionist painter Georges Seurat created paintings with an enormous number of dots of pure pigment, each of which was approximately 2.00 mm in diameter. The idea was to have colors such as red and green next to each other to form a scintillating canvas (Fig. P38.17). Outside what distance would one be unable to discern individual dots on the canvas? (Assume that $\lambda = 500$ nm and that the pupil diameter is 4.00 mm.)

SuperStock

Figure P38.17 *Sunday Afternoon on the Island of La Grande Jatte*, by Georges Seurat.

18. A binary star system in the constellation Orion has an angular interstellar separation of 1.00×10^{-5} rad. If $\lambda = 500$ nm, what is the smallest diameter the telescope can have to just resolve the two stars?

19. A spy satellite can consist essentially of a large-diameter concave mirror forming an image on a digital-camera detector and sending the picture to a ground receiver by radio waves. In effect, it is an astronomical telescope in orbit, looking down instead of up. Can a spy satellite read a license plate? Can it read the date on a dime? Argue for your answers by making an order-of-magnitude calculation, specifying the data you estimate.

20. A circular radar antenna on a Coast Guard ship has a diameter of 2.10 m and radiates at a frequency of 15.0 GHz. Two small boats are located 9.00 km away from the ship. How close together could the boats be and still be detected as two objects?

21. Grote Reber was a pioneer in radio astronomy. He constructed a radio telescope with a 10.0-m-diameter receiving dish. What was the telescope's angular resolution for 2.00-m radio waves?

22. When Mars is nearest the Earth, the distance separating the two planets is 88.6×10^6 km. Mars is viewed through a telescope whose mirror has a diameter of 30.0 cm. (a) If the wavelength of the light is 590 nm, what is the angular resolution of the telescope? (b) What is the smallest distance that can be resolved between two points on Mars?

Section 38.4   The Diffraction Grating

Note: In the following problems, assume that the light is incident normally on the gratings.

23. White light is spread out into its spectral components by a diffraction grating. If the grating has 2 000 grooves per centimeter, at what angle does red light of wavelength 640 nm appear in first order?

24. Light from an argon laser strikes a diffraction grating that has 5 310 grooves per centimeter. The central and first-order principal maxima are separated by 0.488 m on a wall 1.72 m from the grating. Determine the wavelength of the laser light.

25. The hydrogen spectrum has a red line at 656 nm and a blue line at 434 nm. What are the angular separations between these two spectral lines obtained with a diffraction grating that has 4 500 grooves/cm?

26. A helium–neon laser ($\lambda = 632.8$ nm) is used to calibrate a diffraction grating. If the first-order maximum occurs at 20.5°, what is the spacing between adjacent grooves in the grating?

27. Three discrete spectral lines occur at angles of 10.09°, 13.71°, and 14.77° in the first-order spectrum of a grating spectrometer. (a) If the grating has 3 660 slits/cm, what are the wavelengths of the light? (b) At what angles are these lines found in the second-order spectrum?

28. Show that, whenever white light is passed through a diffraction grating of any spacing size, the violet end of the continuous visible spectrum in third order always overlaps with red light at the other end of the second-order spectrum.

29. A diffraction grating of width 4.00 cm has been ruled with 3 000 grooves/cm. (a) What is the resolving power of this grating in the first three orders? (b) If two monochromatic waves incident on this grating have a mean wavelength of 400 nm, what is their wavelength separation if they are just resolved in the third order?

30. The laser in a CD player must precisely follow the spiral track, along which the distance between one loop of the spiral and the next is only about 1.25 μm. A feedback mechanism lets the player know if the laser drifts off the track, so that the player can steer it back again. Figure P38.30 shows how a diffraction grating is used to provide information to keep the beam on track. The laser light passes through a diffraction grating just before it reaches the disk. The strong central maximum of the diffraction pattern is used to read the information in the track of pits. The two first-order side maxima are used for steering. The grating is designed so that the first-order maxima fall on the flat surfaces on both sides of the information track. Both side beams are reflected into their own detectors. As long as both beams are reflecting from smooth nonpitted surfaces, they are detected with constant high intensity. If the main beam wanders off the track, however, one of the side beams will begin to strike pits on the information track and the reflected light will diminish. This change is used with an electronic circuit to guide the beam back to

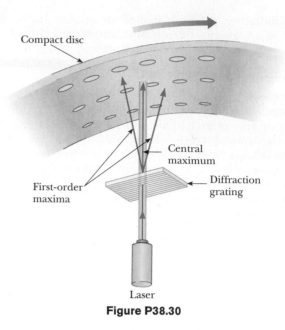

Figure P38.30

the desired location. Assume that the laser light has a wavelength of 780 nm and that the diffraction grating is positioned 6.90 μm from the disk. Assume that the first-order beams are to fall on the disk 0.400 μm on either side of the information track. What should be the number of grooves per millimeter in the grating?

31. A source emits 531.62-nm and 531.81-nm light. (a) What minimum number of grooves is required for a grating that resolves the two wavelengths in the first-order spectrum? (b) Determine the slit spacing for a grating 1.32 cm wide that has the required minimum number of grooves.

32. A diffraction grating has 4 200 rulings/cm. On a screen 2.00 m from the grating, it is found that for a particular order m, the maxima corresponding to two closely spaced wavelengths of sodium (589.0 nm and 589.6 nm) are separated by 1.59 mm. Determine the value of m.

33. A grating with 250 grooves/mm is used with an incandescent light source. Assume the visible spectrum to range in wavelength from 400 to 700 nm. In how many orders can one see (a) the entire visible spectrum and (b) the short-wavelength region?

34. A wide beam of laser light with a wavelength of 632.8 nm is directed through several narrow parallel slits, separated by 1.20 mm, and falls on a sheet of photographic film 1.40 m away. The exposure time is chosen so that the film stays unexposed everywhere except at the central region of each bright fringe. (a) Find the distance between these interference maxima. The film is printed as a transparency—it is opaque everywhere except at the exposed lines. Next, the same beam of laser light is directed through the transparency and allowed to fall on a screen 1.40 m beyond. (b) Argue that several narrow parallel bright regions, separated by 1.20 mm, will appear on the screen, as real images of the original slits. If at last the screen is removed, light will diverge from the images of the original slits with the same reconstructed wave fronts as the original slits produced. (*Suggestion:* You may find it useful to draw diagrams similar to Figure 38.16. A train of thought like this, at a soccer game, led Dennis Gabor to the invention of holography.)

Section 38.5 Diffraction of X-Rays by Crystals

35. Potassium iodide (KI) has the same crystalline structure as NaCl, with atomic planes separated by 0.353 nm. A monochromatic x-ray beam shows a first-order diffraction maximum when the grazing angle is 7.60°. Calculate the x-ray wavelength.

36. A wavelength of 0.129 nm characterizes K_α x-rays from zinc. When a beam of these x-rays is incident on the surface of a crystal whose structure is similar to that of NaCl, a first-order maximum is observed at 8.15°. Calculate the interplanar spacing based on this information.

37. If the interplanar spacing of NaCl is 0.281 nm, what is the predicted angle at which 0.140-nm x-rays are diffracted in a first-order maximum?

38. The first-order diffraction maximum is observed at 12.6° for a crystal in which the interplanar spacing is 0.240 nm. How many other orders can be observed?

39. In water of uniform depth, a wide pier is supported on pilings in several parallel rows 2.80 m apart. Ocean waves of uniform wavelength roll in, moving in a direction that makes an angle of 80.0° with the rows of posts. Find the three longest wavelengths of waves that will be strongly reflected by the pilings.

Section 38.6 Polarization of Light Waves

Problem 34 in Chapter 34 can be assigned with this section.

40. Unpolarized light passes through two polaroid sheets. The axis of the first is vertical, and that of the second is at 30.0° to the vertical. What fraction of the incident light is transmitted?

41. Plane-polarized light is incident on a single polarizing disk with the direction of $\mathbf{E}_0$ parallel to the direction of the transmission axis. Through what angle should the disk be rotated so that the intensity in the transmitted beam is reduced by a factor of (a) 3.00, (b) 5.00, (c) 10.0?

42. Three polarizing disks whose planes are parallel are centered on a common axis. The direction of the transmission axis in each case is shown in Figure P38.42 relative to the

common vertical direction. A plane-polarized beam of light with $\mathbf{E}_0$ parallel to the vertical reference direction is incident from the left on the first disk with intensity $I_i = 10.0$ units (arbitrary). Calculate the transmitted intensity I_f when (a) $\theta_1 = 20.0°$, $\theta_2 = 40.0°$, and $\theta_3 = 60.0°$; (b) $\theta_1 = 0°$, $\theta_2 = 30.0°$, and $\theta_3 = 60.0°$.

43. The angle of incidence of a light beam onto a reflecting surface is continuously variable. The reflected ray is found to be completely polarized when the angle of incidence is 48.0°. What is the index of refraction of the reflecting material?

44. Review Problem. (a) A transparent plate with index of refraction n_2 is immersed in a medium with index n_1. Light traveling in the surrounding medium strikes the top surface of the plate at Brewster's angle. Show that if and only if the surfaces of the plate are parallel, the refracted light will strike the bottom surface of the plate at Brewster's angle for that interface. (b) **What If?** Instead of a plate, consider a prism of index of refraction n_2 separating media of different refractive indices n_1 and n_3. Is there one particular apex angle between the surfaces of the prism for which light can fall on both of its surfaces at Brewster's angle as it passes through the prism? If so, determine it.

45. The critical angle for total internal reflection for sapphire surrounded by air is 34.4°. Calculate the polarizing angle for sapphire.

46. For a particular transparent medium surrounded by air, show that the critical angle for total internal reflection and the polarizing angle are related by $\cot \theta_p = \sin \theta_c$.

47. How far above the horizon is the Moon when its image reflected in calm water is completely polarized? ($n_{\text{water}} = 1.33$)

Additional Problems

48. In Figure P38.42, suppose that the transmission axes of the left and right polarizing disks are perpendicular to each other. Also, let the center disk be rotated on the common axis with an angular speed ω. Show that if unpolarized light is incident on the left disk with an intensity $I_{\max}$, the intensity of the beam emerging from the right disk is

$$I = \tfrac{1}{16} I_{\max} (1 - \cos 4\omega t)$$

This means that the intensity of the emerging beam is modulated at a rate that is four times the rate of rotation of the center disk. [*Suggestion:* Use the trigonometric identities $\cos^2 \theta = (1 + \cos 2\theta)/2$ and $\sin^2 \theta = (1 - \cos 2\theta)/2$, and recall that $\theta = \omega t$.]

49. You want to rotate the plane of polarization of a polarized light beam by 45.0° with a maximum intensity reduction of 10.0%. (a) How many sheets of perfect polarizers do you need to achieve your goal? (b) What is the angle between adjacent polarizers?

50. Figure P38.50 shows a megaphone in use. Construct a theoretical description of how a megaphone works. You may assume that the sound of your voice radiates just through

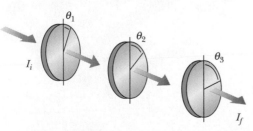

Figure P38.42 Problems 42 and 48.

Figure P38.50

the opening of your mouth. Most of the information in speech is carried not in a signal at the fundamental frequency, but in noises and in harmonics, with frequencies of a few thousand hertz. Does your theory allow any prediction that is simple to test?

51. Light from a helium–neon laser ($\lambda = 632.8$ nm) is incident on a single slit. What is the maximum width of the slit for which no diffraction minima are observed?

52. What are the approximate dimensions of the smallest object on Earth that astronauts can resolve by eye when they are orbiting 250 km above the Earth? Assume that $\lambda = 500$ nm and that a pupil diameter is 5.00 mm.

53. **Review problem.** A beam of 541-nm light is incident on a diffraction grating that has 400 grooves/mm. (a) Determine the angle of the second-order ray. (b) **What If?** If the entire apparatus is immersed in water, what is the new second-order angle of diffraction? (c) Show that the two diffracted rays of parts (a) and (b) are related through the law of refraction.

54. The *Very Large Array* (VLA) is a set of 27 radio telescope dishes in Caton and Socorro Counties, New Mexico (Fig. P38.54). The antennas can be moved apart on railroad tracks, and their combined signals give the resolving power of a synthetic aperture 36.0 km in diameter. (a) If the detectors are tuned to a frequency of 1.40 GHz, what is the angular resolution of the VLA? (b) Clouds of hydrogen radiate at this frequency. What must be the separation distance of two clouds 26 000 lightyears away at the center of the galaxy, if they are to be resolved? (c) **What If?** As the telescope looks up, a circling hawk looks down. Find the

angular resolution of the hawk's eye. Assume that the hawk is most sensitive to green light having a wavelength of 500 nm and that it has a pupil of diameter 12.0 mm. (d) A mouse is on the ground 30.0 m below. By what distance must the mouse's whiskers be separated if the hawk can resolve them?

55. A 750-nm light beam hits the flat surface of a certain liquid, and the beam is split into a reflected ray and a refracted ray. If the reflected ray is completely polarized at 36.0°, what is the wavelength of the refracted ray?

56. Iridescent peacock feathers are shown in Figure P38.56a. The surface of one microscopic barbule is composed of transparent keratin that supports rods of dark brown melanin in a regular lattice, represented in Figure P38.56b. (Your fingernails are made of keratin, and melanin is the dark pigment giving color to human skin.) In a portion of the feather that can appear turquoise, assume that the melanin rods are uniformly separated by 0.25 μm, with air between them. (a) Explain how this structure can appear blue-green when it contains no blue or green pigment.

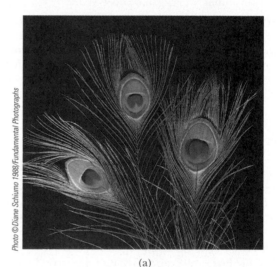

(a)

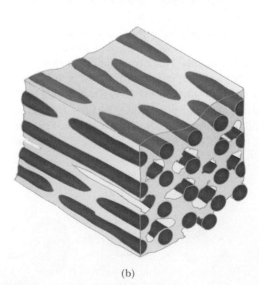

(b)

Figure P38.56 (a) Iridescent peacock feathers. (b) Microscopic section of a feather showing dark melanin rods in a pale keratin matrix.

Figure P38.54 Some of the radio telescope dishes in the Very Large Array.

(b) Explain how it can also appear violet if light falls on it in a different direction. (c) Explain how it can present different colors to your two eyes at the same time—a characteristic of iridescence. (d) A compact disc can appear to be any color of the rainbow. Explain why this portion of the feather cannot appear yellow or red. (e) What could be different about the array of melanin rods in a portion of the feather that does appear to be red?

57. Light of wavelength 500 nm is incident normally on a diffraction grating. If the third-order maximum of the diffraction pattern is observed at 32.0°, (a) what is the number of rulings per centimeter for the grating? (b) Determine the total number of primary maxima that can be observed in this situation.

58. Light strikes a water surface at the polarizing angle. The part of the beam refracted into the water strikes a submerged glass slab (index of refraction, 1.50), as shown in Figure P38.58. The light reflected from the upper surface of the slab is completely polarized. Find the angle between the water surface and the glass slab.

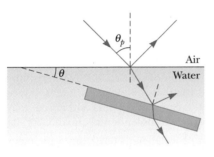

Figure P38.58

59. A beam of bright red light of wavelength 654 nm passes through a diffraction grating. Enclosing the space beyond the grating is a large screen forming one half of a cylinder centered on the grating, with its axis parallel to the slits in the grating. Fifteen bright spots appear on the screen. Find the maximum and minimum possible values for the slit separation in the diffraction grating.

60. A *pinhole camera* has a small circular aperture of diameter D. Light from distant objects passes through the aperture into an otherwise dark box, falling on a screen located a distance L away. If D is too large, the display on the screen will be fuzzy, because a bright point in the field of view will send light onto a circle of diameter slightly larger than D. On the other hand, if D is too small, diffraction will blur the display on the screen. The screen shows a reasonably sharp image if the diameter of the central disk of the diffraction pattern, specified by Equation 38.9, is equal to D at the screen. (a) Show that for monochromatic light with plane wave fronts and $L \gg D$, the condition for a sharp view is fulfilled if $D^2 = 2.44\lambda L$. (b) Find the optimum pinhole diameter for 500-nm light projected onto a screen 15.0 cm away.

61. An American standard television picture is composed of about 485 horizontal lines of varying light intensity. Assume that your ability to resolve the lines is limited only by the Rayleigh criterion and that the pupils of your eyes are 5.00 mm in diameter. Calculate the ratio of minimum viewing distance to the vertical dimension of the picture such that you will not be able to resolve the lines. Assume

that the average wavelength of the light coming from the screen is 550 nm.

62. (a) Light traveling in a medium of index of refraction n_1 is incident at an angle θ on the surface of a medium of index n_2. The angle between reflected and refracted rays is β. Show that

$$\tan \theta = \frac{n_2 \sin \beta}{n_1 - n_2 \cos \beta}$$

(*Suggestion:* Use the identity $\sin(A + B) = \sin A \cos B + \cos A \sin B$.) (b) **What If?** Show that this expression for $\tan \theta$ reduces to Brewster's law when $\beta = 90°$, $n_1 = 1$, and $n_2 = n$.

63. Suppose that the single slit in Figure 38.6 is 6.00 cm wide and in front of a microwave source operating at 7.50 GHz. (a) Calculate the angle subtended by the first minimum in the diffraction pattern. (b) What is the relative intensity $I/I_{\max}$ at $\theta = 15.0°$? (c) Assume that two such sources, separated laterally by 20.0 cm, are behind the slit. What must the maximum distance between the plane of the sources and the slit be if the diffraction patterns are to be resolved? (In this case, the approximation $\sin \theta \approx \tan \theta$ is not valid because of the relatively small value of a/λ.)

64. Two polarizing sheets are placed together with their transmission axes crossed so that no light is transmitted. A third sheet is inserted between them with its transmission axis at an angle of 45.0° with respect to each of the other axes. Find the fraction of incident unpolarized light intensity transmitted by the three-sheet combination. (Assume each polarizing sheet is ideal.)

65. Two wavelengths λ and $\lambda + \Delta\lambda$ (with $\Delta\lambda \ll \lambda$) are incident on a diffraction grating. Show that the angular separation between the spectral lines in the mth-order spectrum is

$$\Delta\theta = \frac{\Delta\lambda}{\sqrt{(d/m)^2 - \lambda^2}}$$

where d is the slit spacing and m is the order number.

66. Two closely spaced wavelengths of light are incident on a diffraction grating. (a) Starting with Equation 38.10, show that the angular dispersion of the grating is given by

$$\frac{d\theta}{d\lambda} = \frac{m}{d \cos \theta}$$

(b) A square grating 2.00 cm on each side containing 8 000 equally spaced slits is used to analyze the spectrum of mercury. Two closely spaced lines emitted by this element have wavelengths of 579.065 nm and 576.959 nm. What is the angular separation of these two wavelengths in the second-order spectrum?

67. The scale of a map is a number of kilometers per centimeter, specifying the distance on the ground that any distance on the map represents. The scale of a spectrum is its *dispersion*, a number of nanometers per centimeter, which specifies the change in wavelength that a distance across the spectrum represents. One must know the dispersion in order to compare one spectrum with another and to make a measurement of (for example) a Doppler shift. Let y represent the position relative to the center of a diffraction pattern projected onto a flat screen at distance L by a diffraction grating with slit spacing d. The dispersion is $d\lambda/dy$.

(a) Prove that the dispersion is given by

$$\frac{d\lambda}{dy} = \frac{L^2 d}{m(L^2 + y^2)^{3/2}}$$

(b) Calculate the dispersion in first order for light with a mean wavelength of 550 nm, analyzed with a grating having 8 000 rulings/cm, and projected onto a screen 2.40 m away.

68. Derive Equation 38.12 for the resolving power of a grating, $R = Nm$, where N is the number of slits illuminated and m is the order in the diffraction pattern. Remember that Rayleigh's criterion (Section 38.3) states that two wavelengths will be resolved when the principal maximum for one falls on the first minimum for the other.

69. Figure P38.69a is a three-dimensional sketch of a birefringent crystal. The dotted lines illustrate how a thin parallel-faced slab of material could be cut from the larger specimen with the optic axis of the crystal parallel to the faces of the plate. A section cut from the crystal in this manner is known as a *retardation plate*. When a beam of light is incident on the plate perpendicular to the direction of the optic axis, as shown in Figure P38.69b, the O ray and the E ray travel along a single straight line, but with different speeds. (a) Let the thickness of the plate be d and show that the phase difference between the O ray and the E ray is

$$\theta = \frac{2\pi d}{\lambda} |n_O - n_E|$$

where λ is the wavelength in air. (b) In a particular case the incident light has a wavelength of 550 nm. Find the minimum value of d for a quartz plate for which $\theta = \pi/2$. Such a plate is called a *quarter-wave plate*. (Use values of n_O and n_E from Table 38.1.)

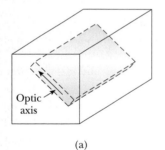

(a)

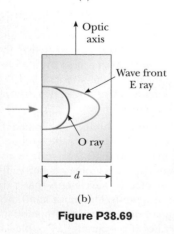

(b)

Figure P38.69

70. How much diffraction spreading does a light beam undergo? One quantitative answer is the *full width at half*

maximum of the central maximum of the single-slit Fraunhofer diffraction pattern. You can evaluate this angle of spreading in this problem and in the next. (a) In Equation 38.4, define $\beta/2 = \phi$ and show that, at the point where $I = 0.5I_{max}$, we must have $\sin\phi = \phi/\sqrt{2}$. (b) Let $y_1 = \sin\phi$ and $y_2 = \phi/\sqrt{2}$. Plot y_1 and y_2 on the same set of axes over a range from $\phi = 1$ rad to $\phi = \pi/2$ rad. Determine ϕ from the point of intersection of the two curves. (c) Then show that, if the fraction λ/a is not large, the angular full width at half maximum of the central diffraction maximum is $\Delta\theta = 0.886\,\lambda/a$.

71. Another method to solve the equation $\phi = \sqrt{2}\sin\phi$ in Problem 70 is to guess a first value of ϕ, use a computer or calculator to see how nearly it fits, and continue to update your estimate until the equation balances. How many steps (iterations) does this take?

72. In the diffraction pattern of a single slit, described by the equation

$$I_\theta = I_{max}\frac{\sin^2(\beta/2)}{(\beta/2)^2}$$

with $\beta = (2\pi a \sin\theta)/\lambda$, the central maximum is at $\beta = 0$ and the side maxima are *approximately* at $\beta/2 = (m + \frac{1}{2})\pi$ for $m = 1, 2, 3, \ldots$. Determine more precisely (a) the location of the first side maximum, where $m = 1$, and (b) the location of the second side maximum. Observe in Figure 38.10a that the graph of intensity versus $\beta/2$ has a horizontal tangent at maxima and also at minima. You will need to solve a transcendental equation.

73. Light of wavelength 632.8 nm illuminates a single slit, and a diffraction pattern is formed on a screen 1.00 m from the slit. Using the data in the table below, plot relative intensity versus position. Choose an appropriate value for the slit width a and on the same graph used for the experimental data, plot the theoretical expression for the relative intensity

$$\frac{I_\theta}{I_{max}} = \frac{\sin^2(\beta/2)}{(\beta/2)^2}$$

What value of a gives the best fit of theory and experiment?

Relative Intensity	Position Relative to Central Maximum (mm)
1.00	0
0.95	0.8
0.80	1.6
0.60	2.4
0.39	3.2
0.21	4.0
0.079	4.8
0.014	5.6
0.003	6.5
0.015	7.3
0.036	8.1
0.047	8.9
0.043	9.7
0.029	10.5
0.013	11.3
0.002	12.1
0.000 3	12.9
0.005	13.7

0.012	14.5
0.016	15.3
0.015	16.1
0.010	16.9
0.004 4	17.7
0.000 6	18.5
0.000 3	19.3
0.003	20.2

Answers to Quick Quizzes

38.1 (a). Equation 38.1 shows that a decrease in a results in an increase in the angles at which the dark fringes appear.

38.2 (c). The space between the slightly open door and the doorframe acts as a single slit. Sound waves have wavelengths that are larger than the opening and so are diffracted and spread throughout the room you are in. Because light wavelengths are much smaller than the slit width, they experience negligible diffraction. As a result, you must have a direct line of sight to detect the light waves.

38.3 The situation is like that depicted in Figure 38.11 except that now the slits are only half as far apart. The diffraction pattern is the same, but the interference pattern is stretched out because d is smaller. Because $d/a = 3$, the $m = 3$ interference maximum coincides with the first diffraction minimum. Your sketch should look like the figure below.

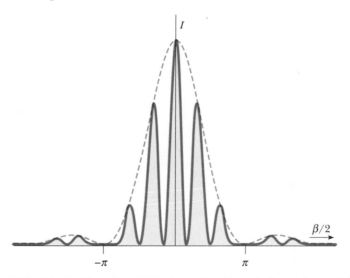

38.4 (c). In Equation 38.7, the ratio d/a is independent of wavelength, so the number of interference fringes in the central diffraction pattern peak remains the same. Equation 38.1 tells us that a decrease in wavelength causes a decrease in the width of the central peak.

38.5 (b). The effective slit width in the vertical direction of the cat's eye is larger than that in the horizontal direction. Thus, the eye has more resolving power for lights separated in the vertical direction and would be more effective at resolving the mast lights on the boat.

38.6 (a). We would like to reduce the minimum angular separation for two objects below the angle subtended by the two stars in the binary system. We can do that by reducing the wavelength of the light—this in essence makes the aperture larger, relative to the light wavelength, increasing the resolving power. Thus, we should choose a blue filter.

38.7 (b). The tracks of information on a compact disc are much closer together than on a phonograph record. As a result, the diffraction maxima from the compact disc will be farther apart than those from the record.

38.8 (c). With the doubled wavelength, the pattern will be wider. Choices (a) and (d) make the pattern even wider. From Equation 38.10, we see that choice (b) causes $\sin\theta$ to be twice as large. Because we cannot use the small angle approximation, however, a doubling of $\sin\theta$ is not the same as a doubling of θ, which would translate to a doubling of the position of a maximum along the screen. If we only consider small-angle maxima, choice (b) would work, but it does not work in the large-angle case.

38.9 (b). Electric field vectors parallel to the metal wires cause electrons in the metal to oscillate parallel to the wires. Thus, the energy from the waves with these electric field vectors is transferred to the metal by accelerating these electrons and is eventually transformed to internal energy through the resistance of the metal. Waves with electric-field vectors perpendicular to the metal wires pass through because they are not able to accelerate electrons in the wires.

38.10 (c). At some intermediate distance, the light rays from the fixtures will strike the floor at Brewster's angle and reflect to your eyes. Because this light is polarized horizontally, it will not pass through your polarized sunglasses. Tilting your head to the side will cause the reflections to reappear.

39.1   The Principle of Galilean Relativity

To describe a physical event, we must establish a frame of reference. You should recall from Chapter 5 that an inertial frame of reference is one in which an object is observed to have no acceleration when no forces act on it. Furthermore, any system moving with constant velocity with respect to an inertial frame must also be in an inertial frame.

There is no absolute inertial reference frame. This means that the results of an experiment performed in a vehicle moving with uniform velocity will be identical to the results of the same experiment performed in a stationary vehicle. The formal statement of this result is called the **principle of Galilean relativity:**

Principle of Galilean relativity

> The laws of mechanics must be the same in all inertial frames of reference.

Let us consider an observation that illustrates the equivalence of the laws of mechanics in different inertial frames. A pickup truck moves with a constant velocity, as shown in Figure 39.1a. If a passenger in the truck throws a ball straight up, and if air effects are neglected, the passenger observes that the ball moves in a vertical path. The motion of the ball appears to be precisely the same as if the ball were thrown by a person at rest on the Earth. The law of universal gravitation and the equations of motion under constant acceleration are obeyed whether the truck is at rest or in uniform motion.

Both observers agree on the laws of physics—they each throw a ball straight up and it rises and falls back into their hand. What about the *path* of the ball thrown by the observer in the truck? Do the observers agree on the path? The observer on the ground sees the path of the ball as a parabola, as illustrated in Figure 39.1b, while, as mentioned earlier, the observer in the truck sees the ball move in a vertical path. Furthermore, according to the observer on the ground, the ball has a horizontal component of velocity equal to the velocity of the truck. Although the two observers disagree on certain aspects of the situation, they agree on the validity of Newton's laws and on such classical principles as conservation of energy and conservation of linear momentum. This agreement implies that no mechanical experiment can detect any difference between the two inertial frames. The only thing that can be detected is the relative motion of one frame with respect to the other.

> **Quick Quiz 39.1**   Which observer in Figure 39.1 sees the ball's *correct* path? (a) the observer in the truck (b) the observer on the ground (c) both observers.

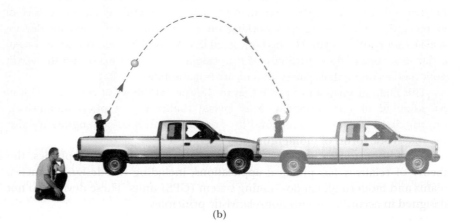

(a)   (b)

Figure 39.1 (a) The observer in the truck sees the ball move in a vertical path when thrown upward. (b) The Earth observer sees the path of the ball as a parabola.

Suppose that some physical phenomenon, which we call an *event,* occurs and is observed by an observer at rest in an inertial reference frame. The event's location and time of occurrence can be specified by the four coordinates (x, y, z, t). We would like to be able to transform these coordinates from those of an observer in one inertial frame to those of another observer in a frame moving with uniform relative velocity compared to the first frame. When we say an observer is "in a frame," we mean that the observer is at rest with respect to the origin of that frame.

Consider two inertial frames S and S′ (Fig. 39.2). The frame S′ moves with a constant velocity **v** along the common x and x' axes, where **v** is measured relative to S. We assume that the origins of S and S′ coincide at $t = 0$ and that an event occurs at point P in space at some instant of time. An observer in S describes the event with space–time coordinates (x, y, z, t), whereas an observer in S′ uses the coordinates (x', y', z', t') to describe the same event. As we see from the geometry in Figure 39.2, the relationships among these various coordinates can be written

$$x' = x - vt \qquad y' = y \qquad z' = z \qquad t' = t \qquad (39.1)$$

These equations are the **Galilean space–time transformation equations.** Note that time is assumed to be the same in both inertial frames. That is, within the framework of classical mechanics, all clocks run at the same rate, regardless of their velocity, so that the time at which an event occurs for an observer in S is the same as the time for the same event in S′. Consequently, the time interval between two successive events should be the same for both observers. Although this assumption may seem obvious, it turns out to be incorrect in situations where v is comparable to the speed of light.

Now suppose that a particle moves through a displacement of magnitude dx along the x axis in a time interval dt as measured by an observer in S. It follows from Equations 39.1 that the corresponding displacement dx' measured by an observer in S′ is $dx' = dx - v\,dt$, where frame S′ is moving with speed v in the x direction relative to frame S. Because $dt = dt'$, we find that

$$\frac{dx'}{dt'} = \frac{dx}{dt} - v$$

or

$$u'_x = u_x - v \qquad (39.2)$$

where u_x and u'_x are the x components of the velocity of the particle measured by observers in S and S′, respectively. (We use the symbol **u** for particle velocity rather than **v**, which is used for the relative velocity of two reference frames.) This is the **Galilean velocity transformation equation.** It is consistent with our intuitive notion of time and space as well as with our discussions in Section 4.6. As we shall soon see, however, it leads to serious contradictions when applied to electromagnetic waves.

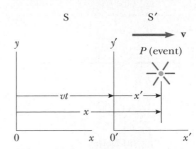

Figure 39.2 An event occurs at a point P. The event is seen by two observers in inertial frames S and S′, where S′ moves with a velocity **v** relative to S.

Galilean transformation equations

▲ **PITFALL PREVENTION**

39.1 The Relationship Between the S and S′ Frames

Many of the mathematical representations in this chapter are true *only* for the specified relationship between the S and S′ frames. The x and x' axes coincide, except that their origins are different. The y and y' axes (and the z and z' axes), are parallel, but do not coincide due to the displacement of the origin of S′ with respect to that of S. We choose the time $t = 0$ to be the instant at which the origins of the two coordinate systems coincide. If the S′ frame is moving in the positive x direction relative to S, v is positive; otherwise it is negative.

Quick Quiz 39.2 A baseball pitcher with a 90-mi/h fastball throws a ball while standing on a railroad flatcar moving at 110 mi/h. The ball is thrown in the same direction as that of the velocity of the train. Applying the Galilean velocity transformation equation, the speed of the ball relative to the Earth is (a) 90 mi/h (b) 110 mi/h (c) 20 mi/h (d) 200 mi/h (e) impossible to determine.

The Speed of Light

It is quite natural to ask whether the principle of Galilean relativity also applies to electricity, magnetism, and optics. Experiments indicate that the answer is no. Recall from Chapter 34 that Maxwell showed that the speed of light in free space is $c = 3.00 \times 10^8$ m/s. Physicists of the late 1800s thought that light waves moved through a medium called the *ether* and that the speed of light was c only in a special, absolute frame

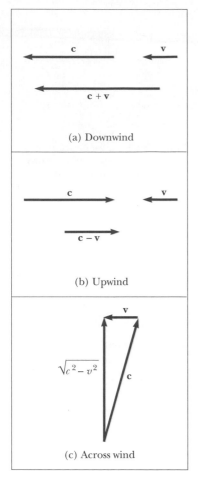

Figure 39.3 If the velocity of the ether wind relative to the Earth is **v** and the velocity of light relative to the ether is **c**, then the speed of light relative to the Earth is (a) $c + v$ in the downwind direction, (b) $c - v$ in the upwind direction, and (c) $(c^2 - v^2)^{1/2}$ in the direction perpendicular to the wind.

at rest with respect to the ether. The Galilean velocity transformation equation was expected to hold for observations of light made by an observer in any frame moving at speed v relative to the absolute ether frame. That is, if light travels along the x axis and an observer moves with velocity **v** along the x axis, the observer will measure the light to have speed $c \pm v$, depending on the directions of travel of the observer and the light.

Because the existence of a preferred, absolute ether frame would show that light was similar to other classical waves and that Newtonian ideas of an absolute frame were true, considerable importance was attached to establishing the existence of the ether frame. Prior to the late 1800s, experiments involving light traveling in media moving at the highest laboratory speeds attainable at that time were not capable of detecting differences as small as that between c and $c \pm v$. Starting in about 1880, scientists decided to use the Earth as the moving frame in an attempt to improve their chances of detecting these small changes in the speed of light.

As observers fixed on the Earth, we can take the view that we are stationary and that the absolute ether frame containing the medium for light propagation moves past us with speed v. Determining the speed of light under these circumstances is just like determining the speed of an aircraft traveling in a moving air current, or wind; consequently, we speak of an "ether wind" blowing through our apparatus fixed to the Earth.

A direct method for detecting an ether wind would use an apparatus fixed to the Earth to measure the ether wind's influence on the speed of light. If v is the speed of the ether relative to the Earth, then light should have its maximum speed $c + v$ when propagating downwind, as in Figure 39.3a. Likewise, the speed of light should have its minimum value $c - v$ when the light is propagating upwind, as in Figure 39.3b, and an intermediate value $(c^2 - v^2)^{1/2}$ in the direction perpendicular to the ether wind, as in Figure 39.3c. If the Sun is assumed to be at rest in the ether, then the velocity of the ether wind would be equal to the orbital velocity of the Earth around the Sun, which has a magnitude of approximately 3×10^4 m/s. Because $c = 3 \times 10^8$ m/s, it is necessary to detect a change in speed of about 1 part in 10^4 for measurements in the upwind or downwind directions. However, while such a change is experimentally measurable, all attempts to detect such changes and establish the existence of the ether wind (and hence the absolute frame) proved futile! We explore the classic experimental search for the ether in Section 39.2.

The principle of Galilean relativity refers only to the laws of mechanics. If it is assumed that the laws of electricity and magnetism are the same in all inertial frames, a paradox concerning the speed of light immediately arises. We can understand this by recognizing that Maxwell's equations seem to imply that the speed of light always has the fixed value 3.00×10^8 m/s in all inertial frames, a result in direct contradiction to what is expected based on the Galilean velocity transformation equation. According to Galilean relativity, the speed of light should *not* be the same in all inertial frames.

To resolve this contradiction in theories, we must conclude that either (1) the laws of electricity and magnetism are not the same in all inertial frames or (2) the Galilean velocity transformation equation is incorrect. If we assume the first alternative, then a preferred reference frame in which the speed of light has the value c must exist and the measured speed must be greater or less than this value in any other reference frame, in accordance with the Galilean velocity transformation equation. If we assume the second alternative, then we are forced to abandon the notions of absolute time and absolute length that form the basis of the Galilean space–time transformation equations.

39.2   The Michelson–Morley Experiment

The most famous experiment designed to detect small changes in the speed of light was first performed in 1881 by Albert A. Michelson (see Section 37.7) and later repeated under various conditions by Michelson and Edward W. Morley (1838–1923). We state at the outset that the outcome of the experiment contradicted the ether hypothesis.

The experiment was designed to determine the velocity of the Earth relative to that of the hypothetical ether. The experimental tool used was the Michelson interferometer, which was discussed in Section 37.7 and is shown again in Figure 39.4. Arm 2 is aligned along the direction of the Earth's motion through space. The Earth moving through the ether at speed v is equivalent to the ether flowing past the Earth in the opposite direction with speed v. This ether wind blowing in the direction opposite the direction of Earth's motion should cause the speed of light measured in the Earth frame to be $c - v$ as the light approaches mirror M_2 and $c + v$ after reflection, where c is the speed of light in the ether frame.

The two light beams reflect from M_1 and M_2 and recombine, and an interference pattern is formed, as discussed in Section 37.7. The interference pattern is observed while the interferometer is rotated through an angle of 90°. This rotation interchanges the speed of the ether wind between the arms of the interferometer. The rotation should cause the fringe pattern to shift slightly but measurably. Measurements failed, however, to show any change in the interference pattern! The Michelson–Morley experiment was repeated at different times of the year when the ether wind was expected to change direction and magnitude, but the results were always the same: **no fringe shift of the magnitude required was ever observed.**[2]

The negative results of the Michelson–Morley experiment not only contradicted the ether hypothesis but also showed that it was impossible to measure the absolute velocity of the Earth with respect to the ether frame. However, Einstein offered a postulate for his special theory of relativity that places quite a different interpretation on these null results. In later years, when more was known about the nature of light, the idea of an ether that permeates all of space was abandoned. **Light is now understood to be an electromagnetic wave, which requires no medium for its propagation.** As a result, the idea of an ether in which these waves travel became unnecessary.

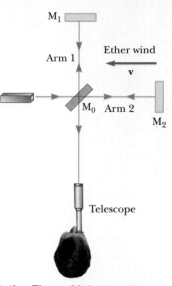

Active Figure 39.4 According to the ether wind theory, the speed of light should be $c - v$ as the beam approaches mirror M_2 and $c + v$ after reflection.

At the Active Figures link at http://www.pse6.com, you can adjust the speed of the ether wind to see the effect on the light beams if there were an ether.

Details of the Michelson–Morley Experiment

To understand the outcome of the Michelson–Morley experiment, let us assume that the two arms of the interferometer in Figure 39.4 are of equal length L. We shall analyze the situation as if there were an ether wind, because that is what Michelson and Morley expected to find. As noted above, the speed of the light beam along arm 2 should be $c - v$ as the beam approaches M_2 and $c + v$ after the beam is reflected. Thus, the time interval for travel to the right is $L/(c - v)$, and the time interval for travel to the left is $L/(c + v)$. The total time interval for the round trip along arm 2 is

$$\Delta t_{\text{arm 2}} = \frac{L}{c + v} + \frac{L}{c - v} = \frac{2Lc}{c^2 - v^2} = \frac{2L}{c}\left(1 - \frac{v^2}{c^2}\right)^{-1}$$

Now consider the light beam traveling along arm 1, perpendicular to the ether wind. Because the speed of the beam relative to the Earth is $(c^2 - v^2)^{1/2}$ in this case (see Fig. 39.3), the time interval for travel for each half of the trip is $L/(c^2 - v^2)^{1/2}$, and the total time interval for the round trip is

$$\Delta t_{\text{arm 1}} = \frac{2L}{(c^2 - v^2)^{1/2}} = \frac{2L}{c}\left(1 - \frac{v^2}{c^2}\right)^{-1/2}$$

Thus, the time difference Δt between the horizontal round trip (arm 2) and the vertical round trip (arm 1) is

$$\Delta t = \Delta t_{\text{arm 2}} - \Delta t_{\text{arm 1}} = \frac{2L}{c}\left[\left(1 - \frac{v^2}{c^2}\right)^{-1} - \left(1 - \frac{v^2}{c^2}\right)^{-1/2}\right]$$

---

[2] From an Earth observer's point of view, changes in the Earth's speed and direction of motion in the course of a year are viewed as ether wind shifts. Even if the speed of the Earth with respect to the ether were zero at some time, six months later the speed of the Earth would be 60 km/s with respect to the ether, and as a result a fringe shift should be noticed. No shift has ever been observed, however.

Because $v^2/c^2 \ll 1$, we can simplify this expression by using the following binomial expansion after dropping all terms higher than second order:

$$(1 - x)^n \approx 1 - nx \qquad (\text{for } x \ll 1)$$

In our case, $x = v^2/c^2$, and we find that

$$\Delta t = \Delta t_{\text{arm } 2} - \Delta t_{\text{arm } 1} \approx \frac{Lv^2}{c^3} \tag{39.3}$$

This time difference between the two instants at which the reflected beams arrive at the viewing telescope gives rise to a phase difference between the beams, producing an interference pattern when they combine at the position of the telescope. A shift in the interference pattern should be detected when the interferometer is rotated through 90° in a horizontal plane, so that the two beams exchange roles. This rotation results in a time difference twice that given by Equation 39.3. Thus, the path difference that corresponds to this time difference is

$$\Delta d = c \, (2 \, \Delta t) = \frac{2Lv^2}{c^2}$$

Because a change in path length of one wavelength corresponds to a shift of one fringe, the corresponding fringe shift is equal to this path difference divided by the wavelength of the light:

$$\text{Shift} = \frac{2Lv^2}{\lambda c^2} \tag{39.4}$$

In the experiments by Michelson and Morley, each light beam was reflected by mirrors many times to give an effective path length L of approximately 11 m. Using this value and taking v to be equal to 3.0×10^4 m/s, the speed of the Earth around the Sun, we obtain a path difference of

$$\Delta d = \frac{2(11 \text{ m}) (3.0 \times 10^4 \text{ m/s})^2}{(3.0 \times 10^8 \text{ m/s})^2} = 2.2 \times 10^{-7} \text{ m}$$

This extra travel distance should produce a noticeable shift in the fringe pattern. Specifically, using 500-nm light, we expect a fringe shift for rotation through 90° of

$$\text{Shift} = \frac{\Delta d}{\lambda} = \frac{2.2 \times 10^{-7} \text{ m}}{5.0 \times 10^{-7} \text{ m}} \approx 0.44$$

The instrument used by Michelson and Morley could detect shifts as small as 0.01 fringe. However, **it detected no shift whatsoever in the fringe pattern.** Since then, the experiment has been repeated many times by different scientists under a wide variety of conditions, and no fringe shift has ever been detected. Thus, it was concluded that the motion of the Earth with respect to the postulated ether cannot be detected.

Many efforts were made to explain the null results of the Michelson–Morley experiment and to save the ether frame concept and the Galilean velocity transformation equation for light. All proposals resulting from these efforts have been shown to be wrong. No experiment in the history of physics received such valiant efforts to explain the absence of an expected result as did the Michelson–Morley experiment. The stage was set for Einstein, who solved the problem in 1905 with his special theory of relativity.

39.3 Einstein's Principle of Relativity

In the previous section we noted the impossibility of measuring the speed of the ether with respect to the Earth and the failure of the Galilean velocity transformation equation in the case of light. Einstein proposed a theory that boldly removed these difficulties and at the same time completely altered our notion of space and time.[3] He based his special theory of relativity on two postulates:

1. **The principle of relativity:** The laws of physics must be the same in all inertial reference frames.
2. **The constancy of the speed of light:** The speed of light in vacuum has the same value, $c = 3.00 \times 10^8$ m/s, in all inertial frames, regardless of the velocity of the observer or the velocity of the source emitting the light.

The first postulate asserts that *all* the laws of physics—those dealing with mechanics, electricity and magnetism, optics, thermodynamics, and so on—are the same in all reference frames moving with constant velocity relative to one another. This postulate is a sweeping generalization of the principle of Galilean relativity, which refers only to the laws of mechanics. From an experimental point of view, Einstein's principle of relativity means that any kind of experiment (measuring the speed of light, for example) performed in a laboratory at rest must give the same result when performed in a laboratory moving at a constant velocity with respect to the first one. Hence, no preferred inertial reference frame exists, and it is impossible to detect absolute motion.

Note that postulate 2 is required by postulate 1: if the speed of light were not the same in all inertial frames, measurements of different speeds would make it possible to distinguish between inertial frames; as a result, a preferred, absolute frame could be identified, in contradiction to postulate 1.

Although the Michelson–Morley experiment was performed before Einstein published his work on relativity, it is not clear whether or not Einstein was aware of the details of the experiment. Nonetheless, the null result of the experiment can be readily understood within the framework of Einstein's theory. According to his principle of relativity, the premises of the Michelson–Morley experiment were incorrect. In the process of trying to explain the expected results, we stated that when light traveled against the ether wind its speed was $c - v$, in accordance with the Galilean velocity transformation equation. However, if the state of motion of the observer or of the source has no influence on the value found for the speed of light, one always measures the value to be c. Likewise, the light makes the return trip after reflection from the mirror at speed c, not at speed $c + v$. Thus, the motion of the Earth does not influence the fringe pattern observed in the Michelson–Morley experiment, and a null result should be expected.

If we accept Einstein's theory of relativity, we must conclude that relative motion is unimportant when measuring the speed of light. At the same time, we shall see that we must alter our common-sense notion of space and time and be prepared for some surprising consequences. It may help as you read the pages ahead to keep in mind that our common-sense ideas are based on a lifetime of everyday experiences and not on observations of objects moving at hundreds of thousands of kilometers per second. Thus, these results will seem strange, but that is only because we have no experience with them.

39.4 Consequences of the Special Theory of Relativity

Before we discuss the consequences of Einstein's special theory of relativity, we must first understand how an observer located in an inertial reference frame describes an event. As mentioned earlier, an event is an occurrence describable by three space

---

[3] A. Einstein, "On the Electrodynamics of Moving Bodies," *Ann. Physik* 17:891, 1905. For an English translation of this article and other publications by Einstein, see the book by H. Lorentz, A. Einstein, H. Minkowski, and H. Weyl, *The Principle of Relativity*, Dover, 1958.

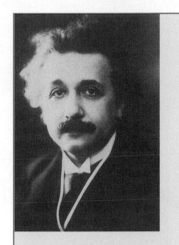

Albert Einstein
German-American Physicist
(1879–1955)

Einstein, one of the greatest physicists of all times, was born in Ulm, Germany. In 1905, at the age of 26, he published four scientific papers that revolutionized physics. Two of these papers were concerned with what is now considered his most important contribution: the special theory of relativity.

In 1916, Einstein published his work on the general theory of relativity. The most dramatic prediction of this theory is the degree to which light is deflected by a gravitational field. Measurements made by astronomers on bright stars in the vicinity of the eclipsed Sun in 1919 confirmed Einstein's prediction, and as a result Einstein became a world celebrity.

Einstein was deeply disturbed by the development of quantum mechanics in the 1920s despite his own role as a scientific revolutionary. In particular, he could never accept the probabilistic view of events in nature that is a central feature of quantum theory. The last few decades of his life were devoted to an unsuccessful search for a unified theory that would combine gravitation and electromagnetism. *(AIP Niels Bohr Library)*

coordinates and one time coordinate. Observers in different inertial frames will describe the same event with coordinates that have different values.

As we examine some of the consequences of relativity in the remainder of this section, we restrict our discussion to the concepts of simultaneity, time intervals, and lengths, all three of which are quite different in relativistic mechanics from what they are in Newtonian mechanics. For example, in relativistic mechanics the distance between two points and the time interval between two events depend on the frame of reference in which they are measured. That is, **in relativistic mechanics there is no such thing as an absolute length or absolute time interval.** Furthermore, **events at different locations that are observed to occur simultaneously in one frame are not necessarily observed to be simultaneous in another frame moving uniformly with respect to the first.**

Simultaneity and the Relativity of Time

A basic premise of Newtonian mechanics is that a universal time scale exists that is the same for all observers. In fact, Newton wrote that "Absolute, true, and mathematical time, of itself, and from its own nature, flows equably without relation to anything external." Thus, Newton and his followers simply took simultaneity for granted. In his special theory of relativity, Einstein abandoned this assumption.

Einstein devised the following thought experiment to illustrate this point. A boxcar moves with uniform velocity, and two lightning bolts strike its ends, as illustrated in Figure 39.5a, leaving marks on the boxcar and on the ground. The marks on the boxcar are labeled A' and B', and those on the ground are labeled A and B. An observer O' moving with the boxcar is midway between A' and B', and a ground observer O is midway between A and B. The events recorded by the observers are the striking of the boxcar by the two lightning bolts.

The light signals emitted from A and B at the instant at which the two bolts strike reach observer O at the same time, as indicated in Figure 39.5b. This observer realizes that the signals have traveled at the same speed over equal distances, and so rightly concludes that the events at A and B occurred simultaneously. Now consider the same events as viewed by observer O'. By the time the signals have reached observer O, observer O' has moved as indicated in Figure 39.5b. Thus, the signal from B' has already swept past O', but the signal from A' has not yet reached O'. In other words, O' sees the signal from B' before seeing the signal from A'. According to Einstein, *the two observers must find that light travels at the same speed.* Therefore, observer O' concludes that the lightning strikes the front of the boxcar before it strikes the back.

This thought experiment clearly demonstrates that the two events that appear to be simultaneous to observer O do not appear to be simultaneous to observer O'.

PITFALL PREVENTION

39.2 Who's Right?

You might wonder which observer in Fig. 39.5 is correct concerning the two lightning strikes. *Both are correct,* because the principle of relativity states that *there is no preferred inertial frame of reference.* Although the two observers reach different conclusions, both are correct in their own reference frame because the concept of simultaneity is not absolute. This, in fact, is the central point of relativity—any uniformly moving frame of reference can be used to describe events and do physics.

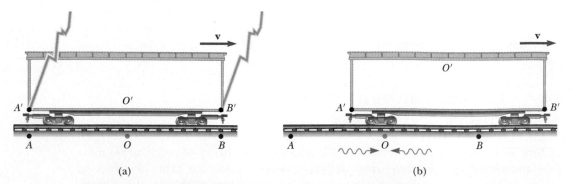

(a)   (b)

Figure 39.5 (a) Two lightning bolts strike the ends of a moving boxcar. (b) The events appear to be simultaneous to the stationary observer O, standing midway between A and B. The events do not appear to be simultaneous to observer O', who claims that the front of the car is struck before the rear. Note that in (b) the leftward-traveling light signal has already passed O' but the rightward-traveling signal has not yet reached O'.

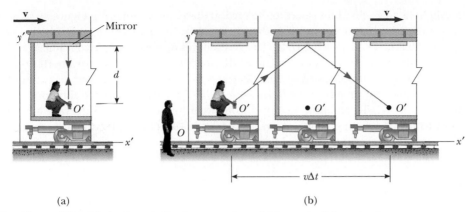

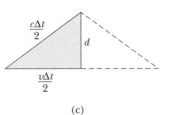

(a)   (b)   (c)

Active Figure 39.6 (a) A mirror is fixed to a moving vehicle, and a light pulse is sent out by observer O' at rest in the vehicle. (b) Relative to a stationary observer O standing alongside the vehicle, the mirror and O' move with a speed v. Note that what observer O measures for the distance the pulse travels is greater than $2d$. (c) The right triangle for calculating the relationship between Δt and Δt_p.

At the Active Figures link at http://www.pse6.com, *you can observe the bouncing of the light pulse for various speeds of the train.*

In other words,

> two events that are simultaneous in one reference frame are in general not simultaneous in a second frame moving relative to the first. That is, simultaneity is not an absolute concept but rather one that depends on the state of motion of the observer.

Einstein's thought experiment demonstrates that two observers can disagree on the simultaneity of two events. **This disagreement, however, depends on the transit time of light to the observers and, therefore, does *not* demonstrate the deeper meaning of relativity.** In relativistic analyses of high-speed situations, relativity shows that simultaneity is relative even when the transit time is subtracted out. In fact, all of the relativistic effects that we will discuss from here on will assume that we are ignoring differences caused by the transit time of light to the observers.

Time Dilation

We can illustrate the fact that observers in different inertial frames can measure different time intervals between a pair of events by considering a vehicle moving to the right with a speed v, such as the boxcar shown in Figure 39.6a. A mirror is fixed to the ceiling of the vehicle, and observer O' at rest in the frame attached to the vehicle holds a flashlight a distance d below the mirror. At some instant, the flashlight emits a pulse of light directed toward the mirror (event 1), and at some later time after reflecting from the mirror, the pulse arrives back at the flashlight (event 2). Observer O' carries a clock and uses it to measure the time interval Δt_p between these two events. (The subscript p stands for *proper*, as we shall see in a moment.) Because the light pulse has a speed c, the time interval required for the pulse to travel from O' to the mirror and back is

$$\Delta t_p = \frac{\text{distance traveled}}{\text{speed}} = \frac{2d}{c} \tag{39.5}$$

Now consider the same pair of events as viewed by observer O in a second frame, as shown in Figure 39.6b. According to this observer, the mirror and flashlight are moving to the right with a speed v, and as a result the sequence of events appears entirely different. By the time the light from the flashlight reaches the mirror, the mirror has moved to the right a distance $v \, \Delta t/2$, where Δt is the time interval required for the light to travel from O' to the mirror and back to O' as measured by O. In other words, O concludes that, because of the motion of the vehicle, if the light is to hit the mirror, it must leave the flashlight at an angle with respect to the vertical direction. Comparing Figure 39.6a and b, we see that the light must travel farther in (b) than in (a). (Note that neither observer "knows" that he or she is moving. Each is at rest in his or her own inertial frame.)

According to the second postulate of the special theory of relativity, both observers must measure c for the speed of light. Because the light travels farther according to O, it follows that the time interval Δt measured by O is longer than the time interval Δt_p measured by O'. To obtain a relationship between these two time intervals, it is convenient to use the right triangle shown in Figure 39.6c. The Pythagorean theorem gives

$$\left(\frac{c\,\Delta t}{2}\right)^2 = \left(\frac{v\,\Delta t}{2}\right)^2 + d^2$$

Solving for Δt gives

$$\Delta t = \frac{2d}{\sqrt{c^2 - v^2}} = \frac{2d}{c\sqrt{1 - \dfrac{v^2}{c^2}}} \tag{39.6}$$

Because $\Delta t_p = 2d/c$, we can express this result as

Time dilation

$$\Delta t = \frac{\Delta t_p}{\sqrt{1 - \dfrac{v^2}{c^2}}} = \gamma\,\Delta t_p \tag{39.7}$$

where

$$\gamma = \frac{1}{\sqrt{1 - \dfrac{v^2}{c^2}}} \tag{39.8}$$

Because γ is always greater than unity, this result says that **the time interval Δt measured by an observer moving with respect to a clock is longer than the time interval Δt_p measured by an observer at rest with respect to the clock.** This effect is known as **time dilation.**

We can see that time dilation is not observed in our everyday lives by considering the factor γ. This factor deviates significantly from a value of 1 only for very high speeds, as shown in Figure 39.7 and Table 39.1. For example, for a speed of $0.1c$, the value of γ is 1.005. Thus, there is a time dilation of only 0.5% at one-tenth the speed of light. Speeds that we encounter on an everyday basis are far slower than this, so we do not see time dilation in normal situations.

The time interval Δt_p in Equations 39.5 and 39.7 is called the **proper time interval.** (In German, Einstein used the term *Eigenzeit*, which means "own-time.") In

Table 39.1

Approximate Values for γ at Various Speeds	
v/c	γ
0.001 0	1.000 000 5
0.010	1.000 05
0.10	1.005
0.20	1.021
0.30	1.048
0.40	1.091
0.50	1.155
0.60	1.250
0.70	1.400
0.80	1.667
0.90	2.294
0.92	2.552
0.94	2.931
0.96	3.571
0.98	5.025
0.99	7.089
0.995	10.01
0.999	22.37

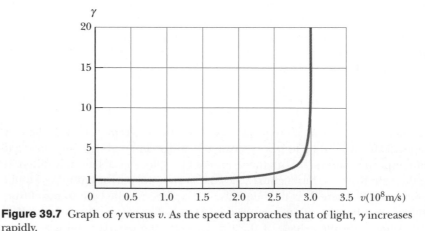

Figure 39.7 Graph of γ versus v. As the speed approaches that of light, γ increases rapidly.

general, **the proper time interval is the time interval between two events measured by an observer who sees the events occur at the same point in space.**

If a clock is moving with respect to you, the time interval between ticks of the moving clock is observed to be longer than the time interval between ticks of an identical clock in your reference frame. Thus, it is often said that a moving clock is measured to run more slowly than a clock in your reference frame by a factor γ. This is true for mechanical clocks as well as for the light clock just described. We can generalize this result by stating that all physical processes, including chemical and biological ones, are measured to slow down when those processes occur in a frame moving with respect to the observer. For example, the heartbeat of an astronaut moving through space would keep time with a clock inside the spacecraft. Both the astronaut's clock and heartbeat would be measured to slow down according to an observer on Earth comparing time intervals with his own clock (although the astronaut would have no sensation of life slowing down in the spacecraft).

> **Quick Quiz 39.3** Suppose the observer O' on the train in Figure 39.6 aims her flashlight at the far wall of the boxcar and turns it on and off, sending a pulse of light toward the far wall. Both O' and O measure the time interval between when the pulse leaves the flashlight and it hits the far wall. Which observer measures the proper time interval between these two events? (a) O' (b) O (c) both observers (d) neither observer.

> **Quick Quiz 39.4** A crew watches a movie that is two hours long in a spacecraft that is moving at high speed through space. Will an Earthbound observer, who is watching the movie through a powerful telescope, measure the duration of the movie to be (a) longer than, (b) shorter than, or (c) equal to two hours?

Strange as it may seem, time dilation is a verifiable phenomenon. An experiment reported by Hafele and Keating provided direct evidence of time dilation.[4] Time intervals measured with four cesium atomic clocks in jet flight were compared with time intervals measured by Earth-based reference atomic clocks. In order to compare these results with theory, many factors had to be considered, including periods of speeding up and slowing down relative to the Earth, variations in direction of travel, and the fact that the gravitational field experienced by the flying clocks was weaker than that experienced by the Earth-based clock. The results were in good agreement with the predictions of the special theory of relativity and can be explained in terms of the relative motion between the Earth and the jet aircraft. In their paper, Hafele and Keating stated that "Relative to the atomic time scale of the U.S. Naval Observatory, the flying clocks lost 59 ± 10 ns during the eastward trip and gained 273 ± 7 ns during the westward trip. . . . These results provide an unambiguous empirical resolution of the famous clock paradox with macroscopic clocks."

Another interesting example of time dilation involves the observation of *muons*, unstable elementary particles that have a charge equal to that of the electron and a mass 207 times that of the electron. (We will study the muon and other particles in Chapter 46.) Muons can be produced by the collision of cosmic radiation with atoms high in the atmosphere. Slow-moving muons in the laboratory have a lifetime which is measured to be the proper time interval $\Delta t_p = 2.2\ \mu s$. If we assume that the speed of atmospheric muons is close to the speed of light, we find that these particles can travel a distance of approximately $(3.0 \times 10^8\ \text{m/s})(2.2 \times 10^{-6}\ \text{s}) \approx 6.6 \times 10^2$ m before they decay (Fig. 39.8a). Hence, they are unlikely to reach the surface of the Earth from

---

[4]   J. C. Hafele and R. E. Keating, "Around the World Atomic Clocks: Relativistic Time Gains Observed," *Science*, 177:168, 1972.

▲ PITFALL PREVENTION

39.3 The Proper Time Interval

It is *very* important in relativistic calculations to correctly identify the observer who measures the proper time interval. The proper time interval between two events is always the time interval measured by an observer for whom the two events take place at the same position.

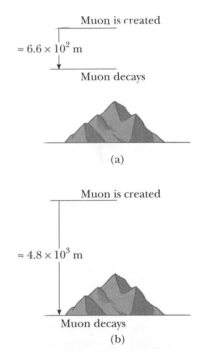

Figure 39.8 (a) Without relativistic considerations, muons created in the atmosphere and traveling downward with a speed of $0.99c$ travel only about 6.6×10^2 m before decaying with an average lifetime of 2.2 μs. Thus, very few muons reach the surface of the Earth. (b) With relativistic considerations, the muon's lifetime is dilated according to an observer on Earth. As a result, according to this observer, the muon can travel about 4.8×10^3 m before decaying. This results in many of them arriving at the surface.

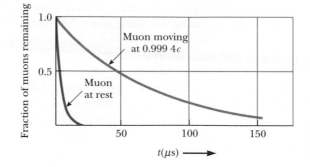

Figure 39.9 Decay curves for muons at rest and for muons traveling at a speed of 0.999 4c.

high in the atmosphere where they are produced. However, experiments show that a large number of muons *do* reach the surface. The phenomenon of time dilation explains this effect. As measured by an observer on Earth, the muons have a dilated lifetime equal to $\gamma \Delta t_p$. For example, for $v = 0.99c$, $\gamma \approx 7.1$ and $\gamma \Delta t_p \approx 16$ μs. Hence, the average distance traveled by the muons in this time as measured by an observer on Earth is approximately $(0.99)(3.0 \times 10^8 \text{ m/s})(16 \times 10^{-6} \text{ s}) \approx 4.8 \times 10^3$ m, as indicated in Figure 39.8b.

In 1976, at the laboratory of the European Council for Nuclear Research (CERN) in Geneva, muons injected into a large storage ring reached speeds of approximately 0.999 4c. Electrons produced by the decaying muons were detected by counters around the ring, enabling scientists to measure the decay rate and hence the muon lifetime. The lifetime of the moving muons was measured to be approximately 30 times as long as that of the stationary muon (Fig. 39.9), in agreement with the prediction of relativity to within two parts in a thousand.

Example 39.1   What Is the Period of the Pendulum?

The period of a pendulum is measured to be 3.00 s in the reference frame of the pendulum. What is the period when measured by an observer moving at a speed of 0.950c relative to the pendulum?

Solution To conceptualize this problem, let us change frames of reference. Instead of the observer moving at 0.950c, we can take the equivalent point of view that the observer is at rest and the pendulum is moving at 0.950c past the stationary observer. Hence, the pendulum is an example of a clock moving at high speed with respect to an observer and we can categorize this problem as one involving time dilation.

To analyze the problem, note that the proper time interval, measured in the rest frame of the pendulum, is $\Delta t_p = 3.00$ s. Because a clock moving with respect to an observer is measured to run more slowly than a stationary clock by a factor γ, Equation 39.7 gives

$$\Delta t = \gamma \Delta t_p = \frac{1}{\sqrt{1 - \dfrac{(0.950c)^2}{c^2}}} \Delta t_p = \frac{1}{\sqrt{1 - 0.902}} \Delta t_p$$

$$= (3.20)(3.00 \text{ s}) = \boxed{9.60 \text{ s}}$$

To finalize this problem, we see that indeed a moving pendulum is measured to take longer to complete a period

than a pendulum at rest does. The period increases by a factor of $\gamma = 3.20$. We see that this is consistent with Table 39.1, where this value lies between those for γ for $v/c = 0.94$ and $v/c = 0.96$.

What If? What if we increase the speed of the observer by 5.00%? Does the dilated time interval increase by 5.00%?

Answer Based on the highly nonlinear behavior of γ as a function of v in Figure 39.7, we would guess that the increase in Δt would be different from 5.00%. Increasing v by 5.00% gives us

$$v_{\text{new}} = (1.050\,0)(0.950c) = 0.997\,5c$$

(Because γ varies so rapidly with v when v is this large, we will keep one additional significant figure until the final answer.) If we perform the time dilation calculation again, we find that

$$\Delta t = \gamma \Delta t_p = \frac{1}{\sqrt{1 - \dfrac{(0.997\,5c)^2}{c^2}}} \Delta t_p = \frac{1}{\sqrt{1 - 0.995\,0}} \Delta t_p$$

$$= (14.15)(3.00 \text{ s}) = 42.5 \text{ s}$$

Thus, the 5.00% increase in speed has caused over a 300% increase in the dilated time!

Example 39.2   How Long Was Your Trip?

Suppose you are driving your car on a business trip and are traveling at 30 m/s. Your boss, who is waiting at your destination, expects the trip to take 5.0 h. When you arrive late, your excuse is that your car clock registered the passage of 5.0 h but that you were driving fast and so your clock ran more slowly than your boss's clock. If your car clock actually did indicate a 5.0-h trip, how much time passed on your boss's clock, which was at rest on the Earth?

Solution We begin by calculating γ from Equation 39.8:

$$\gamma = \frac{1}{\sqrt{1 - \dfrac{v^2}{c^2}}} = \frac{1}{\sqrt{1 - \dfrac{(3 \times 10^1 \text{ m/s})^2}{(3 \times 10^8 \text{ m/s})^2}}}$$

$$= \frac{1}{\sqrt{1 - 10^{-14}}}$$

If you try to determine this value on your calculator, you will probably obtain $\gamma = 1$. However, if we perform a binomial expansion, we can more precisely determine the value as

$$\gamma = (1 - 10^{-14})^{-1/2} \approx 1 + \tfrac{1}{2}(10^{-14}) = 1 + 5.0 \times 10^{-15}$$

This result indicates that at typical automobile speeds, γ is not much different from 1.

Applying Equation 39.7, we find Δt, the time interval measured by your boss, to be

$$\Delta t = \gamma \, \Delta t_p = (1 + 5.0 \times 10^{-15})(5.0 \text{ h})$$

$$= 5.0 \text{ h} + 2.5 \times 10^{-14} \text{ h} = \boxed{5.0 \text{ h} + 0.09 \text{ ns}}$$

Your boss's clock would be only 0.09 ns ahead of your car clock. You might want to think of another excuse!

The Twin Paradox

An intriguing consequence of time dilation is the so-called *twin paradox* (Fig. 39.10). Consider an experiment involving a set of twins named Speedo and Goslo. When they are 20 yr old, Speedo, the more adventuresome of the two, sets out on an epic journey to Planet X, located 20 ly from the Earth. (Note that 1 lightyear (ly) is the distance light travels through free space in 1 year.) Furthermore, Speedo's spacecraft is capable of reaching a speed of $0.95c$ relative to the inertial frame of his twin brother back home. After reaching Planet X, Speedo becomes homesick and immediately returns to the Earth at the same speed $0.95c$. Upon his return, Speedo is shocked to discover that Goslo has aged 42 yr and is now 62 yr old. Speedo, on the other hand, has aged only 13 yr.

At this point, it is fair to raise the following question—which twin is the traveler and which is really younger as a result of this experiment? From Goslo's frame of reference, he was at rest while his brother traveled at a high speed away from him and then came back. According to Speedo, however, he himself remained stationary while Goslo and the Earth raced away from him and then headed back. This leads to an apparent

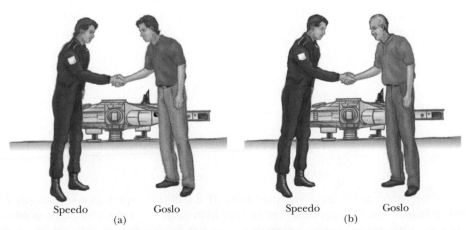

Speedo	Goslo	Speedo	Goslo
(a)		(b)	

Figure 39.10 (a) As one twin leaves his brother on the Earth, both are the same age. (b) When Speedo returns from his journey to Planet X, he is younger than his twin Goslo.

contradiction due to the apparent symmetry of the observations. Which twin has developed signs of excess aging?

The situation in our current problem is actually not symmetrical. To resolve this apparent paradox, recall that the special theory of relativity describes observations made in inertial frames of reference moving relative to each other. Speedo, the space traveler, must experience a series of accelerations during his journey because he must fire his rocket engines to slow down and start moving back toward Earth. As a result, his speed is not always uniform, and consequently he is not in an inertial frame. Therefore, there is no paradox—only Goslo, who is always in a single inertial frame, can make correct predictions based on special relativity. During each passing year noted by Goslo, slightly less than 4 months elapses for Speedo.

Only Goslo, who is in a single inertial frame, can apply the simple time-dilation formula to Speedo's trip. Thus, Goslo finds that instead of aging 42 yr, Speedo ages only $(1 - v^2/c^2)^{1/2}(42 \text{ yr}) = 13 \text{ yr}$. Thus, according to Goslo, Speedo spends 6.5 yr traveling to Planet X and 6.5 yr returning, for a total travel time of 13 yr, in agreement with our earlier statement.

Quick Quiz 39.5 Suppose astronauts are paid according to the amount of time they spend traveling in space. After a long voyage traveling at a speed approaching c, would a crew rather be paid according to (a) an Earth-based clock, (b) their spacecraft's clock, or (c) either clock?

Length Contraction

▲ **PITFALL PREVENTION**

39.4 The Proper Length

As with the proper time interval, it is *very* important in relativistic calculations to correctly identify the observer who measures the proper length. The proper length between two points in space is always the length measured by an observer at rest with respect to the points. Often the proper time interval and the proper length are *not* measured by the same observer.

The measured distance between two points also depends on the frame of reference. **The proper length L_p of an object is the length measured by someone at rest relative to the object.** The length of an object measured by someone in a reference frame that is moving with respect to the object is always less than the proper length. This effect is known as **length contraction.**

Consider a spacecraft traveling with a speed v from one star to another. There are two observers: one on the Earth and the other in the spacecraft. The observer at rest on the Earth (and also assumed to be at rest with respect to the two stars) measures the distance between the stars to be the proper length L_p. According to this observer, the time interval required for the spacecraft to complete the voyage is $\Delta t = L_p/v$. The passages of the two stars by the spacecraft occur at the same position for the space traveler. Thus, the space traveler measures the proper time interval Δt_p. Because of time dilation, the proper time interval is related to the Earth-measured time interval by $\Delta t_p = \Delta t / \gamma$. Because the space traveler reaches the second star in the time Δt_p, he or she concludes that the distance L between the stars is

$$L = v \, \Delta t_p = v \, \frac{\Delta t}{\gamma}$$

Because the proper length is $L_p = v \, \Delta t$, we see that

Length contraction

$$L = \frac{L_p}{\gamma} = L_p \sqrt{1 - \frac{v^2}{c^2}} \tag{39.9}$$

where $\sqrt{1 - v^2/c^2}$ is a factor less than unity. **If an object has a proper length L_p when it is measured by an observer at rest with respect to the object, then when it moves with speed v in a direction parallel to its length, its length L is measured to be shorter according to $L = L_p \sqrt{1 - v^2/c^2} = L_p/\gamma$.**

For example, suppose that a meter stick moves past a stationary Earth observer with speed v, as in Figure 39.11. The length of the stick as measured by an observer in a frame attached to the stick is the proper length L_p shown in Figure 39.11a. The length of the stick L measured by the Earth observer is shorter than L_p by the factor $(1 - v^2/c^2)^{1/2}$. Note that **length contraction takes place only along the direction of motion.**

The proper length and the proper time interval are defined differently. The proper length is measured by an observer for whom the end points of the length remain fixed in space. The proper time interval is measured by someone for whom the two events take place at the same position in space. As an example of this point, let us return to the decaying muons moving at speeds close to the speed of light. An observer in the muon's reference frame would measure the proper lifetime, while an Earth-based observer would measure the proper length (the distance from creation to decay in Figure 39.8). In the muon's reference frame, there is no time dilation but the distance of travel to the surface is observed to be shorter when measured in this frame. Likewise, in the Earth observer's reference frame, there is time dilation, but the distance of travel is measured to be the proper length. Thus, when calculations on the muon are performed in both frames, the outcome of the experiment in one frame is the same as the outcome in the other frame—more muons reach the surface than would be predicted without relativistic effects.

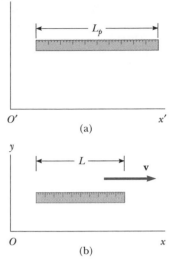

Active Figure 39.11 (a) A meter stick measured by an observer in a frame attached to the stick (that is, both have the same velocity) has its proper length L_p. (b) The stick measured by an observer in a frame in which the stick has a velocity **v** relative to the frame is measured to be shorter than its proper length L_p by a factor $(1 - v^2/c^2)^{1/2}$.

At the Active Figures link at http://www.pse6.com, *you can view the meter stick from the points of view of two observers to compare the measured length of the stick.*

Quick Quiz 39.6 You are packing for a trip to another star. During the journey, you will be traveling at $0.99c$. You are trying to decide whether you should buy smaller sizes of your clothing, because you will be thinner on your trip, due to length contraction. Also, you are considering saving money by reserving a smaller cabin to sleep in, because you will be shorter when you lie down. Should you (a) buy smaller sizes of clothing, (b) reserve a smaller cabin, (c) do neither of these, or (d) do both of these?

Quick Quiz 39.7 You are observing a spacecraft moving away from you. You measure it to be shorter than when it was at rest on the ground next to you. You also see a clock through the spacecraft window, and you observe that the passage of time on the clock is measured to be slower than that of the watch on your wrist. Compared to when the spacecraft was on the ground, what do you measure if the spacecraft turns around and comes *toward* you at the same speed? (a) The spacecraft is measured to be longer and the clock runs faster. (b) The spacecraft is measured to be longer and the clock runs slower. (c) The spacecraft is measured to be shorter and the clock runs faster. (d) The spacecraft is measured to be shorter and the clock runs slower.

Space–Time Graphs

It is sometimes helpful to make a *space–time graph*, in which ct is the ordinate and position x is the abscissa. The twin paradox is displayed in such a graph in Figure 39.12

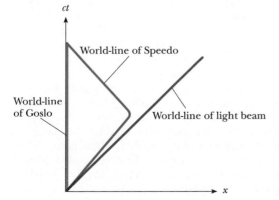

Figure 39.12 The twin paradox on a space–time graph. The twin who stays on the Earth has a world-line along the ct axis. The path of the traveling twin through space–time is represented by a world-line that changes direction.

from the point of view of Goslo. A path through space–time is called a **world-line.** At the origin, the world-lines of Speedo and Goslo coincide because the twins are in the same location at the same time. After Speedo leaves on his trip, his world-line diverges from that of his brother. Goslo's world-line is vertical because he remains fixed in location. At their reunion, the two world-lines again come together. Note that it would be impossible for Speedo to have a world-line that crossed the path of a light beam that left the Earth when he did. To do so would require him to have a speed greater than c (not possible, as shown in Sections 39.6 and 39.7).

World-lines for light beams are diagonal lines on space–time graphs, typically drawn at 45° to the right or left of vertical (assuming that the x and ct axes have the same scales), depending on whether the light beam is traveling in the direction of increasing or decreasing x. These two world-lines mean that all possible future events for Goslo and Speedo lie within two 45° lines extending from the origin. Either twin's presence at an event outside this "light cone" would require that twin to move at a speed greater than c, which we have said is not possible. Also, the only past events that Goslo and Speedo could have experienced occurred within two similar 45° world-lines that approach the origin from below the x axis.

Example 39.3   The Contraction of a Spacecraft

A spacecraft is measured to be 120.0 m long and 20.0 m in diameter while at rest relative to an observer. If this spacecraft now flies by the observer with a speed of $0.99c$, what length and diameter does the observer measure?

Solution From Equation 39.9, the length measured by the observer is

$$L = L_p \sqrt{1 - \frac{v^2}{c^2}} = (120.0 \text{ m}) \sqrt{1 - \frac{(0.99c)^2}{c^2}} = \boxed{17 \text{ m}}$$

The diameter measured by the observer is still 20.0 m because the diameter is a dimension perpendicular to the motion and length contraction occurs only along the direction of motion.

Example 39.4   The Pole-in-the-Barn Paradox   `Interactive`

The twin paradox, discussed earlier, is a classic "paradox" in relativity. Another classic "paradox" is this: Suppose a runner moving at $0.75c$ carries a horizontal pole 15 m long toward a barn that is 10 m long. The barn has front and rear doors. An observer on the ground can instantly and simultaneously open and close the two doors by remote control. When the runner and the pole are inside the barn, the ground observer closes and then opens both doors so that the runner and pole are momentarily captured inside the barn and then proceed to exit the barn from the back door. Do both the runner and the ground observer agree that the runner makes it safely through the barn?

Solution From our everyday experience, we would be surprised to see a 15-m pole fit inside a 10-m barn. But the pole is in motion with respect to the ground observer, who measures the pole to be contracted to a length L_{pole}, where

$$L_{\text{pole}} = L_p \sqrt{1 - \frac{v^2}{c^2}} = (15 \text{ m}) \sqrt{1 - (0.75)^2} = 9.9 \text{ m}$$

Thus, the ground observer measures the pole to be slightly shorter than the barn and there is no problem with momentarily capturing the pole inside it. The "paradox" arises when we consider the runner's point of view. The runner

sees the barn contracted to

$$L_{\text{barn}} = L_p \sqrt{1 - \frac{v^2}{c^2}} = (10 \text{ m}) \sqrt{1 - (0.75)^2} = \boxed{6.6 \text{ m}}$$

Because the pole is in the rest frame of the runner, the runner measures it to have its proper length of 15 m. How can a 15-m pole fit inside a 6.6-m barn? While this is the classic question that is often asked, this is not the question we have asked, because it is not the important question. We asked *if the runner can make it safely through the barn.*

The resolution of the "paradox" lies in the relativity of simultaneity. The closing of the two doors is measured to be simultaneous by the ground observer. Because the doors are at different positions, however, they do not close simultaneously as measured by the runner. The rear door closes and then opens first, allowing the leading edge of the pole to exit. The front door of the barn does not close until the trailing edge of the pole passes by.

We can analyze this using a space-time graph. Figure 39.13a is a space–time graph from the ground observer's point of view. We choose $x = 0$ as the position of the front door of the barn and $t = 0$ as the instant at which the leading end of the pole is located at the front door of the barn. The world-lines for the two ends of the barn are separated by 10 m and are vertical because the barn is not moving relative to this observer. For the pole, we follow two tilted world-lines, one

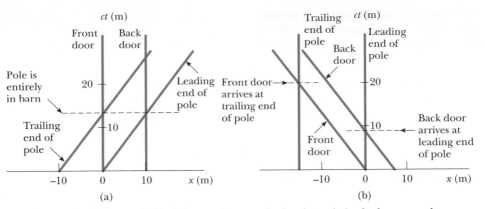

Figure 39.13 (Example 39.4) Space–time graphs for the pole-in-the-barn paradox. (a) From the ground observer's point of view, the world-lines for the front and back doors of the barn are vertical lines. The world-lines for the ends of the pole are tilted and are 9.9 m apart horizontally. The front door of the barn is at $x = 0$, and the leading end of the pole enters the front door at $t = 0$. The entire pole is inside the barn at the time indicated by the dashed line. (b) From the runner's point of view, the world-lines for the ends of the pole are vertical. The barn is moving in the negative direction, so the world-lines for the front and back doors are tilted to the left. The leading end of the pole exits the back door before the trailing end arrives at the front door.

for each end of the moving pole. These world-lines are 9.9 m apart horizontally, which is the contracted length seen by the ground observer. As seen in Figure 39.13a, at one instant, the pole is entirely within the barn.

Figure 39.13b shows the space–time graph according to the runner. Here, the world-lines for the pole are separated by 15 m and are vertical because the pole is at rest in the runner's frame of reference. The barn is hurtling *toward* the runner, so the world-lines for the front and rear doors of the barn are tilted in the opposite direction compared to Figure 39.13a. The world-lines for the barn are separated by 6.6 m, the contracted length as seen by the runner. Notice that the front of the pole leaves the rear door of the barn long before the back of the pole enters the barn. Thus, the opening of the rear door occurs before the closing of the front door.

From the ground observer's point of view, the time at which the trailing end of the pole enters the barn is found from

$$\Delta t = t - 0 = t = \frac{\Delta x}{v} = \frac{9.9 \text{ m}}{0.75c} = \frac{13.2 \text{ m}}{c}$$

Thus, the pole should be completely inside the barn at a time corresponding to $ct = 13.2$ m. This is consistent with the point on the ct axis in Figure 39.13a where the pole is inside the barn.

From the runner's point of view, the time at which the leading end of the pole leaves the barn is found from

$$\Delta t = t - 0 = t = \frac{\Delta x}{v} = \frac{6.6 \text{ m}}{0.75c} = \frac{8.8 \text{ m}}{c}$$

leading to $ct = 8.8$ m. This is consistent with the point on the ct axis in Figure 39.13b where the back door of the barn arrives at the leading end of the pole. Finally, the time at which the trailing end of the pole enters the front door of the barn is found from

$$\Delta t = t - 0 = t = \frac{\Delta x}{v} = \frac{15 \text{ m}}{0.75c} = \frac{20 \text{ m}}{c}$$

This gives $ct = 20$ m, which agrees with the instant shown in Figure 39.13b.

Investigate the pole-in-the-barn paradox at the Interactive Worked Example link at **http://www.pse6.com.**

Example 39.5   A Voyage to Sirius

An astronaut takes a trip to Sirius, which is located a distance of 8 lightyears from the Earth. The astronaut measures the time of the one-way journey to be 6 yr. If the spaceship moves at a constant speed of 0.8c, how can the 8-ly distance be reconciled with the 6-yr trip time measured by the astronaut?

Solution The distance of 8 ly represents the proper length from the Earth to Sirius measured by an observer seeing both objects nearly at rest. The astronaut sees Sirius approaching her at 0.8c but also sees the distance

contracted to

$$\frac{8 \text{ ly}}{\gamma} = (8 \text{ ly}) \sqrt{1 - \frac{v^2}{c^2}} = (8 \text{ ly}) \sqrt{1 - \frac{(0.8c)^2}{c^2}} = 5 \text{ ly}$$

Thus, the travel time measured on her clock is

$$\Delta t = \frac{d}{v} = \frac{5 \text{ ly}}{0.8c} = 6 \text{ yr}$$

Note that we have used the value for the speed of light as $c = 1$ ly/yr.

What If? What if this trip is observed with a very powerful telescope by a technician in Mission Control on Earth? At what time will this technician *see* that the astronaut has arrived at Sirius?

Answer The time interval that the technician will measure for the astronaut to arrive is

$$\Delta t = \frac{d}{v} = \frac{8 \text{ ly}}{0.8c} = 10 \text{ yr}$$

In order for the technician to *see* the arrival, the light from the scene of the arrival must travel back to Earth and enter the telescope. This will require a time interval of

$$\Delta t = \frac{d}{v} = \frac{8 \text{ ly}}{c} = 8 \text{ yr}$$

Thus, the technician sees the arrival after 10 yr + 8 yr = 18 yr. Notice that if the astronaut immediately turns around and comes back home, she arrives, according to the technician, 20 years after leaving, only 2 years after he *saw* her arrive! In addition, she would have aged by only 12 years.

The Relativistic Doppler Effect

Another important consequence of time dilation is the shift in frequency found for light emitted by atoms in motion as opposed to light emitted by atoms at rest. This phenomenon, known as the Doppler effect, was introduced in Chapter 17 as it pertains to sound waves. In the case of sound, the motion of the source with respect to the medium of propagation can be distinguished from the motion of the observer with respect to the medium. Light waves must be analyzed differently, however, because they require no medium of propagation, and no method exists for distinguishing the motion of a light source from the motion of the observer.

If a light source and an observer approach each other with a relative speed v, the frequency f_{obs} measured by the observer is

$$f_{obs} = \frac{\sqrt{1 + v/c}}{\sqrt{1 - v/c}} f_{source} \tag{39.10}$$

where f_{source} is the frequency of the source measured in its rest frame. Note that this relativistic Doppler shift equation, unlike the Doppler shift equation for sound, depends only on the relative speed v of the source and observer and holds for relative speeds as great as c. As you might expect, the equation predicts that $f_{obs} > f_{source}$ when the source and observer approach each other. We obtain the expression for the case in which the source and observer recede from each other by substituting negative values for v in Equation 39.10.

The most spectacular and dramatic use of the relativistic Doppler effect is the measurement of shifts in the frequency of light emitted by a moving astronomical object such as a galaxy. Light emitted by atoms and normally found in the extreme violet region of the spectrum is shifted toward the red end of the spectrum for atoms in other galaxies—indicating that these galaxies are *receding* from us. The American astronomer Edwin Hubble (1889–1953) performed extensive measurements of this *red shift* to confirm that most galaxies are moving away from us, indicating that the Universe is expanding.

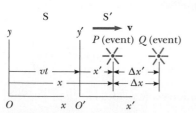

Figure 39.14 Events occur at points P and Q and are observed by an observer at rest in the S frame and another in the S′ frame, which is moving to the right with a speed v.

39.5   The Lorentz Transformation Equations

Suppose an event that occurs at some point P is reported by two observers, one at rest in a frame S and another in a frame S′ that is moving to the right with speed v as in Figure 39.14. The observer in S reports the event with space–time coordinates (x, y, z, t), while the observer in S′ reports the same event using the coordinates (x', y', z', t'). If two events occur at P and Q, Equation 39.1 predicts that $\Delta x = \Delta x'$, that is, the distance between the two points in space at which the events occur does not depend on motion of the observer. Because this is contradictory to the notion of length contraction, the Galilean transformation is not valid when v approaches the speed of light. In this section, we state the correct transformation equations that apply for all speeds in the range $0 \leq v < c$.

The equations that are valid for all speeds and enable us to transform coordinates from S to S′ are the **Lorentz transformation equations:**

$$x' = \gamma(x - vt) \qquad y' = y \qquad z' = z \qquad t' = \gamma\left(t - \frac{v}{c^2}x\right) \tag{39.11}$$

Lorentz transformation for S → S′

These transformation equations were developed by Hendrik A. Lorentz (1853–1928) in 1890 in connection with electromagnetism. However, it was Einstein who recognized their physical significance and took the bold step of interpreting them within the framework of the special theory of relativity.

Note the difference between the Galilean and Lorentz time equations. In the Galilean case, $t = t'$, but in the Lorentz case the value for t' assigned to an event by an observer O' in the S′ frame in Figure 39.14 depends both on the time t and on the coordinate x as measured by an observer O in the S frame. This is consistent with the notion that an event is characterized by four space–time coordinates (x, y, z, t). In other words, in relativity, space and time are *not* separate concepts but rather are closely interwoven with each other.

If we wish to transform coordinates in the S′ frame to coordinates in the S frame, we simply replace v by $-v$ and interchange the primed and unprimed coordinates in Equations 39.11:

$$x = \gamma(x' + vt') \qquad y = y' \qquad z = z' \qquad t = \gamma\left(t' + \frac{v}{c^2}x'\right) \tag{39.12}$$

Inverse Lorentz transformation for S′ → S

When $v \ll c$, the Lorentz transformation equations should reduce to the Galilean equations. To verify this, note that as v approaches zero, $v/c \ll 1$; thus, $\gamma \to 1$, and Equations 39.11 reduce to the Galilean space–time transformation equations:

$$x' = x - vt \qquad y' = y \qquad z' = z \qquad t' = t$$

In many situations, we would like to know the difference in coordinates between two events or the time interval between two events as seen by observers O and O'. We can accomplish this by writing the Lorentz equations in a form suitable for describing pairs of events. From Equations 39.11 and 39.12, we can express the differences between the four variables x, x', t, and t' in the form

$$\left.\begin{array}{l} \Delta x' = \gamma(\Delta x - v\,\Delta t) \\[2mm] \Delta t' = \gamma\left(\Delta t - \dfrac{v}{c^2}\,\Delta x\right) \end{array}\right\} \text{S} \to \text{S}' \tag{39.13}$$

$$\left.\begin{array}{l} \Delta x = \gamma(\Delta x' + v\,\Delta t') \\[2mm] \Delta t = \gamma\left(\Delta t' + \dfrac{v}{c^2}\,\Delta x'\right) \end{array}\right\} \text{S}' \to \text{S} \tag{39.14}$$

where $\Delta x' = x'_2 - x'_1$ and $\Delta t' = t'_2 - t'_1$ are the differences measured by observer O' and $\Delta x = x_2 - x_1$ and $\Delta t = t_2 - t_1$ are the differences measured by observer O. (We have not included the expressions for relating the y and z coordinates because they are unaffected by motion along the x direction.[5])

---

[5] Although relative motion of the two frames along the x axis does not change the y and z coordinates of an object, it does change the y and z velocity components of an object moving in either frame, as noted in Section 39.6.

Example 39.6 **Simultaneity and Time Dilation Revisited**

Use the Lorentz transformation equations in difference form to show that

(A) simultaneity is not an absolute concept and that

(B) a moving clock is measured to run more slowly than a clock that is at rest with respect to an observer.

Solution (A) Suppose that two events are simultaneous and separated in space such that $\Delta t' = 0$ and $\Delta x' \neq 0$ according to an observer O' who is moving with speed v relative to O. From the expression for Δt given in Equation 39.14, we see that in this case the time interval Δt measured by observer O is $\Delta t = \gamma v \, \Delta x'/c^2$. That is, the

time interval for the same two events as measured by O is nonzero, and so the events do not appear to be simultaneous to O.

(B) Suppose that observer O' carries a clock that he uses to measure a time interval $\Delta t'$. He finds that two events occur at the same place in his reference frame ($\Delta x' = 0$) but at different times ($\Delta t' \neq 0$). Observer O' is moving with speed v relative to O, who measures the time interval between the events to be Δt. In this situation, the expression for Δt given in Equation 39.14 becomes $\Delta t = \gamma \, \Delta t'$. This is the equation for time dilation found earlier (Eq. 39.7), where $\Delta t' = \Delta t_p$ is the proper time measured by the clock carried by observer O'. Thus, O measures the moving clock to run slow.

39.6 The Lorentz Velocity Transformation Equations

Suppose two observers in relative motion with respect to each other are both observing the motion of an object. Previously, we defined an event as occurring at an instant of time. Now, we wish to interpret the "event" as the motion of the object. We know that the Galilean velocity transformation (Eq. 39.2) is valid for low speeds. How do the observers' measurements of the velocity of the object relate to each other if the speed of the object is close to that of light? Once again S′ is our frame moving at a speed v relative to S. Suppose that an object has a velocity component u'_x measured in the S′ frame, where

$$u'_x = \frac{dx'}{dt'} \tag{39.15}$$

Using Equation 39.11, we have

$$dx' = \gamma(dx - v\,dt)$$

$$dt' = \gamma\left(dt - \frac{v}{c^2}\,dx\right)$$

Substituting these values into Equation 39.15 gives

$$u'_x = \frac{dx'}{dt'} = \frac{dx - v\,dt}{dt - \dfrac{v}{c^2}\,dx} = \frac{\dfrac{dx}{dt} - v}{1 - \dfrac{v}{c^2}\dfrac{dx}{dt}}$$

But dx/dt is just the velocity component u_x of the object measured by an observer in S, and so this expression becomes

Lorentz velocity transformation for S → S′

$$u'_x = \frac{u_x - v}{1 - \dfrac{u_x v}{c^2}} \tag{39.16}$$

If the object has velocity components along the y and z axes, the components as measured by an observer in S′ are

$$u'_y = \frac{u_y}{\gamma\left(1 - \dfrac{u_x v}{c^2}\right)} \qquad \text{and} \qquad u'_z = \frac{u_z}{\gamma\left(1 - \dfrac{u_x v}{c^2}\right)} \tag{39.17}$$

Note that u'_y and u'_z do not contain the parameter v in the numerator because the relative velocity is along the x axis.

When v is much smaller than c (the nonrelativistic case), the denominator of Equation 39.16 approaches unity, and so $u'_x \approx u_x - v$, which is the Galilean velocity transformation equation. In another extreme, when $u_x = c$, Equation 39.16 becomes

$$u'_x = \frac{c - v}{1 - \dfrac{cv}{c^2}} = \frac{c\left(1 - \dfrac{v}{c}\right)}{1 - \dfrac{v}{c}} = c$$

From this result, we see that a speed measured as c by an observer in S is also measured as c by an observer in S'—independent of the relative motion of S and S'. Note that this conclusion is consistent with Einstein's second postulate—that the speed of light must be c relative to all inertial reference frames. Furthermore, we find that the speed of an object can never be measured as larger than c. That is, the speed of light is the ultimate speed. We return to this point later.

To obtain u_x in terms of u'_x, we replace v by $-v$ in Equation 39.16 and interchange the roles of u_x and u'_x:

$$u_x = \frac{u'_x + v}{1 + \dfrac{u'_x v}{c^2}} \tag{39.18}$$

39.5 What Can the Observers Agree On?

We have seen several measurements that the two observers O and O' do *not* agree on: (1) the time interval between events that take place in the same position in one of the frames, (2) the distance between two points that remain fixed in one of their frames, (3) the velocity components of a moving particle, and (4) whether two events occurring at different locations in both frames are simultaneous or not. Note that the two observers *can* agree on (1) their relative speed of motion v with respect to each other, (2) the speed c of any ray of light, and (3) the simultaneity of two events which take place at the same position *and* time in some frame.

Quick Quiz 39.8 You are driving on a freeway at a relativistic speed. Straight ahead of you, a technician standing on the ground turns on a searchlight and a beam of light moves exactly vertically upward, as seen by the technician. As you observe the beam of light, you measure the magnitude of the vertical component of its velocity as (a) equal to c (b) greater than c (c) less than c.

Quick Quiz 39.9 Consider the situation in Quick Quiz 39.8 again. If the technician aims the searchlight directly at you instead of upward, you measure the magnitude of the horizontal component of its velocity as (a) equal to c (b) greater than c (c) less than c.

Example 39.7   Relative Velocity of Two Spacecraft

Two spacecraft A and B are moving in opposite directions, as shown in Figure 39.15. An observer on the Earth measures the speed of craft A to be $0.750c$ and the speed of craft B to be $0.850c$. Find the velocity of craft B as observed by the crew on craft A.

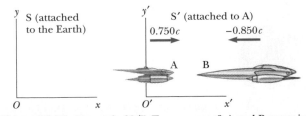

Figure 39.15 (Example 39.7) Two spacecraft A and B move in opposite directions. The speed of B relative to A is *less* than c and is obtained from the relativistic velocity transformation equation.

Solution To conceptualize this problem, we carefully identify the observers and the event. The two observers are on the Earth and on spacecraft A. The event is the motion of spacecraft B. Because the problem asks to find an observed velocity, we categorize this problem as one requiring the Lorentz velocity transformation. To analyze the problem, we note that the Earth observer makes two measurements, one of each spacecraft. We identify this observer as being at rest in the S frame. Because the velocity of spacecraft B is what we wish to measure, we identify the speed u_x as $-0.850c$. The velocity of spacecraft A is also the velocity of the observer at rest in the S' frame, which is attached to the spacecraft, relative to the observer at rest in S. Thus, $v = 0.750c$. Now we can obtain the velocity u'_x of craft B relative to craft A by using Equation 39.16:

$$u'_x = \frac{u_x - v}{1 - \dfrac{u_x v}{c^2}} = \frac{-0.850c - 0.750c}{1 - \dfrac{(-0.850c)(0.750c)}{c^2}}$$

$$= -0.977c$$

To finalize this problem, note that the negative sign indicates that craft B is moving in the negative x direction as observed by the crew on craft A. Is this consistent with your expectation from Figure 39.15? Note that the speed is less than c. That is, an object whose speed is less than c in one frame of reference must have a speed less than c in any other frame. (If the Galilean velocity transformation equation were used in

this example, we would find that $u'_x = u_x - v = -0.850c - 0.750c = -1.60c$, which is impossible. The Galilean transformation equation does not work in relativistic situations.)

What If? What if the two spacecraft pass each other? Now what is their relative speed?

Answer The calculation using Equation 39.16 involves only the velocities of the two spacecraft and does not depend on their locations. After they pass each other, they have the same velocities, so the velocity of craft B as observed by the crew on craft A is the same, $-0.977c$. The only difference after they pass is that B is receding from A whereas it was approaching A before it passed.

Example 39.8   The Speeding Motorcycle

Imagine a motorcycle moving with a speed $0.80c$ past a stationary observer, as shown in Figure 39.16. If the rider

tosses a ball in the forward direction with a speed of $0.70c$ relative to himself, what is the speed of the ball relative to the stationary observer?

Solution The speed of the motorcycle relative to the stationary observer is $v = 0.80c$. The speed of the ball in the frame of reference of the motorcyclist is $u'_x = 0.70c$. Therefore, the speed u_x of the ball relative to the stationary observer is

$$u_x = \frac{u'_x + v}{1 + \dfrac{u'_x v}{c^2}} = \frac{0.70c + 0.80c}{1 + \dfrac{(0.70c)(0.80c)}{c^2}} = 0.96c$$

Figure 39.16 (Example 39.8) A motorcyclist moves past a stationary observer with a speed of $0.80c$ and throws a ball in the direction of motion with a speed of $0.70c$ relative to himself.

Example 39.9   Relativistic Leaders of the Pack

Interactive

Two motorcycle pack leaders named David and Emily are racing at relativistic speeds along perpendicular paths, as shown in Figure 39.17. How fast does Emily recede as seen by David over his right shoulder?

Solution Figure 39.17 represents the situation as seen by a police officer at rest in frame S, who observes the

following:

David: $u_x = 0.75c$ $u_y = 0$

Emily: $u_x = 0$ $u_y = -0.90c$

To calculate Emily's speed of recession as seen by David, we take S′ to move along with David and then calculate u'_x and

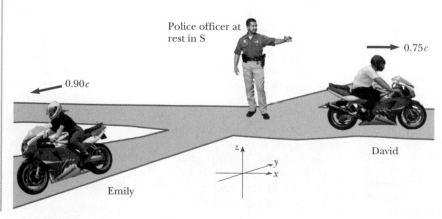

Figure 39.17 (Example 39.9) David moves to the east with a speed $0.75c$ relative to the police officer, and Emily travels south at a speed $0.90c$ relative to the officer.

u_y' for Emily using Equations 39.16 and 39.17:

$$u_x' = \frac{u_x - v}{1 - \dfrac{u_x v}{c^2}} = \frac{0 - 0.75c}{1 - \dfrac{(0)(0.75c)}{c^2}} = -0.75c$$

$$u_y' = \frac{u_y}{\gamma\left(1 - \dfrac{u_x v}{c^2}\right)} = \frac{\sqrt{1 - \dfrac{(0.75c)^2}{c^2}}\,(-0.90c)}{\left(1 - \dfrac{(0)(0.75c)}{c^2}\right)}$$

$$= -0.60c$$

Thus, the speed of Emily as observed by David is

$$u' = \sqrt{(u_x')^2 + (u_y')^2} = \sqrt{(-0.75c)^2 + (-0.60c)^2}$$

$$= \boxed{0.96c}$$

Note that this speed is less than c, as required by the special theory of relativity.

Investigate this situation with various speeds of David and Emily at the Interactive Worked Example link at http://www.pse6.com.

39.7 Relativistic Linear Momentum and the Relativistic Form of Newton's Laws

We have seen that in order to describe properly the motion of particles within the framework of the special theory of relativity, we must replace the Galilean transformation equations by the Lorentz transformation equations. Because the laws of physics must remain unchanged under the Lorentz transformation, we must generalize Newton's laws and the definitions of linear momentum and energy to conform to the Lorentz transformation equations and the principle of relativity. These generalized definitions should reduce to the classical (nonrelativistic) definitions for $v \ll c$.

First, recall that the law of conservation of linear momentum states that when two particles (or objects that can be modeled as particles) collide, the total momentum of the isolated system of the two particles remains constant. Suppose that we observe this collision in a reference frame S and confirm that the momentum of the system is conserved. Now imagine that the momenta of the particles are measured by an observer in a second reference frame S′ moving with velocity **v** relative to the first frame. Using the Lorentz velocity transformation equation and the classical definition of linear momentum, $\mathbf{p} = m\mathbf{u}$ (where **u** is the velocity of a particle), we find that linear momentum is *not* measured to be conserved by the observer in S′. However, because the laws of physics are the same in all inertial frames, linear momentum of the system must be conserved in all frames. We have a contradiction. In view of this contradiction and assuming that the Lorentz velocity transformation equation is correct, we must modify the definition of linear momentum to satisfy the following conditions:

- The linear momentum of an isolated system must be conserved in all collisions.

- The relativistic value calculated for the linear momentum **p** of a particle must approach the classical value $m\mathbf{u}$ as **u** approaches zero.

For any particle, the correct relativistic equation for linear momentum that satisfies these conditions is

$$\mathbf{p} \equiv \frac{m\mathbf{u}}{\sqrt{1 - \dfrac{u^2}{c^2}}} = \gamma m\mathbf{u} \tag{39.19}$$

Definition of relativistic linear momentum

where **u** is the velocity of the particle and m is the mass of the particle. When u is much less than c, $\gamma = (1 - u^2/c^2)^{-1/2}$ approaches unity and **p** approaches $m\mathbf{u}$. Therefore,

▲ **PITFALL PREVENTION**

39.6 Watch Out for "Relativistic Mass"

Some older treatments of relativity maintained the conservation of momentum principle at high speeds by using a model in which the mass of a particle increases with speed. You might still encounter this notion of "relativistic mass" in your outside reading, especially in older books. Be aware that this notion is no longer widely accepted and mass is considered as *invariant*, independent of speed. The mass of an object in all frames is considered to be the mass as measured by an observer at rest with respect to the object.

SPEED
LIMIT
3×10^8m/s

The speed of light is the speed limit of the Universe. It is the maximum possible speed for energy transfer and for information transfer. Any object with mass must move at a lower speed.

the relativistic equation for **p** does indeed reduce to the classical expression when u is much smaller than c.

The relativistic force **F** acting on a particle whose linear momentum is **p** is defined as

$$\mathbf{F} \equiv \frac{d\mathbf{p}}{dt} \tag{39.20}$$

where **p** is given by Equation 39.19. This expression, which is the relativistic form of Newton's second law, is reasonable because it preserves classical mechanics in the limit of low velocities and is consistent with conservation of linear momentum for an isolated system (**F** = 0) both relativistically and classically.

It is left as an end-of-chapter problem (Problem 69) to show that under relativistic conditions, the acceleration **a** of a particle decreases under the action of a constant force, in which case $a \propto (1 - u^2/c^2)^{3/2}$. From this proportionality, we see that as the particle's speed approaches c, the acceleration caused by any finite force approaches zero. Hence, it is impossible to accelerate a particle from rest to a speed $u \geq c$. This argument shows that the speed of light is the ultimate speed, as noted at the end of the preceding section.

Example 39.10   Linear Momentum of an Electron

An electron, which has a mass of 9.11×10^{-31} kg, moves with a speed of $0.750c$. Find its relativistic momentum and compare this value with the momentum calculated from the classical expression.

Solution Using Equation 39.19 with $u = 0.750c$, we have

$$p = \frac{m_e u}{\sqrt{1 - \dfrac{u^2}{c^2}}}$$

$$p = \frac{(9.11 \times 10^{-31}\ \text{kg})(0.750)(3.00 \times 10^8\ \text{m/s})}{\sqrt{1 - \dfrac{(0.750c)^2}{c^2}}}$$

$$p = \boxed{3.10 \times 10^{-22}\ \text{kg} \cdot \text{m/s}}$$

The classical expression (used incorrectly here) gives

$$p_{\text{classical}} = m_e u = 2.05 \times 10^{-22}\ \text{kg} \cdot \text{m/s}$$

Hence, the correct relativistic result is 50% greater than the classical result!

39.8   Relativistic Energy

We have seen that the definition of linear momentum requires generalization to make it compatible with Einstein's postulates. This implies that most likely the definition of kinetic energy must also be modified.

To derive the relativistic form of the work–kinetic energy theorem, let us imagine a particle moving in one dimension along the x axis. A force in the x direction causes the momentum of the particle to change according to Equation 39.20. The work done by the force F on the particle is

$$W = \int_{x_1}^{x_2} F\, dx = \int_{x_1}^{x_2} \frac{dp}{dt}\, dx \tag{39.21}$$

In order to perform this integration and find the work done on the particle and the relativistic kinetic energy as a function of u, we first evaluate dp/dt:

$$\frac{dp}{dt} = \frac{d}{dt}\frac{mu}{\sqrt{1 - \dfrac{u^2}{c^2}}} = \frac{m(du/dt)}{\left(1 - \dfrac{u^2}{c^2}\right)^{3/2}}$$

Substituting this expression for dp/dt and $dx = u\,dt$ into Equation 39.21 gives

$$W = \int_0^t \frac{m(du/dt)\,u\,dt}{\left(1 - \dfrac{u^2}{c^2}\right)^{3/2}} = m \int_0^u \frac{u}{\left(1 - \dfrac{u^2}{c^2}\right)^{3/2}}\,du$$

where we use the limits 0 and u in the integral because the integration variable has been changed from t to u. We assume that the particle is accelerated from rest to some final speed u. Evaluating the integral, we find that

$$W = \frac{mc^2}{\sqrt{1 - \dfrac{u^2}{c^2}}} - mc^2 \tag{39.22}$$

Recall from Chapter 7 that the work done by a force acting on a system consisting of a single particle equals the change in kinetic energy of the particle. Because we assumed that the initial speed of the particle is zero, we know that its initial kinetic energy is zero. We therefore conclude that the work W in Equation 39.22 is equivalent to the relativistic kinetic energy K:

$$K = \frac{mc^2}{\sqrt{1 - \dfrac{u^2}{c^2}}} - mc^2 = \gamma mc^2 - mc^2 = (\gamma - 1)mc^2 \tag{39.23}$$

Relativistic kinetic energy

This equation is routinely confirmed by experiments using high-energy particle accelerators.

At low speeds, where $u/c \ll 1$, Equation 39.23 should reduce to the classical expression $K = \frac{1}{2}mu^2$. We can check this by using the binomial expansion $(1 - \beta^2)^{-1/2} \approx 1 + \frac{1}{2}\beta^2 + \cdots$ for $\beta \ll 1$, where the higher-order powers of β are neglected in the expansion. (In treatments of relativity, β is a common symbol used to represent u/c or v/c.) In our case, $\beta = u/c$, so that

$$\gamma = \frac{1}{\sqrt{1 - \dfrac{u^2}{c^2}}} = \left(1 - \frac{u^2}{c^2}\right)^{-1/2} \approx 1 + \frac{1}{2}\frac{u^2}{c^2}$$

Substituting this into Equation 39.23 gives

$$K \approx \left[\left(1 + \frac{1}{2}\frac{u^2}{c^2}\right) - 1\right]mc^2 = \frac{1}{2}mu^2 \qquad (\text{for } u/c \ll 1)$$

which is the classical expression for kinetic energy. A graph comparing the relativistic and nonrelativistic expressions is given in Figure 39.18. In the relativistic case, the particle speed never exceeds c, regardless of the kinetic energy. The two curves are in good agreement when $u \ll c$.

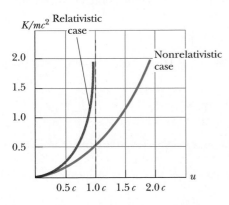

Figure 39.18 A graph comparing relativistic and nonrelativistic kinetic energy of a moving particle. The energies are plotted as a function of particle speed u. In the relativistic case, u is always less than c.

The constant term mc^2 in Equation 39.23, which is independent of the speed of the particle, is called the **rest energy** E_R of the particle:

Rest energy

$$E_R = mc^2 \tag{39.24}$$

The term γmc^2, which does depend on the particle speed, is therefore the sum of the kinetic and rest energies. We define γmc^2 to be the **total energy** E:

Total energy = kinetic energy + rest energy

$$E = K + mc^2 \tag{39.25}$$

or

Total energy of a relativistic particle

$$E = \frac{mc^2}{\sqrt{1 - \dfrac{u^2}{c^2}}} = \gamma mc^2 \tag{39.26}$$

The relationship $E = K + mc^2$ shows that **mass is a form of energy,** where c^2 in the rest energy term is just a constant conversion factor. This expression also shows that a small mass corresponds to an enormous amount of energy, a concept fundamental to nuclear and elementary-particle physics.

In many situations, the linear momentum or energy of a particle is measured rather than its speed. It is therefore useful to have an expression relating the total energy E to the relativistic linear momentum p. This is accomplished by using the expressions $E = \gamma mc^2$ and $p = \gamma mu$. By squaring these equations and subtracting, we can eliminate u (Problem 43). The result, after some algebra, is[6]

Energy–momentum relationship for a relativistic particle

$$E^2 = p^2c^2 + (mc^2)^2 \tag{39.27}$$

When the particle is at rest, $p = 0$ and so $E = E_R = mc^2$.

In Section 35.1, we introduced the concept of a particle of light, called a **photon.** For particles that have zero mass, such as photons, we set $m = 0$ in Equation 39.27 and find that

$$E = pc \tag{39.28}$$

This equation is an exact expression relating total energy and linear momentum for photons, which always travel at the speed of light (in vacuum).

Finally, note that because the mass m of a particle is independent of its motion, m must have the same value in all reference frames. For this reason, m is often called the **invariant mass.** On the other hand, because the total energy and linear momentum of a particle both depend on velocity, these quantities depend on the reference frame in which they are measured.

When we are dealing with subatomic particles, it is convenient to express their energy in electron volts (Section 25.1) because the particles are usually given this energy by acceleration through a potential difference. The conversion factor, as you recall from Equation 25.5, is

$$1\ \text{eV} = 1.60 \times 10^{-19}\ \text{J}$$

For example, the mass of an electron is 9.11×10^{-31} kg. Hence, the rest energy of the electron is

$$m_ec^2 = (9.11 \times 10^{-31}\ \text{kg})(3.00 \times 10^8\ \text{m/s})^2 = 8.20 \times 10^{-14}\ \text{J}$$
$$= (8.20 \times 10^{-14}\ \text{J})(1\ \text{eV}/1.60 \times 10^{-19}\ \text{J}) = 0.511\ \text{MeV}$$

---

[6] One way to remember this relationship is to draw a right triangle having a hypotenuse of length E and legs of lengths pc and mc^2.

Quick Quiz 39.10 The following *pairs* of energies represent the rest energy and total energy of three different particles: particle 1: E, $2E$; particle 2: E, $3E$; particle 3: $2E$, $4E$. Rank the particles, from greatest to least, according to their (a) mass; (b) kinetic energy; (c) speed.

Example 39.11   The Energy of a Speedy Electron

An electron in a television picture tube typically moves with a speed $u = 0.250c$. Find its total energy and kinetic energy in electron volts.

Solution Using the fact that the rest energy of the electron is 0.511 MeV together with Equation 39.26, we have

$$E = \frac{m_e c^2}{\sqrt{1 - \dfrac{u^2}{c^2}}} = \frac{0.511 \text{ MeV}}{\sqrt{1 - \dfrac{(0.250c)^2}{c^2}}}$$

$$= 1.03(0.511 \text{ MeV}) = \boxed{0.528 \text{ MeV}}$$

This is 3% greater than the rest energy.

We obtain the kinetic energy by subtracting the rest energy from the total energy:

$$K = E - m_e c^2 = 0.528 \text{ MeV} - 0.511 \text{ MeV}$$

$$= \boxed{0.017 \text{ MeV}}$$

Example 39.12   The Energy of a Speedy Proton

(A) Find the rest energy of a proton in electron volts.

Solution Using Equation 39.24,

$$E_R = m_p c^2 = (1.67 \times 10^{-27} \text{ kg})(3.00 \times 10^8 \text{ m/s})^2$$

$$= (1.50 \times 10^{-10} \text{ J}) \left(\frac{1.00 \text{ eV}}{1.60 \times 10^{-19} \text{ J}} \right)$$

$$= \boxed{938 \text{ MeV}}$$

(B) If the total energy of a proton is three times its rest energy, what is the speed of the proton?

Solution Equation 39.26 gives

$$E = 3m_p c^2 = \frac{m_p c^2}{\sqrt{1 - \dfrac{u^2}{c^2}}}$$

$$3 = \frac{1}{\sqrt{1 - \dfrac{u^2}{c^2}}}$$

Solving for u gives

$$\left(1 - \frac{u^2}{c^2}\right) = \frac{1}{9}$$

$$\frac{u^2}{c^2} = \frac{8}{9}$$

$$u = \frac{\sqrt{8}}{3}c = 0.943c = \boxed{2.83 \times 10^8 \text{ m/s}}$$

(C) Determine the kinetic energy of the proton in electron volts.

Solution From Equation 39.25,

$$K = E - m_p c^2 = 3m_p c^2 - m_p c^2 = 2m_p c^2$$

Because $m_p c^2 = 938$ MeV, we see that $K = \boxed{1\,880 \text{ MeV}}$.

(D) What is the proton's momentum?

Solution We can use Equation 39.27 to calculate the momentum with $E = 3m_p c^2$:

$$E^2 = p^2 c^2 + (m_p c^2)^2 = (3m_p c^2)^2$$

$$p^2 c^2 = 9(m_p c^2)^2 - (m_p c^2)^2 = 8(m_p c^2)^2$$

$$p = \sqrt{8} \, \frac{m_p c^2}{c} = \sqrt{8} \, \frac{(938 \text{ MeV})}{c} = \boxed{2\,650 \text{ MeV}/c}$$

The unit of momentum is written MeV/c, which is a common unit in particle physics.

What If? In classical physics, if the momentum of a particle doubles, the kinetic energy increases by a factor of 4. What happens to the kinetic energy of the speedy proton in this example if its momentum doubles?

Answer Based on what we have seen so far in relativity, it is likely that you would predict that its kinetic energy does not increase by a factor of 4. If the momentum doubles, the new momentum is

$$p_{\text{new}} = 2\left(\sqrt{8} \, \frac{m_p c^2}{c}\right) = 4\sqrt{2} \, \frac{m_p c^2}{c}$$

Using Equation 39.27, we find the square of the new total energy:

$$E_{\text{new}}^2 = p_{\text{new}}^2 c^2 + (m_p c^2)^2$$

$$E_{\text{new}}^2 = \left(4\sqrt{2}\ \frac{m_p c^2}{c}\right)^2 c^2 + (m_p c^2)^2 = 33(m_p c^2)^2$$

$$E_{\text{new}} = \sqrt{33}(m_p c^2) = 5.7 m_p c^2$$

Now, using Equation 39.25, we find the new kinetic energy:

$$K_{\text{new}} = E_{\text{new}} - m_p c^2 = 5.7 m_p c^2 - m_p c^2 = 4.7 m_p c^2$$

Notice that this is only 2.35 times as large as the kinetic energy we found in part (C), not four times as large. In general, the factor by which the kinetic energy increases if the momentum doubles will depend on the initial momentum, but will approach 4 as the momentum approaches zero. In this latter situation, classical physics correctly describes the situation.

39.9 Mass and Energy

Equation 39.26, $E = \gamma m c^2$, which represents the total energy of a particle, suggests that even when a particle is at rest ($\gamma = 1$) it still possesses enormous energy through its mass. The clearest experimental proof of the equivalence of mass and energy occurs in nuclear and elementary particle interactions in which the conversion of mass into kinetic energy takes place. Because of this, in relativistic situations, we cannot use the principle of conservation of energy as it was outlined in Chapters 7 and 8. We must include rest energy as another form of energy storage.

This concept is important in atomic and nuclear processes, in which the change in mass is a relatively large fraction of the initial mass. For example, in a conventional nuclear reactor, the uranium nucleus undergoes *fission*, a reaction that results in several lighter fragments having considerable kinetic energy. In the case of ^{235}U, which is used as fuel in nuclear power plants, the fragments are two lighter nuclei and a few neutrons. The total mass of the fragments is less than that of the ^{235}U by an amount Δm. The corresponding energy $\Delta m c^2$ associated with this mass difference is exactly equal to the total kinetic energy of the fragments. The kinetic energy is absorbed as the fragments move through water, raising the internal energy of the water. This internal energy is used to produce steam for the generation of electrical power.

Next, consider a basic *fusion* reaction in which two deuterium atoms combine to form one helium atom. The decrease in mass that results from the creation of one helium atom from two deuterium atoms is $\Delta m = 4.25 \times 10^{-29}$ kg. Hence, the corresponding energy that results from one fusion reaction is $\Delta m c^2 = 3.83 \times 10^{-12}$ J = 23.9 MeV. To appreciate the magnitude of this result, if only 1 g of deuterium is converted to helium, the energy released is on the order of 10^{12} J! At the year 2003 cost of electrical energy, this would be worth about \$30 000. We shall present more details of these nuclear processes in Chapter 45 of the extended version of this textbook.

Example 39.13   Mass Change in a Radioactive Decay

The ^{216}Po nucleus is unstable and exhibits radioactivity (Chapter 44). It decays to ^{212}Pb by emitting an alpha particle, which is a helium nucleus, ^{4}He. Find

(A) the mass change in this decay and

(B) the energy that this represents.

Solution Using values in Table A.3, we see that the initial and final masses are

$$m_i = m(^{216}\text{Po}) = 216.001\,905\ \text{u}$$

$$m_f = m(^{212}\text{Pb}) + m(^4\text{He}) = 211.991\,888\ \text{u} + 4.002\,603\ \text{u}$$

$$= 215.994\,491\ \text{u}$$

Thus, the mass change is

$$\Delta m = 216.001\,905\ \text{u} - 215.994\,491\ \text{u} = 0.007\,414\ \text{u}$$

$$= \boxed{1.23 \times 10^{-29}\ \text{kg}}$$

(B) The energy associated with this mass change is

$$E = \Delta m c^2 = (1.23 \times 10^{-29}\ \text{kg})(3.00 \times 10^8\ \text{m/s})^2$$

$$= 1.11 \times 10^{-12}\ \text{J} = \boxed{6.92\ \text{MeV}}$$

This energy appears as the kinetic energy of the alpha particle and the ^{212}Pb nucleus after the decay.

39.10 The General Theory of Relativity

Up to this point, we have sidestepped a curious puzzle. Mass has two seemingly different properties: a *gravitational attraction* for other masses and an *inertial* property that represents a resistance to acceleration. To designate these two attributes, we use the subscripts *g* and *i* and write

$$\text{Gravitational property} \quad F_g = m_g g$$

$$\text{Inertial property} \quad \sum F = m_i a$$

The value for the gravitational constant *G* was chosen to make the magnitudes of m_g and m_i numerically equal. Regardless of how *G* is chosen, however, the strict proportionality of m_g and m_i has been established experimentally to an extremely high degree: a few parts in 10^{12}. Thus, it appears that gravitational mass and inertial mass may indeed be exactly proportional.

But why? They seem to involve two entirely different concepts: a force of mutual gravitational attraction between two masses, and the resistance of a single mass to being accelerated. This question, which puzzled Newton and many other physicists over the years, was answered by Einstein in 1916 when he published his theory of gravitation, known as the *general theory of relativity*. Because it is a mathematically complex theory, we offer merely a hint of its elegance and insight.

In Einstein's view, the dual behavior of mass was evidence for a very intimate and basic connection between the two behaviors. He pointed out that no mechanical experiment (such as dropping an object) could distinguish between the two situations illustrated in Figures 39.19a and 39.19b. In Figure 39.19a, a person is standing in an elevator on the surface of a planet, and feels pressed into the floor, due to the gravitational force. In Figure 39.19b, the person is in an elevator in empty space accelerating upward with *a* = *g*. The person feels pressed into the floor with the same force as in Figure 39.19a. In each case, an object released by the observer undergoes a downward acceleration of magnitude *g* relative to the floor. In Figure 39.19a, the person is in an inertial frame in a gravitational field. In Figure 39.19b, the person is in a noninertial frame accelerating in gravity-free space. Einstein's claim is that these two situations are completely equivalent.

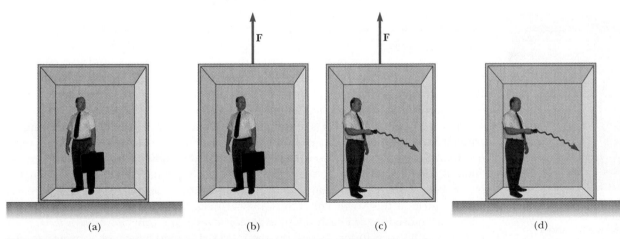

(a)	(b)	(c)	(d)

Figure 39.19 (a) The observer is at rest in a uniform gravitational field **g**, directed downward. (b) The observer is in a region where gravity is negligible, but the frame is accelerated by an external force **F** that produces an acceleration **g** directed upward. According to Einstein, the frames of reference in parts (a) and (b) are equivalent in every way. No local experiment can distinguish any difference between the two frames. (c) In the accelerating frame, a ray of light would appear to bend downward due to the acceleration of the elevator. (d) If parts (a) and (b) are truly equivalent, as Einstein proposed, then part (c) suggests that a ray of light would bend downward in a gravitational field.

Einstein carried this idea further and proposed that *no* experiment, mechanical or otherwise, could distinguish between the two cases. This extension to include all phenomena (not just mechanical ones) has interesting consequences. For example, suppose that a light pulse is sent horizontally across an elevator that is accelerating upward in empty space, as in Figure 39.19c. From the point of view of an observer in an inertial frame outside of the elevator, the light travels in a straight line while the floor of the elevator accelerates upward. According to the observer on the elevator, however, the trajectory of the light pulse bends downward as the floor of the elevator (and the observer) accelerates upward. Therefore, based on the equality of parts (a) and (b) of the figure for all phenomena, Einstein proposed that **a beam of light should also be bent downward by a gravitational field,** as in Figure 39.19d. Experiments have verified the effect, although the bending is small. A laser aimed at the horizon falls less than 1 cm after traveling 6 000 km. (No such bending is predicted in Newton's theory of gravitation.)

The two postulates of Einstein's **general theory of relativity** are

Postulates of the general theory of relativity

- All the laws of nature have the same form for observers in any frame of reference, whether accelerated or not.

- The results of experiments based on the laws of physics, as measured by an observer at rest in an inertial reference frame in a uniform gravitational field, are equivalent to those measured by an observer at rest in a uniformly accelerated reference frame in gravity-free space.

One interesting effect predicted by the general theory is that time is altered by gravity. A clock in the presence of gravity runs slower than one located where gravity is negligible. Consequently, the frequencies of radiation emitted by atoms in the presence of a strong gravitational field are *red-shifted* to lower frequencies when compared with the same emissions in the presence of a weak field. This gravitational red shift has been detected in spectral lines emitted by atoms in massive stars. It has also been verified on the Earth by comparing the frequencies of gamma rays emitted from nuclei separated vertically by about 20 m.

The second postulate suggests that a gravitational field may be "transformed away" at any point if we choose an appropriate accelerated frame of reference—a freely falling one. Einstein developed an ingenious method of describing the acceleration necessary to make the gravitational field "disappear." He specified a concept, the *curvature of space–time,* that describes the gravitational effect at every point. In fact, the curvature of space–time completely replaces Newton's gravitational theory. According to Einstein, there is no such thing as a gravitational force. Rather, the presence of a mass causes a curvature of space–time in the vicinity of the mass, and this curvature dictates the space–time path that all freely moving objects must follow. In 1979, John Wheeler summarized Einstein's general theory of relativity in a single sentence: "Space tells matter how to move and matter tells space how to curve."

As an example of the effects of curved space–time, imagine two travelers moving on parallel paths a few meters apart on the surface of the Earth and maintaining an exact northward heading along two longitude lines. As they observe each other near the equator, they will claim that their paths are exactly parallel. As they approach the North Pole, however, they notice that they are moving closer together, and they will actually meet at the North Pole. Thus, they will claim that they moved along parallel paths, but moved toward each other, *as if there were an attractive force between them.* They will make this conclusion based on their everyday experience of moving on flat surfaces. From our mental representation, however, we realize that they are walking on a curved surface, and it is the geometry of the curved surface that causes them to converge, rather than an attractive force. In a similar way, general relativity replaces the notion of forces with the movement of objects through curved space–time.

One prediction of the general theory of relativity is that a light ray passing near the Sun should be deflected in the curved space–time created by the Sun's mass. This prediction was confirmed when astronomers detected the bending of starlight near the

Courtesy of NASA

Einstein's cross. The four bright spots are images of the same galaxy that have been bent around a massive object located between the galaxy and the Earth. The massive object acts like a lens, causing the rays of light that were diverging from the distant galaxy to converge on the Earth. (If the intervening massive object had a uniform mass distribution, we would see a bright ring instead of four spots.)

Figure 39.20 Deflection of starlight passing near the Sun. Because of this effect, the Sun or some other remote object can act as a *gravitational lens*. In his general theory of relativity, Einstein calculated that starlight just grazing the Sun's surface should be deflected by an angle of 1.75 s of arc.

Sun during a total solar eclipse that occurred shortly after World War I (Fig. 39.20). When this discovery was announced, Einstein became an international celebrity.

If the concentration of mass becomes very great, as is believed to occur when a large star exhausts its nuclear fuel and collapses to a very small volume, a **black hole** may form. Here, the curvature of space–time is so extreme that, within a certain distance from the center of the black hole, all matter and light become trapped, as discussed in Section 13.7.

SUMMARY

The two basic postulates of the special theory of relativity are

- The laws of physics must be the same in all inertial reference frames.
- The speed of light in vacuum has the same value, $c = 3.00 \times 10^8$ m/s, in all inertial frames, regardless of the velocity of the observer or the velocity of the source emitting the light.

Three consequences of the special theory of relativity are

- Events that are measured to be simultaneous for one observer are not necessarily measured to be simultaneous for another observer who is in motion relative to the first.
- Clocks in motion relative to an observer are measured to run slower by a factor $\gamma = (1 - v^2/c^2)^{-1/2}$. This phenomenon is known as **time dilation.**
- The length of objects in motion are measured to be contracted in the direction of motion by a factor $1/\gamma = (1 - v^2/c^2)^{1/2}$. This phenomenon is known as **length contraction.**

To satisfy the postulates of special relativity, the Galilean transformation equations must be replaced by the **Lorentz transformation equations:**

$$x' = \gamma(x - vt) \qquad y' = y \qquad z' = z \qquad t' = \gamma\left(t - \frac{v}{c^2}x\right) \qquad (39.11)$$

where $\gamma = (1 - v^2/c^2)^{-1/2}$ and the S′ frame moves in the x direction relative to the S frame.

The relativistic form of the **velocity transformation equation** is

$$u_x' = \frac{u_x - v}{1 - \dfrac{u_x v}{c^2}} \qquad (39.16)$$

where u_x is the speed of an object as measured in the S frame and u_x' is its speed measured in the S′ frame.

Take a practice test for this chapter by clicking on the Practice Test link at http://www.pse6.com.

The relativistic expression for the **linear momentum** of a particle moving with a velocity **u** is

$$\mathbf{p} \equiv \frac{m\mathbf{u}}{\sqrt{1 - \dfrac{u^2}{c^2}}} = \gamma m\mathbf{u} \tag{39.19}$$

The relativistic expression for the **kinetic energy** of a particle is

$$K = \frac{mc^2}{\sqrt{1 - \dfrac{u^2}{c^2}}} - mc^2 = (\gamma - 1)\,mc^2 \tag{39.23}$$

The constant term mc^2 in Equation 39.23 is called the **rest energy** E_R of the particle:

$$E_R = mc^2 \tag{39.24}$$

The total energy E of a particle is given by

$$E = \frac{mc^2}{\sqrt{1 - \dfrac{u^2}{c^2}}} = \gamma mc^2 \tag{39.26}$$

The relativistic linear momentum of a particle is related to its total energy through the equation

$$E^2 = p^2 c^2 + (mc^2)^2 \tag{39.27}$$

QUESTIONS

1. What two speed measurements do two observers in relative motion always agree on?

2. A spacecraft with the shape of a sphere moves past an observer on Earth with a speed $0.5c$. What shape does the observer measure for the spacecraft as it moves past?

3. The speed of light in water is 230 Mm/s. Suppose an electron is moving through water at 250 Mm/s. Does this violate the principle of relativity?

4. Two identical clocks are synchronized. One is then put in orbit directed eastward around the Earth while the other remains on the Earth. Which clock runs slower? When the moving clock returns to the Earth, are the two still synchronized?

5. Explain why it is necessary, when defining the length of a rod, to specify that the positions of the ends of the rod are to be measured simultaneously.

6. A train is approaching you at very high speed as you stand next to the tracks. Just as an observer on the train passes you, you both begin to play the same Beethoven symphony on portable compact disc players. (a) According to you, whose CD player finishes the symphony first? (b) **What If?** According to the observer on the train, whose CD player finishes the symphony first? (c) Whose CD player really finishes the symphony first?

7. List some ways our day-to-day lives would change if the speed of light were only 50 m/s.

8. Does saying that a moving clock runs slower than a stationary one imply that something is physically unusual about the moving clock?

9. How is acceleration indicated on a space–time graph?

10. A particle is moving at a speed less than $c/2$. If the speed of the particle is doubled, what happens to its momentum?

11. Give a physical argument that shows that it is impossible to accelerate an object of mass m to the speed of light, even with a continuous force acting on it.

12. The upper limit of the speed of an electron is the speed of light c. Does that mean that the momentum of the electron has an upper limit?

13. Because mass is a measure of energy, can we conclude that the mass of a compressed spring is greater than the mass of the same spring when it is not compressed?

14. It is said that Einstein, in his teenage years, asked the question, "What would I see in a mirror if I carried it in my hands and ran at the speed of light?" How would you answer this question?

15. Some distant astronomical objects, called quasars, are receding from us at half the speed of light (or greater). What is the speed of the light we receive from these quasars?

16. Photons of light have zero mass. How is it possible that they have momentum?

17. "Newtonian mechanics correctly describes objects moving at ordinary speeds and relativistic mechanics correctly describes objects moving very fast." "Relativistic mechanics must make a smooth transition as it reduces to Newtonian mechanics in a case where the speed of an object becomes small compared to the speed of light." Argue for or against each of these two statements.

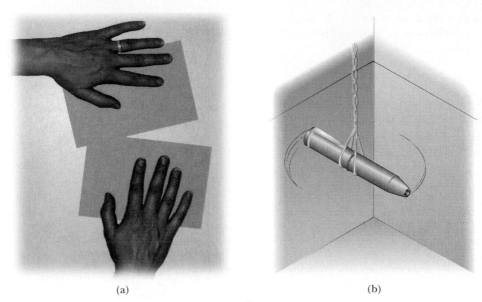

(a)   (b)

Figure Q39.18

18. Two cards have straight edges. Suppose that the top edge of one card crosses the bottom edge of another card at a small angle, as in Figure Q39.18a. A person slides the cards together at a moderately high speed. In what direction does the intersection point of the edges move? Show that it can move at a speed greater than the speed of light.

A small flashlight is suspended in a horizontal plane and set into rapid rotation. Show that the spot of light it produces on a distant screen can move across the screen at a speed greater than the speed of light. (If you use a laser pointer, as in Figure Q39.18b, make sure the direct laser light cannot enter a person's eyes.) Argue that these experiments do not invalidate the principle that no material, no energy, and no information can move faster than light moves in a vacuum.

19. Describe how the results of Example 39.7 would change if, instead of fast space vehicles, two ordinary cars were approaching each other at highway speeds.

20. Two objects are identical except that one is hotter than the other. Compare how they respond to identical forces.

21. With regard to reference frames, how does general relativity differ from special relativity?

22. Two identical clocks are in the same house, one upstairs in a bedroom, and the other downstairs in the kitchen. Which clock runs more slowly? Explain.

23. *A thought experiment.* Imagine ants living on a merry-go-round turning at relativistic speed, which is their two-dimensional world. From measurements on small circles they are thoroughly familiar with the number π. When they measure the circumference of their world, and divide it by the diameter, they expect to calculate the number $\pi = 3.141\ 59.\ .\ .\ .$ We see the merry-go-round turning at relativistic speed. From our point of view, the ants' measuring rods on the circumference are experiencing length contraction in the tangential direction; hence the ants will need some extra rods to fill that entire distance. The rods measuring the diameter, however, do not contract, because their motion is perpendicular to their lengths. As a result, the computed ratio does not agree with the number π. If you were an ant, you would say that the rest of the universe is spinning in circles, and your disk is stationary. What possible explanation can you then give for the discrepancy, in light of the general theory of relativity?

PROBLEMS

1, 2, 3 = straightforward, intermediate, challenging   ☐ = full solution available in the *Student Solutions Manual and Study Guide*

🕸 = coached solution with hints available at http://www.pse6.com   💻 = computer useful in solving problem

▨ = paired numerical and symbolic problems

Section 39.1   The Principle of Galilean Relativity

1. A 2 000-kg car moving at 20.0 m/s collides and locks together with a 1 500-kg car at rest at a stop sign. Show that momentum is conserved in a reference frame moving at 10.0 m/s in the direction of the moving car.

2. A ball is thrown at 20.0 m/s inside a boxcar moving along the tracks at 40.0 m/s. What is the speed of the ball

relative to the ground if the ball is thrown (a) forward (b) backward (c) out the side door?

3. In a laboratory frame of reference, an observer notes that Newton's second law is valid. Show that it is also valid for an observer moving at a constant speed, small compared with the speed of light, relative to the laboratory frame.

4. Show that Newton's second law is *not* valid in a reference frame moving past the laboratory frame of Problem 3 with a constant acceleration.

Section 39.2 The Michelson–Morley Experiment
Section 39.3 Einstein's Principle of Relativity
Section 39.4 Consequences of the Special Theory of Relativity

Problem 43 in Chapter 4 can be assigned with this section.

5. How fast must a meter stick be moving if its length is measured to shrink to 0.500 m?

6. At what speed does a clock move if it is measured to run at a rate that is half the rate of a clock at rest with respect to an observer?

7. An astronaut is traveling in a space vehicle that has a speed of $0.500c$ relative to the Earth. The astronaut measures her pulse rate at 75.0 beats per minute. Signals generated by the astronaut's pulse are radioed to Earth when the vehicle is moving in a direction perpendicular to the line that connects the vehicle with an observer on the Earth. (a) What pulse rate does the Earth observer measure? (b) **What If?** What would be the pulse rate if the speed of the space vehicle were increased to $0.990c$?

8. An astronomer on Earth observes a meteoroid in the southern sky approaching the Earth at a speed of $0.800c$. At the time of its discovery the meteoroid is 20.0 ly from the Earth. Calculate (a) the time interval required for the meteoroid to reach the Earth as measured by the Earth-bound astronomer, (b) this time interval as measured by a tourist on the meteoroid, and (c) the distance to the Earth as measured by the tourist.

9. An atomic clock moves at 1 000 km/h for 1.00 h as measured by an identical clock on the Earth. How many nanoseconds slow will the moving clock be compared with the Earth clock, at the end of the 1.00-h interval?

10. A muon formed high in the Earth's atmosphere travels at speed $v = 0.990c$ for a distance of 4.60 km before it decays into an electron, a neutrino, and an antineutrino $(\mu^- \rightarrow e^- + \nu + \overline{\nu})$. (a) How long does the muon live, as measured in its reference frame? (b) How far does the Earth travel, as measured in the frame of the muon?

11. A spacecraft with a proper length of 300 m takes 0.750 μs to pass an Earth observer. Determine the speed of the spacecraft as measured by the Earth observer.

12. (a) An object of proper length L_p takes a time interval Δt to pass an Earth observer. Determine the speed of the object as measured by the Earth observer. (b) A column of tanks, 300 m long, takes 75.0 s to pass a child waiting at a street corner on her way to school. Determine the speed of the armored vehicles. (c) Show that the answer to part (a) includes the answer to Problem 11 as a special case, and includes the answer to part (b) as another special case.

13. **Review problem.** In 1963 Mercury astronaut Gordon Cooper orbited the Earth 22 times. The press stated that for each orbit he aged 2 millionths of a second less than he would have if he had remained on the Earth. (a) Assuming that he was 160 km above the Earth in a circular orbit, determine the time difference between someone on the Earth and the orbiting astronaut for the 22 orbits. You will need to use the approximation $\sqrt{1 - x} \approx 1 - x/2$, for small x. (b) Did the press report accurate information? Explain.

14. For what value of v does $\gamma = 1.010\,0$? Observe that for speeds lower than this value, time dilation and length contraction are effects amounting to less than 1%.

15. A friend passes by you in a spacecraft traveling at a high speed. He tells you that his craft is 20.0 m long and that the identically constructed craft you are sitting in is 19.0 m long. According to your observations, (a) how long is your spacecraft, (b) how long is your friend's craft, and (c) what is the speed of your friend's craft?

16. The identical twins Speedo and Goslo join a migration from the Earth to Planet X. It is 20.0 ly away in a reference frame in which both planets are at rest. The twins, of the same age, depart at the same time on different spacecraft. Speedo's craft travels steadily at $0.950c$, and Goslo's at $0.750c$. Calculate the age difference between the twins after Goslo's spacecraft lands on Planet X. Which twin is the older?

17. An interstellar space probe is launched from the Earth. After a brief period of acceleration it moves with a constant velocity, with a magnitude of 70.0% of the speed of light. Its nuclear-powered batteries supply the energy to keep its data transmitter active continuously. The batteries have a lifetime of 15.0 yr as measured in a rest frame. (a) How long do the batteries on the space probe last as measured by Mission Control on the Earth? (b) How far is the probe from the Earth when its batteries fail, as measured by Mission Control? (c) How far is the probe from the Earth when its batteries fail, as measured by its built-in trip odometer? (d) For what total time interval after launch are data received from the probe by Mission Control? Note that radio waves travel at the speed of light and fill the space between the probe and the Earth at the time of battery failure.

18. **Review problem.** An alien civilization occupies a brown dwarf, nearly stationary relative to the Sun, several lightyears away. The extraterrestrials have come to love original broadcasts of *I Love Lucy*, on our television channel 2, at carrier frequency 57.0 MHz. Their line of sight to us is in the plane of the Earth's orbit. Find the difference between the highest and lowest frequencies they receive due to the Earth's orbital motion around the Sun.

19. Police radar detects the speed of a car (Fig. P39.19) as follows. Microwaves of a precisely known frequency are broadcast toward the car. The moving car reflects the microwaves with a Doppler shift. The reflected waves are received and combined with an attenuated version of the transmitted wave. Beats occur between the two microwave signals. The beat frequency is measured. (a) For an electromagnetic wave reflected back to its source from a mirror approaching at speed v, show that the reflected

wave has frequency

$$f = f_{source} \frac{c + v}{c - v}$$

where f_{source} is the source frequency. (b) When v is much less than c, the beat frequency is much smaller than the transmitted frequency. In this case use the approximation $f + f_{source} \approx 2 f_{source}$ and show that the beat frequency can be written as $f_{beat} = 2v/\lambda$. (c) What beat frequency is measured for a car speed of 30.0 m/s if the microwaves have frequency 10.0 GHz? (d) If the beat frequency measurement is accurate to ± 5 Hz, how accurate is the velocity measurement?

Figure P39.19

20. *The red shift.* A light source recedes from an observer with a speed v_{source} that is small compared with c. (a) Show that the fractional shift in the measured wavelength is given by the approximate expression

$$\frac{\Delta\lambda}{\lambda} \approx \frac{v_{source}}{c}$$

This phenomenon is known as the red shift, because the visible light is shifted toward the red. (b) Spectroscopic measurements of light at $\lambda = 397$ nm coming from a galaxy in Ursa Major reveal a red shift of 20.0 nm. What is the recessional speed of the galaxy?

21. A physicist drives through a stop light. When he is pulled over, he tells the police officer that the Doppler shift made the red light of wavelength 650 nm appear green to him, with a wavelength of 520 nm. The police officer writes out a traffic citation for speeding. How fast was the physicist traveling, according to his own testimony?

Section 39.5 The Lorentz Transformation Equations

22. Suzanne observes two light pulses to be emitted from the same location, but separated in time by 3.00 μs. Mark sees the emission of the same two pulses separated in time by 9.00 μs. (a) How fast is Mark moving relative to Suzanne? (b) According to Mark, what is the separation in space of the two pulses?

23. A moving rod is observed to have a length of 2.00 m and to be oriented at an angle of 30.0° with respect to the direction of motion, as shown in Figure P39.23. The rod has a speed of 0.995c. (a) What is the proper length of the rod? (b) What is the orientation angle in the proper frame?

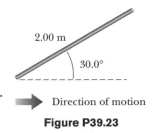

2.00 m

30.0°

Direction of motion

Figure P39.23

24. An observer in reference frame S sees two events as simultaneous. Event *A* occurs at the point (50.0 m, 0, 0) at the instant 9:00:00 Universal time, 15 January 2004. Event *B* occurs at the point (150 m, 0, 0) at the same moment. A second observer, moving past with a velocity of $0.800c\hat{\mathbf{i}}$, also observes the two events. In her reference frame S′, which event occurred first and what time interval elapsed between the events?

25. A red light flashes at position $x_R = 3.00$ m and time $t_R = 1.00 \times 10^{-9}$ s, and a blue light flashes at $x_B = 5.00$ m and $t_B = 9.00 \times 10^{-9}$ s, all measured in the S reference frame. Reference frame S′ has its origin at the same point as S at $t = t' = 0$; frame S′ moves uniformly to the right. Both flashes are observed to occur at the same place in S′. (a) Find the relative speed between S and S′. (b) Find the location of the two flashes in frame S′. (c) At what time does the red flash occur in the S′ frame?

Section 39.6 The Lorentz Velocity Transformation Equations

26. A Klingon spacecraft moves away from the Earth at a speed of 0.800c (Fig. P39.26). The starship *Enterprise* pursues at a speed of 0.900c relative to the Earth. Observers on the Earth see the *Enterprise* overtaking the Klingon craft at a relative speed of 0.100c. With what speed is the *Enterprise* overtaking the Klingon craft as seen by the crew of the *Enterprise*?

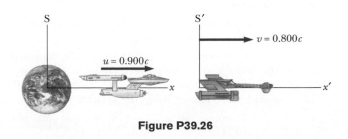

S   S′

$v = 0.800c$

$u = 0.900c$

x x'

Figure P39.26

27. 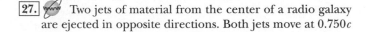 Two jets of material from the center of a radio galaxy are ejected in opposite directions. Both jets move at 0.750c

relative to the galaxy. Determine the speed of one jet relative to the other.

28. A spacecraft is launched from the surface of the Earth with a velocity of $0.600c$ at an angle of $50.0°$ above the horizontal positive x axis. Another spacecraft is moving past, with a velocity of $0.700c$ in the negative x direction. Determine the magnitude and direction of the velocity of the first spacecraft as measured by the pilot of the second spacecraft.

Section 39.7   Relativistic Linear Momentum and the Relativistic Form of Newton's Laws

29. Calculate the momentum of an electron moving with a speed of (a) $0.010\,0c$, (b) $0.500c$, and (c) $0.900c$.

30. The nonrelativistic expression for the momentum of a particle, $p = mu$, agrees with experiment if $u \ll c$. For what speed does the use of this equation give an error in the momentum of (a) 1.00% and (b) 10.0%?

31. A golf ball travels with a speed of 90.0 m/s. By what fraction does its relativistic momentum magnitude p differ from its classical value mu? That is, find the ratio $(p - mu)/mu$.

32. Show that the speed of an object having momentum of magnitude p and mass m is

$$u = \frac{c}{\sqrt{1 + (mc/p)^2}}$$

33. An unstable particle at rest breaks into two fragments of unequal mass. The mass of the first fragment is 2.50×10^{-28} kg, and that of the other is 1.67×10^{-27} kg. If the lighter fragment has a speed of $0.893c$ after the breakup, what is the speed of the heavier fragment?

Section 39.8   Relativistic Energy

34. Determine the energy required to accelerate an electron from (a) $0.500c$ to $0.900c$ and (b) $0.900c$ to $0.990c$.

35. A proton in a high-energy accelerator moves with a speed of $c/2$. Use the work–kinetic energy theorem to find the work required to increase its speed to (a) $0.750c$ and (b) $0.995c$.

36. Show that, for any object moving at less than one-tenth the speed of light, the relativistic kinetic energy agrees with the result of the classical equation $K = \frac{1}{2}mu^2$ to within less than 1%. Thus for most purposes, the classical equation is good enough to describe these objects, whose motion we call *nonrelativistic*.

37. Find the momentum of a proton in MeV/c units assuming its total energy is twice its rest energy.

38. Find the kinetic energy of a 78.0-kg spacecraft launched out of the solar system with speed 106 km/s by using (a) the classical equation $K = \frac{1}{2}mu^2$. (b) **What If?** Calculate its kinetic energy using the relativistic equation.

39. A proton moves at $0.950c$. Calculate its (a) rest energy, (b) total energy, and (c) kinetic energy.

40. A cube of steel has a volume of 1.00 cm^3 and a mass of 8.00 g when at rest on the Earth. If this cube is now given a speed $u = 0.900c$, what is its density as measured by a stationary observer? Note that relativistic density is defined as E_R/c^2V.

41. An unstable particle with a mass of 3.34×10^{-27} kg is initially at rest. The particle decays into two fragments that fly off along the x axis with velocity components $0.987c$ and $-0.868c$. Find the masses of the fragments. (*Suggestion:* Conserve both energy and momentum.)

42. An object having mass 900 kg and traveling at speed $0.850c$ collides with a stationary object having mass $1\,400$ kg. The two objects stick together. Find (a) the speed and (b) the mass of the composite object.

43. Show that the energy–momentum relationship $E^2 = p^2c^2 + (mc^2)^2$ follows from the expressions $E = \gamma mc^2$ and $p = \gamma mu$.

44. In a typical color television picture tube, the electrons are accelerated through a potential difference of $25\,000$ V. (a) What speed do the electrons have when they strike the screen? (b) What is their kinetic energy in joules?

45. Consider electrons accelerated to an energy of 20.0 GeV in the 3.00-km-long Stanford Linear Accelerator. (a) What is the γ factor for the electrons? (b) What is their speed? (c) How long does the accelerator appear to them?

46. Compact high-power lasers can produce a 2.00-J light pulse of duration 100 fs, focused to a spot 1 μm in diameter. (See Mourou and Umstader, "Extreme Light," *Scientific American*, May 2002, page 81.) The electric field in the light accelerates electrons in the target material to near the speed of light. (a) What is the average power of the laser during the pulse? (b) How many electrons can be accelerated to $0.999\,9c$ if $0.010\,0\%$ of the pulse energy is converted into energy of electron motion?

47. A pion at rest $(m_\pi = 273m_e)$ decays to a muon $(m_\mu = 207m_e)$ and an antineutrino $(m_{\bar{\nu}} \approx 0)$. The reaction is written $\pi^- \rightarrow \mu^- + \bar{\nu}$. Find the kinetic energy of the muon and the energy of the antineutrino in electron volts. (*Suggestion:* Conserve both energy and momentum.)

48. According to observer A, two objects of equal mass and moving along the x axis collide head on and stick to each other. Before the collision, this observer measures that object 1 moves to the right with a speed of $3c/4$, while object 2 moves to the left with the same speed. According to observer B, however, object 1 is initially at rest. (a) Determine the speed of object 2 as seen by observer B. (b) Compare the total initial energy of the system in the two frames of reference.

Section 39.9   Mass and Energy

49. Make an order-of-magnitude estimate of the ratio of mass increase to the original mass of a flag, as you run it up a flagpole. In your solution explain what quantities you take as data and the values you estimate or measure for them.

50. When 1.00 g of hydrogen combines with 8.00 g of oxygen, 9.00 g of water is formed. During this chemical reaction, 2.86×10^5 J of energy is released. How much mass do the constituents of this reaction lose? Is the loss of mass likely to be detectable?

51. In a nuclear power plant the fuel rods last 3 yr before they are replaced. If a plant with rated thermal power 1.00 GW

operates at 80.0% capacity for 3.00 yr, what is the loss of mass of the fuel?

52. **Review problem.** The total volume of water in the oceans is approximately 1.40×10^9 km³. The density of sea water is 1 030 kg/m³, and the specific heat of the water is 4 186 J/(kg·°C). Find the increase in mass of the oceans produced by an increase in temperature of 10.0°C.

53. The power output of the Sun is 3.77×10^{26} W. How much mass is converted to energy in the Sun each second?

54. A gamma ray (a high-energy photon) can produce an electron (e⁻) and a positron (e⁺) when it enters the electric field of a heavy nucleus: $\gamma \rightarrow e^+ + e^-$. What minimum gamma-ray energy is required to accomplish this task? (*Note:* The masses of the electron and the positron are equal.)

Section 39.10   The General Theory of Relativity

55. An Earth satellite used in the global positioning system moves in a circular orbit with period 11 h 58 min. (a) Determine the radius of its orbit. (b) Determine its speed. (c) The satellite contains an oscillator producing the principal nonmilitary GPS signal. Its frequency is 1 575.42 MHz in the reference frame of the satellite. When it is received on the Earth's surface, what is the fractional change in this frequency due to time dilation, as described by special relativity? (d) The gravitational blue shift of the frequency according to general relativity is a separate effect. The magnitude of that fractional change is given by

$$\frac{\Delta f}{f} = \frac{\Delta U_g}{mc^2}$$

where ΔU_g is the change in gravitational potential energy of an object–Earth system when the object of mass m is moved between the two points at which the signal is observed. Calculate this fractional change in frequency. (e) What is the overall fractional change in frequency? Superposed on both of these relativistic effects is a Doppler shift that is generally much larger. It can be a red shift or a blue shift, depending on the motion of a particular satellite relative to a GPS receiver (Fig. P39.55).

Figure P39.55 This global positioning system (GPS) receiver incorporates relativistically corrected time calculations in its analysis of signals it receives from orbiting satellites. This allows the unit to determine its position on the Earth's surface to within a few meters. If these corrections were not made, the location error would be about 1 km.

Additional Problems

56. An astronaut wishes to visit the Andromeda galaxy, making a one-way trip that will take 30.0 yr in the spacecraft's frame of reference. Assume that the galaxy is 2.00×10^6 ly away and that the astronaut's speed is constant. (a) How fast must he travel relative to the Earth? (b) What will be the kinetic energy of his 1 000-metric-ton spacecraft? (c) What is the cost of this energy if it is purchased at a typical consumer price for electric energy: $0.130/kWh?

57. The cosmic rays of highest energy are protons that have kinetic energy on the order of 10^{13} MeV. (a) How long would it take a proton of this energy to travel across the Milky Way galaxy, having a diameter $\sim 10^5$ ly, as measured in the proton's frame? (b) From the point of view of the proton, how many kilometers across is the galaxy?

58. An electron has a speed of $0.750c$. (a) Find the speed of a proton that has the same kinetic energy as the electron. (b) **What If?** Find the speed of a proton that has the same momentum as the electron.

59. Ted and Mary are playing a game of catch in frame S′, which is moving at $0.600c$ with respect to frame S, while Jim, at rest in frame S, watches the action (Fig. P39.59). Ted throws the ball to Mary at $0.800c$ (according to Ted) and their separation (measured in S′) is 1.80×10^{12} m. (a) According to Mary, how fast is the ball moving? (b) According to Mary, how long does it take the ball to reach her? (c) According to Jim, how far apart are Ted and Mary, and how fast is the ball moving? (d) According to Jim, how long does it take the ball to reach Mary?

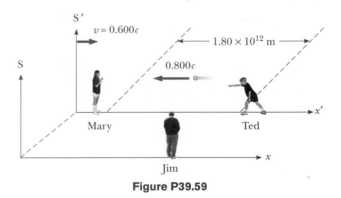

Figure P39.59

60. A rechargeable AA battery with a mass of 25.0 g can supply a power of 1.20 W for 50.0 min. (a) What is the difference in mass between a charged and an uncharged battery? (b) What fraction of the total mass is this mass difference?

61. The net nuclear fusion reaction inside the Sun can be written as $4\,^1\text{H} \rightarrow\,^4\text{He} + \Delta E$. The rest energy of each hydrogen atom is 938.78 MeV and the rest energy of the helium-4 atom is 3 728.4 MeV. Calculate the percentage of the starting mass that is transformed to other forms of energy.

62. An object disintegrates into two fragments. One of the fragments has mass 1.00 MeV/c^2 and momentum 1.75 MeV/c in the positive x direction. The other fragment has mass 1.50 MeV/c^2 and momentum 2.00 MeV/c in the positive y direction. Find (a) the mass and (b) the speed of the original object.

63. An alien spaceship traveling at $0.600c$ toward the Earth launches a landing craft with an advance guard of purchasing agents and physics teachers. The lander travels in the same direction with a speed of $0.800c$ relative to the mother ship. As observed on the Earth, the spaceship is 0.200 ly from the Earth when the lander is launched. (a) What speed do the Earth observers measure for the approaching lander? (b) What is the distance to the Earth at the time of lander launch, as observed by the aliens? (c) How long does it take the lander to reach the Earth as observed by the aliens on the mother ship? (d) If the lander has a mass of 4.00×10^5 kg, what is its kinetic energy as observed in the Earth reference frame?

64. A physics professor on the Earth gives an exam to her students, who are in a spacecraft traveling at speed v relative to the Earth. The moment the craft passes the professor, she signals the start of the exam. She wishes her students to have a time interval T_0 (spacecraft time) to complete the exam. Show that she should wait a time interval (Earth time) of

$$T = T_0 \sqrt{\frac{1 - v/c}{1 + v/c}}$$

before sending a light signal telling them to stop. (*Suggestion:* Remember that it takes some time for the second light signal to travel from the professor to the students.)

65. Spacecraft I, containing students taking a physics exam, approaches the Earth with a speed of $0.600c$ (relative to the Earth), while spacecraft II, containing professors proctoring the exam, moves at $0.280c$ (relative to the Earth) directly toward the students. If the professors stop the exam after 50.0 min have passed on their clock, how long does the exam last as measured by (a) the students (b) an observer on the Earth?

66. Energy reaches the upper atmosphere of the Earth from the Sun at the rate of 1.79×10^{17} W. If all of this energy were absorbed by the Earth and not re-emitted, how much would the mass of the Earth increase in 1.00 yr?

67. A supertrain (proper length 100 m) travels at a speed of $0.950c$ as it passes through a tunnel (proper length 50.0 m). As seen by a trackside observer, is the train ever completely within the tunnel? If so, with how much space to spare?

68. Imagine that the entire Sun collapses to a sphere of radius R_g such that the work required to remove a small mass m from the surface would be equal to its rest energy mc^2. This radius is called the *gravitational radius* for the Sun. Find R_g. (It is believed that the ultimate fate of very massive stars is to collapse beyond their gravitational radii into black holes.)

69. A particle with electric charge q moves along a straight line in a uniform electric field **E** with a speed of u. The electric force exerted on the charge is q**E**. The motion and the electric field are both in the x direction. (a) Show that the acceleration of the particle in the x direction is given by

$$a = \frac{du}{dt} = \frac{qE}{m} \left(1 - \frac{u^2}{c^2} \right)^{3/2}$$

(b) Discuss the significance of the dependence of the acceleration on the speed. (c) **What If?** If the particle

starts from rest at $x = 0$ at $t = 0$, how would you proceed to find the speed of the particle and its position at time t?

70. An observer in a coasting spacecraft moves toward a mirror at speed v relative to the reference frame labeled by S in Figure P39.70. The mirror is stationary with respect to S. A light pulse emitted by the spacecraft travels toward the mirror and is reflected back to the craft. The front of the craft is a distance d from the mirror (as measured by observers in S) at the moment the light pulse leaves the craft. What is the total travel time of the pulse as measured by observers in (a) the S frame and (b) the front of the spacecraft?

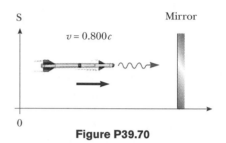

Figure P39.70

71. The creation and study of new elementary particles is an important part of contemporary physics. Especially interesting is the discovery of a very massive particle. To create a particle of mass M requires an energy Mc^2. With enough energy, an exotic particle can be created by allowing a fast moving particle of ordinary matter, such as a proton, to collide with a similar target particle. Let us consider a perfectly inelastic collision between two protons: an incident proton with mass m_p, kinetic energy K, and momentum magnitude p joins with an originally stationary target proton to form a single product particle of mass M. You might think that the creation of a new product particle, nine times more massive than in a previous experiment, would require just nine times more energy for the incident proton. Unfortunately not all of the kinetic energy of the incoming proton is available to create the product particle, since conservation of momentum requires that after the collision the system as a whole still must have some kinetic energy. Only a fraction of the energy of the incident particle is thus available to create a new particle. You will determine how the energy available for particle creation depends on the energy of the moving proton. Show that the energy available to create a product particle is given by

$$Mc^2 = 2m_p c^2 \sqrt{1 + \frac{K}{2m_p c^2}}$$

From this result, when the kinetic energy K of the incident proton is large compared to its rest energy $m_p c^2$, we see that M approaches $(2m_p K)^{1/2}/c$. Thus if the energy of the incoming proton is increased by a factor of nine, the mass you can create increases only by a factor of three. This disappointing result is the main reason that most modern accelerators, such as those at CERN (in Europe), at Fermilab (near Chicago), at SLAC (at Stanford), and at DESY (in Germany), use *colliding beams*. Here the total momentum of a pair of interacting particles can be zero. The center of mass can be at rest after the collision, so in principle all of the initial kinetic energy can be used for particle creation, according to

$$Mc^2 = 2mc^2 + K = 2mc^2\left(1 + \frac{K}{2mc^2}\right)$$

where K is the total kinetic energy of two identical colliding particles. Here if $K \gg mc^2$, we have M directly proportional to K, as we would desire. These machines are difficult to build and to operate, but they open new vistas in physics.

72. A particle of mass m moving along the x axis with a velocity component $+ u$ collides head-on and sticks to a particle of mass $m/3$ moving along the x axis with the velocity component $- u$. What is the mass M of the resulting particle?

73. A rod of length L_0 moving with a speed v along the horizontal direction makes an angle θ_0 with respect to the x' axis. (a) Show that the length of the rod as measured by a stationary observer is $L = L_0[1 - (v^2/c^2)\cos^2\theta_0]^{1/2}$. (b) Show that the angle that the rod makes with the x axis is given by $\tan\theta = \gamma\tan\theta_0$. These results show that the rod is both contracted and rotated. (Take the lower end of the rod to be at the origin of the primed coordinate system.)

74. Suppose our Sun is about to explode. In an effort to escape, we depart in a spacecraft at $v = 0.800c$ and head toward the star Tau Ceti, 12.0 ly away. When we reach the midpoint of our journey from the Earth, we see our Sun explode and, unfortunately, at the same instant we see Tau Ceti explode as well. (a) In the spacecraft's frame of reference, should we conclude that the two explosions occurred simultaneously? If not, which occurred first? (b) **What If?** In a frame of reference in which the Sun and Tau Ceti are at rest, did they explode simultaneously? If not, which exploded first?

75. A ^{57}Fe nucleus at rest emits a 14.0-keV photon. Use conservation of energy and momentum to deduce the kinetic energy of the recoiling nucleus in electron volts. (Use $Mc^2 = 8.60 \times 10^{-9}$ J for the final state of the ^{57}Fe nucleus.)

76. ▭ Prepare a graph of the relativistic kinetic energy and the classical kinetic energy, both as a function of speed, for an object with a mass of your choice. At what speed does the classical kinetic energy underestimate the experimental value by 1%? by 5%? by 50%?

Answers to Quick Quizzes

39.1 (c). While the observers' measurements differ, both are correct.

39.2 (d). The Galilean velocity transformation gives us $u_x = u_x' + v = 110$ mi/h $+ 90$ mi/h $= 200$ mi/h.

39.3 (d). The two events (the pulse leaving the flashlight and the pulse hitting the far wall) take place at different locations for both observers, so neither measures the proper time interval.

39.4 (a). The two events are the beginning and the end of the movie, both of which take place at rest with respect to the spacecraft crew. Thus, the crew measures the proper

time interval of 2 h. Any observer in motion with respect to the spacecraft, which includes the observer on Earth, will measure a longer time interval due to time dilation.

39.5 (a). If their on-duty time is based on clocks that remain on the Earth, they will have larger paychecks. A shorter time interval will have passed for the astronauts in their frame of reference than for their employer back on the Earth.

39.6 (c). Both your body and your sleeping cabin are at rest in your reference frame; thus, they will have their proper length according to you. There will be no change in measured lengths of objects, including yourself, within your spacecraft.

39.7 (d). Time dilation and length contraction depend only on the relative speed of one observer relative to another, not on whether the observers are receding or approaching each other.

39.8 (c). Because of your motion toward the source of the light, the light beam has a horizontal component of velocity as measured by you. The magnitude of the vector sum of the horizontal and vertical component vectors must be equal to c, so the magnitude of the vertical component must be smaller than c.

39.9 (a). In this case, there is only a horizontal component of the velocity of the light, and you must measure a speed of c.

39.10 (a) $m_3 > m_2 = m_1$; the rest energy of particle 3 is $2E$, while it is E for particles 1 and 2. (b) $K_3 = K_2 > K_1$; the kinetic energy is the difference between the total energy and the rest energy. The kinetic energy is $4E - 2E = 2E$ for particle 3, $3E - E = 2E$ for particle 2, and $2E - E = E$ for particle 1. (c) $u_2 > u_3 = u_1$; from Equation 39.26, $E = \gamma E_R$. Solving this for the square of the particle speed u, we find $u^2 = c^2(1 - (E_R/E)^2)$. Thus, the particle with the smallest ratio of rest energy to total energy will have the largest speed. Particles 1 and 3 have the same ratio as each other, and the ratio of particle 2 is smaller.

Table A.1

Conversion Factors

Length

	m	cm	km	in.	ft	mi
1 meter	1	10^2	10^{-3}	39.37	3.281	6.214×10^{-4}
1 centimeter	10^{-2}	1	10^{-5}	0.393 7	3.281×10^{-2}	6.214×10^{-6}
1 kilometer	10^3	10^5	1	3.937×10^4	3.281×10^3	0.621 4
1 inch	2.540×10^{-2}	2.540	2.540×10^{-5}	1	8.333×10^{-2}	1.578×10^{-5}
1 foot	0.304 8	30.48	3.048×10^{-4}	12	1	1.894×10^{-4}
1 mile	1 609	1.609×10^5	1.609	6.336×10^4	5 280	1

Mass

	kg	g	slug	u
1 kilogram	1	10^3	6.852×10^{-2}	6.024×10^{26}
1 gram	10^{-3}	1	6.852×10^{-5}	6.024×10^{23}
1 slug	14.59	1.459×10^4	1	8.789×10^{27}
1 atomic mass unit	1.660×10^{-27}	1.660×10^{-24}	1.137×10^{-28}	1

Note: 1 metric ton = 1 000 kg.

Time

	s	min	h	day	yr
1 second	1	1.667×10^{-2}	2.778×10^{-4}	1.157×10^{-5}	3.169×10^{-8}
1 minute	60	1	1.667×10^{-2}	6.994×10^{-4}	1.901×10^{-6}
1 hour	3 600	60	1	4.167×10^{-2}	1.141×10^{-4}
1 day	8.640×10^4	1 440	24	1	2.738×10^{-5}
1 year	3.156×10^7	5.259×10^5	8.766×10^3	365.2	1

Speed

	m/s	cm/s	ft/s	mi/h
1 meter per second	1	10^2	3.281	2.237
1 centimeter per second	10^{-2}	1	3.281×10^{-2}	2.237×10^{-2}
1 foot per second	0.304 8	30.48	1	0.681 8
1 mile per hour	0.447 0	44.70	1.467	1

Note: 1 mi/min = 60 mi/h = 88 ft/s.

Force

	N	lb
1 newton	1	0.224 8
1 pound	4.448	1

continued

Table A.1

Conversion Factors *continued*			

Work, Energy, Heat

	J	ft·lb	eV
1 joule	1	0.737 6	6.242×10^{18}
1 foot-pound	1.356	1	8.464×10^{18}
1 electron volt	1.602×10^{-19}	1.182×10^{-19}	1
1 calorie	4.186	3.087	2.613×10^{19}
1 British thermal unit	1.055×10^3	7.779×10^2	6.585×10^{21}
1 kilowatt hour	3.600×10^6	2.655×10^6	2.247×10^{25}

	cal	Btu	kWh
1 joule	0.238 9	9.481×10^{-4}	2.778×10^{-7}
1 foot-pound	0.323 9	1.285×10^{-3}	3.766×10^{-7}
1 electron volt	3.827×10^{-20}	1.519×10^{-22}	4.450×10^{-26}
1 calorie	1	3.968×10^{-3}	1.163×10^{-6}
1 British thermal unit	2.520×10^2	1	2.930×10^{-4}
1 kilowatt hour	8.601×10^5	3.413×10^2	1

Pressure

	Pa	atm	
1 pascal	1	9.869×10^{-6}	
1 atmosphere	1.013×10^5	1	
1 centimeter mercury[a]	1.333×10^3	1.316×10^{-2}	
1 pound per square inch	6.895×10^3	6.805×10^{-2}	
1 pound per square foot	47.88	4.725×10^{-4}	

	cm Hg	lb/in.^{2}	lb/ft^2
1 pascal	7.501×10^{-4}	1.450×10^{-4}	2.089×10^{-2}
1 atmosphere	76	14.70	2.116×10^3
1 centimeter mercury[a]	1	0.194 3	27.85
1 pound per square inch	5.171	1	144
1 pound per square foot	3.591×10^{-2}	6.944×10^{-3}	1

[a] At 0°C and at a location where the free-fall acceleration has its "standard" value, 9.806 65 m/s^2.

Table A.2

Symbols, Dimensions, and Units of Physical Quantities				
Quantity	Common Symbol	Unit[a]	Dimensions[b]	Unit in Terms of Base SI Units
Acceleration	**a**	m/s^2	L/T^2	m/s^2
Amount of substance	n	MOLE		mol
Angle	θ, ϕ	radian (rad)	1	
Angular acceleration	**α**	rad/s^2	T^{-2}	s^{-2}
Angular frequency	ω	rad/s	T^{-1}	s^{-1}
Angular momentum	**L**	kg·m^2/s	ML^2/T	kg·m^2/s
Angular velocity	**ω**	rad/s	T^{-1}	s^{-1}
Area	A	m^2	L^2	m^2
Atomic number	Z			

continued

Table A.2

Symbols, Dimensions, and Units of Physical Quantities *continued*

Quantity	Common Symbol	Unit[a]	Dimensions[b]	Unit in Terms of Base SI Units
Capacitance	C	farad (F)	Q^2T^2/ML^2	$A^2 \cdot s^4/kg \cdot m^2$
Charge	q, Q, e	coulomb (C)	Q	$A \cdot s$
Charge density				
Line	λ	C/m	Q/L	$A \cdot s/m$
Surface	σ	C/m^2	Q/L^2	$A \cdot s/m^2$
Volume	ρ	C/m^3	Q/L^3	$A \cdot s/m^3$
Conductivity	σ	$1/\Omega \cdot m$	Q^2T/ML^3	$A^2 \cdot s^3/kg \cdot m^3$
Current	I	AMPERE	Q/T	A
Current density	**J**	A/m^2	Q/T^2	A/m^2
Density	ρ	kg/m^3	M/L^3	kg/m^3
Dielectric constant	κ			
Length	ℓ, L	METER	L	m
Position	$x, y, z, \mathbf{r}$			
Displacement	$\Delta x, \Delta \mathbf{r}$			
Distance	d, h			
Electric dipole moment	**p**	C·m	QL	$A \cdot s \cdot m$
Electric field	**E**	V/m	ML/QT^2	$kg \cdot m/A \cdot s^3$
Electric flux	Φ_E	V·m	ML^3/QT^2	$kg \cdot m^3/A \cdot s^3$
Electromotive force	$\mathcal{E}$	volt (V)	ML^2/QT^2	$kg \cdot m^2/A \cdot s^3$
Energy	E, U, K	joule (J)	ML^2/T^2	$kg \cdot m^2/s^2$
Entropy	S	J/K	$ML^2/T^2 \cdot K$	$kg \cdot m^2/s^2 \cdot K$
Force	**F**	newton (N)	ML/T^2	$kg \cdot m/s^2$
Frequency	f	hertz (Hz)	T^{-1}	s^{-1}
Heat	Q	joule (J)	ML^2/T^2	$kg \cdot m^2/s^2$
Inductance	L	henry (H)	ML^2/Q^2	$kg \cdot m^2/A^2 \cdot s^2$
Magnetic dipole moment	$\boldsymbol{\mu}$	N·m/T	QL^2/T	$A \cdot m^2$
Magnetic field	**B**	tesla (T) (= Wb/m^2)	M/QT	$kg/A \cdot s^2$
Magnetic flux	Φ_B	weber (Wb)	ML^2/QT	$kg \cdot m^2/A \cdot s^2$
Mass	m, M	KILOGRAM	M	kg
Molar specific heat	C	J/mol·K		$kg \cdot m^2/s^2 \cdot mol \cdot K$
Moment of inertia	I	kg·m^2	ML^2	$kg \cdot m^2$
Momentum	**p**	kg·m/s	ML/T	$kg \cdot m/s$
Period	T	s	T	s
Permeability of free space	μ_0	N/A^2 (= H/m)	ML/Q^2T	$kg \cdot m/A^2 \cdot s^2$
Permittivity of free space	ϵ_0	C^2/N·m^2 (= F/m)	Q^2T^2/ML^3	$A^2 \cdot s^4/kg \cdot m^3$
Potential	V	volt (V) (= J/C)	ML^2/QT^2	$kg \cdot m^2/A \cdot s^3$
Power	$\mathcal{P}$	watt (W) (= J/s)	ML^2/T^3	$kg \cdot m^2/s^3$
Pressure	P	pascal (Pa) (= N/m^2)	M/LT^2	$kg/m \cdot s^2$
Resistance	R	ohm (Ω) (= V/A)	ML^2/Q^2T	$kg \cdot m^2/A^2 \cdot s^3$
Specific heat	c	J/kg·K	$L^2/T^2 \cdot K$	$m^2/s^2 \cdot K$
Speed	v	m/s	L/T	m/s
Temperature	T	KELVIN	K	K
Time	t	SECOND	T	s
Torque	τ	N·m	ML^2/T^2	$kg \cdot m^2/s^2$
Velocity	**v**	m/s	L/T	m/s
Volume	V	m^3	L^3	m^3
Wavelength	λ	m	L	m
Work	W	joule (J) (= N·m)	ML^2/T^2	$kg \cdot m^2/s^2$

[a] The base SI units are given in uppercase letters.

[b] The symbols M, L, T, and Q denote mass, length, time, and charge, respectively.

Table A.3

Table of Atomic Masses[a]

Atomic Number Z	Element	Symbol	Chemical Atomic Mass (u)	Mass Number (*Indicates Radioactive) A	Atomic Mass (u)	Percent Abundance	Half-Life (If Radioactive) $T_{1/2}$
0	(Neutron)	n		1*	1.008 665		10.4 min
1	Hydrogen	H	1.007 94	1	1.007 825	99.988 5	
	Deuterium	D		2	2.014 102	0.011 5	
	Tritium	T		3*	3.016 049		12.33 yr
2	Helium	He	4.002 602	3	3.016 029	0.000 137	
				4	4.002 603	99.999 863	
				6*	6.018 888		0.81 s
3	Lithium	Li	6.941	6	6.015 122	7.5	
				7	7.016 004	92.5	
				8*	8.022 487		0.84 s
4	Beryllium	Be	9.012 182	7*	7.016 929		53.3 days
				9	9.012 182	100	
				10*	10.013 534		1.5×10^6 yr
5	Boron	B	10.811	10	10.012 937	19.9	
				11	11.009 306	80.1	
				12*	12.014 352		0.020 2 s
6	Carbon	C	12.010 7	10*	10.016 853		19.3 s
				11*	11.011 434		20.4 min
				12	12.000 000	98.93	
				13	13.003 355	1.07	
				14*	14.003 242		5 730 yr
				15*	15.010 599		2.45 s
7	Nitrogen	N	14.006 7	12*	12.018 613		0.011 0 s
				13*	13.005 739		9.96 min
				14	14.003 074	99.632	
				15	15.000 109	0.368	
				16*	16.006 101		7.13 s
				17*	17.008 450		4.17 s
8	Oxygen	O	15.999 4	14*	14.008 595		70.6 s
				15*	15.003 065		122 s
				16	15.994 915	99.757	
				17	16.999 132	0.038	
				18	17.999 160	0.205	
				19*	19.003 579		26.9 s
9	Fluorine	F	18.998 403 2	17*	17.002 095		64.5 s
				18*	18.000 938		109.8 min
				19	18.998 403	100	
				20*	19.999 981		11.0 s
				21*	20.999 949		4.2 s
10	Neon	Ne	20.179 7	18*	18.005 697		1.67 s
				19*	19.001 880		17.2 s
				20	19.992 440	90.48	
				21	20.993 847	0.27	
				22	21.991 385	9.25	
				23*	22.994 467		37.2 s
11	Sodium	Na	22.989 77	21*	20.997 655		22.5 s
				22*	21.994 437		2.61 yr

continued

Table A.3

Atomic Number Z	Element	Symbol	Chemical Atomic Mass (u)	Mass Number (*Indicates Radioactive) A	Atomic Mass (u)	Percent Abundance	Half-Life (If Radioactive) $T_{1/2}$
(11)	Sodium			23	22.989 770	100	
				24*	23.990 963		14.96 h
12	Magnesium	Mg	24.305 0	23*	22.994 125		11.3 s
				24	23.985 042	78.99	
				25	24.985 837	10.00	
				26	25.982 593	11.01	
				27*	26.984 341		9.46 min
13	Aluminum	Al	26.981 538	26*	25.986 892		7.4×10^5 yr
				27	26.981 539	100	
				28*	27.981 910		2.24 min
14	Silicon	Si	28.085 5	28	27.976 926	92.229 7	
				29	28.976 495	4.683 2	
				30	29.973 770	3.087 2	
				31*	30.975 363		2.62 h
				32*	31.974 148		172 yr
15	Phosphorus	P	30.973 761	30*	29.978 314		2.50 min
				31	30.973 762	100	
				32*	31.973 907		14.26 days
				33*	32.971 725		25.3 days
16	Sulfur	S	32.066	32	31.972 071	94.93	
				33	32.971 458	0.76	
				34	33.967 869	4.29	
				35*	34.969 032		87.5 days
				36	35.967 081	0.02	
17	Chlorine	Cl	35.452 7	35	34.968 853	75.78	
				36*	35.968 307		3.0×10^5 yr
				37	36.965 903	24.22	
18	Argon	Ar	39.948	36	35.967 546	0.336 5	
				37*	36.966 776		35.04 days
				38	37.962 732	0.063 2	
				39*	38.964 313		269 yr
				40	39.962 383	99.600 3	
				42*	41.963 046		33 yr
19	Potassium	K	39.098 3	39	38.963 707	93.258 1	
				40*	39.963 999	0.011 7	1.28×10^9 yr
				41	40.961 826	6.730 2	
20	Calcium	Ca	40.078	40	39.962 591	96.941	
				41*	40.962 278		1.0×10^5 yr
				42	41.958 618	0.647	
				43	42.958 767	0.135	
				44	43.955 481	2.086	
				46	45.953 693	0.004	
				48	47.952 534	0.187	
21	Scandium	Sc	44.955 910	41*	40.969 251		0.596 s
				45	44.955 910	100	
22	Titanium	Ti	47.867	44*	43.959 690		49 yr
				46	45.952 630	8.25	

continued

Table A.3

Atomic Number Z	Element	Symbol	Chemical Atomic Mass (u)	Mass Number (*Indicates Radioactive) A	Atomic Mass (u)	Percent Abundance	Half-Life (If Radioactive) $T_{1/2}$
(22)	Titanium			47	46.951 764	7.44	
				48	47.947 947	73.72	
				49	48.947 871	5.41	
				50	49.944 792	5.18	
23	Vanadium	V	50.941 5	48*	47.952 254		15.97 days
				50*	49.947 163	0.250	1.5×10^{17} yr
				51	50.943 964	99.750	
24	Chromium	Cr	51.996 1	48*	47.954 036		21.6 h
				50	49.946 050	4.345	
				52	51.940 512	83.789	
				53	52.940 654	9.501	
				54	53.938 885	2.365	
25	Manganese	Mn	54.938 049	54*	53.940 363		312.1 days
				55	54.938 050	100	
26	Iron	Fe	55.845	54	53.939 615	5.845	
				55*	54.938 298		2.7 yr
				56	55.934 942	91.754	
				57	56.935 399	2.119	
				58	57.933 280	0.282	
				60*	59.934 077		1.5×10^{6} yr
27	Cobalt	Co	58.933 200	59	58.933 200	100	
				60*	59.933 822		5.27 yr
28	Nickel	Ni	58.693 4	58	57.935 348	68.076 9	
				59*	58.934 351		7.5×10^{4} yr
				60	59.930 790	26.223 1	
				61	60.931 060	1.139 9	
				62	61.928 349	3.634 5	
				63*	62.929 673		100 yr
				64	63.927 970	0.925 6	
29	Copper	Cu	63.546	63	62.929 601	69.17	
				65	64.927 794	30.83	
30	Zinc	Zn	65.39	64	63.929 147	48.63	
				66	65.926 037	27.90	
				67	66.927 131	4.10	
				68	67.924 848	18.75	
				70	69.925 325	0.62	
31	Gallium	Ga	69.723	69	68.925 581	60.108	
				71	70.924 705	39.892	
32	Germanium	Ge	72.61	70	69.924 250	20.84	
				72	71.922 076	27.54	
				73	72.923 459	7.73	
				74	73.921 178	36.28	
				76	75.921 403	7.61	
33	Arsenic	As	74.921 60	75	74.921 596	100	
34	Selenium	Se	78.96	74	73.922 477	0.89	
				76	75.919 214	9.37	
				77	76.919 915	7.63	

continued

Table A.3

Atomic Number Z	Element	Symbol	Chemical Atomic Mass (u)	Mass Number (*Indicates Radioactive) A	Atomic Mass (u)	Percent Abundance	Half-Life (If Radioactive) $T_{1/2}$
(34)	Selenium			78	77.917 310	23.77	
				79*	78.918 500		$\leq 6.5 \times 10^4$ yr
				80	79.916 522	49.61	
				82*	81.916 700	8.73	1.4×10^{20} yr
35	Bromine	Br	79.904	79	78.918 338	50.69	
				81	80.916 291	49.31	
36	Krypton	Kr	83.80	78	77.920 386	0.35	
				80	79.916 378	2.28	
				81*	80.916 592		2.1×10^5 yr
				82	81.913 485	11.58	
				83	82.914 136	11.49	
				84	83.911 507	57.00	
				85*	84.912 527		10.76 yr
				86	85.910 610	17.30	
37	Rubidium	Rb	85.467 8	85	84.911 789	72.17	
				87*	86.909 184	27.83	4.75×10^{10} yr
38	Strontium	Sr	87.62	84	83.913 425	0.56	
				86	85.909 262	9.86	
				87	86.908 880	7.00	
				88	87.905 614	82.58	
				90*	89.907 738		29.1 yr
39	Yttrium	Y	88.905 85	89	88.905 848	100	
40	Zirconium	Zr	91.224	90	89.904 704	51.45	
				91	90.905 645	11.22	
				92	91.905 040	17.15	
				93*	92.906 476		1.5×10^6 yr
				94	93.906 316	17.38	
				96	95.908 276	2.80	
41	Niobium	Nb	92.906 38	91*	90.906 990		6.8×10^2 yr
				92*	91.907 193		3.5×10^7 yr
				93	92.906 378	100	
				94*	93.907 284		2×10^4 yr
42	Molybdenum	Mo	95.94	92	91.906 810	14.84	
				93*	92.906 812		3.5×10^3 yr
				94	93.905 088	9.25	
				95	94.905 842	15.92	
				96	95.904 679	16.68	
				97	96.906 021	9.55	
				98	97.905 408	24.13	
				100	99.907 477	9.63	
43	Technetium	Tc		97*	96.906 365		2.6×10^6 yr
				98*	97.907 216		4.2×10^6 yr
				99*	98.906 255		2.1×10^5 yr
44	Ruthenium	Ru	101.07	96	95.907 598	5.54	
				98	97.905 287	1.87	
				99	98.905 939	12.76	
				100	99.904 220	12.60	

continued

Table A.3

Table of Atomic Masses[a] *continued*

Atomic Number Z	Element	Symbol	Chemical Atomic Mass (u)	Mass Number (*Indicates Radioactive) A	Atomic Mass (u)	Percent Abundance	Half-Life (If Radioactive) $T_{1/2}$
(44)	Ruthenium			101	100.905 582	17.06	
				102	101.904 350	31.55	
				104	103.905 430	18.62	
45	Rhodium	Rh	102.905 50	103	102.905 504	100	
46	Palladium	Pd	106.42	102	101.905 608	1.02	
				104	103.904 035	11.14	
				105	104.905 084	22.33	
				106	105.903 483	27.33	
				107*	106.905 128		6.5×10^6 yr
				108	107.903 894	26.46	
				110	109.905 152	11.72	
47	Silver	Ag	107.868 2	107	106.905 093	51.839	
				109	108.904 756	48.161	
48	Cadmium	Cd	112.411	106	105.906 458	1.25	
				108	107.904 183	0.89	
				109*	108.904 986		462 days
				110	109.903 006	12.49	
				111	110.904 182	12.80	
				112	111.902 757	24.13	
				113*	112.904 401	12.22	9.3×10^{15} yr
				114	113.903 358	28.73	
				116	115.904 755	7.49	
49	Indium	In	114.818	113	112.904 061	4.29	
				115*	114.903 878	95.71	4.4×10^{14} yr
50	Tin	Sn	118.710	112	111.904 821	0.97	
				114	113.902 782	0.66	
				115	114.903 346	0.34	
				116	115.901 744	14.54	
				117	116.902 954	7.68	
				118	117.901 606	24.22	
				119	118.903 309	8.59	
				120	119.902 197	32.58	
				121*	120.904 237		55 yr
				122	121.903 440	4.63	
				124	123.905 275	5.79	
51	Antimony	Sb	121.760	121	120.903 818	57.21	
				123	122.904 216	42.79	
				125*	124.905 248		2.7 yr
52	Tellurium	Te	127.60	120	119.904 020	0.09	
				122	121.903 047	2.55	
				123*	122.904 273	0.89	1.3×10^{13} yr
				124	123.902 820	4.74	
				125	124.904 425	7.07	
				126	125.903 306	18.84	
				128*	127.904 461	31.74	$>8 \times 10^{24}$ yr
				130*	129.906 223	34.08	$\leq 1.25 \times 10^{21}$ yr

continued

Table A.3

Table of Atomic Masses[a] *continued*

Atomic Number Z	Element	Symbol	Chemical Atomic Mass (u)	Mass Number (*Indicates Radioactive) A	Atomic Mass (u)	Percent Abundance	Half-Life (If Radioactive) $T_{1/2}$
53	Iodine	I	126.904 47	127	126.904 468	100	
				129*	128.904 988		1.6×10^7 yr
54	Xenon	Xe	131.29	124	123.905 896	0.09	
				126	125.904 269	0.09	
				128	127.903 530	1.92	
				129	128.904 780	26.44	
				130	129.903 508	4.08	
				131	130.905 082	21.18	
				132	131.904 145	26.89	
				134	133.905 394	10.44	
				136*	135.907 220	8.87	$\geq 2.36 \times 10^{21}$ yr
55	Cesium	Cs	132.905 45	133	132.905 447	100	
				134*	133.906 713		2.1 yr
				135*	134.905 972		2×10^6 yr
				137*	136.907 074		30 yr
56	Barium	Ba	137.327	130	129.906 310	0.106	
				132	131.905 056	0.101	
				133*	132.906 002		10.5 yr
				134	133.904 503	2.417	
				135	134.905 683	6.592	
				136	135.904 570	7.854	
				137	136.905 821	11.232	
				138	137.905 241	71.698	
57	Lanthanum	La	138.905 5	137*	136.906 466		6×10^4 yr
				138*	137.907 107	0.090	1.05×10^{11} yr
				139	138.906 349	99.910	
58	Cerium	Ce	140.116	136	135.907 144	0.185	
				138	137.905 986	0.251	
				140	139.905 434	88.450	
				142*	141.909 240	11.114	$>5 \times 10^{16}$ yr
59	Praseodymium	Pr	140.907 65	141	140.907 648	100	
60	Neodymium	Nd	144.24	142	141.907 719	27.2	
				143	142.909 810	12.2	
				144*	143.910 083	23.8	2.3×10^{15} yr
				145	144.912 569	8.3	
				146	145.913 112	17.2	
				148	147.916 888	5.7	
				150*	149.920 887	5.6	$>1 \times 10^{18}$ yr
61	Promethium	Pm		143*	142.910 928		265 days
				145*	144.912 744		17.7 yr
				146*	145.914 692		5.5 yr
				147*	146.915 134		2.623 yr
62	Samarium	Sm	150.36	144	143.911 995	3.07	
				146*	145.913 037		1.0×10^8 yr
				147*	146.914 893	14.99	1.06×10^{11} yr
				148*	147.914 818	11.24	7×10^{15} yr

continued

Table A.3

Table of Atomic Masses [a] *continued*

Atomic Number Z	Element	Symbol	Chemical Atomic Mass (u)	Mass Number (*Indicates Radioactive) A	Atomic Mass (u)	Percent Abundance	Half-Life (If Radioactive) $T_{1/2}$
(62)	Samarium			149*	148.917 180	13.82	$> 2 \times 10^{15}$ yr
				150	149.917 272	7.38	
				151*	150.919 928		90 yr
				152	151.919 728	26.75	
				154	153.922 205	22.75	
63	Europium	Eu	151.964	151	150.919 846	47.81	
				152*	151.921 740		13.5 yr
				153	152.921 226	52.19	
				154*	153.922 975		8.59 yr
				155*	154.922 889		4.7 yr
64	Gadolinium	Gd	157.25	148*	147.918 110		75 yr
				150*	149.918 656		1.8×10^{6} yr
				152*	151.919 788	0.20	1.1×10^{14} yr
				154	153.920 862	2.18	
				155	154.922 619	14.80	
				156	155.922 120	20.47	
				157	156.923 957	15.65	
				158	157.924 100	24.84	
				160	159.927 051	21.86	
65	Terbium	Tb	158.925 34	159	158.925 343	100	
66	Dysprosium	Dy	162.50	156	155.924 278	0.06	
				158	157.924 405	0.10	
				160	159.925 194	2.34	
				161	160.926 930	18.91	
				162	161.926 795	25.51	
				163	162.928 728	24.90	
				164	163.929 171	28.18	
67	Holmium	Ho	164.930 32	165	164.930 320	100	
				166*	165.932 281		1.2×10^{3} yr
68	Erbium	Er	167.6	162	161.928 775	0.14	
				164	163.929 197	1.61	
				166	165.930 290	33.61	
				167	166.932 045	22.93	
				168	167.932 368	26.78	
				170	169.935 460	14.93	
69	Thulium	Tm	168.934 21	169	168.934 211	100	
				171*	170.936 426		1.92 yr
70	Ytterbium	Yb	173.04	168	167.933 894	0.13	
				170	169.934 759	3.04	
				171	170.936 322	14.28	
				172	171.936 378	21.83	
				173	172.938 207	16.13	
				174	173.938 858	31.83	
				176	175.942 568	12.76	
71	Lutecium	Lu	174.967	173*	172.938 927		1.37 yr
				175	174.940 768	97.41	
				176*	175.942 682	2.59	3.78×10^{10} yr

continued

Table A.3

| Table of Atomic Masses[a] *continued* | | | | | | | |

Atomic Number Z	Element	Symbol	Chemical Atomic Mass (u)	Mass Number (*Indicates Radioactive) A	Atomic Mass (u)	Percent Abundance	Half-Life (If Radioactive) $T_{1/2}$
72	Hafnium	Hf	178.49	174*	173.940 040	0.16	2.0×10^{15} yr
				176	175.941 402	5.26	
				177	176.943 220	18.60	
				178	177.943 698	27.28	
				179	178.945 815	13.62	
				180	179.946 549	35.08	
73	Tantalum	Ta	180.947 9	180*	179.947 466	0.012	8.152 h
				181	180.947 996	99.988	
74	Tungsten (Wolfram)	W	183.84	180	179.946 706	0.12	
				182	181.948 206	26.50	
				183	182.950 224	14.31	
				184*	183.950 933	30.64	$>3 \times 10^{17}$ yr
				186	185.954 362	28.43	
75	Rhenium	Re	186.207	185	184.952 956	37.40	
				187*	186.955 751	62.60	4.4×10^{10} yr
76	Osmium	Os	190.23	184	183.952 491	0.02	
				186*	185.953 838	1.59	2.0×10^{15} yr
				187	186.955 748	1.96	
				188	187.955 836	13.24	
				189	188.958 145	16.15	
				190	189.958 445	26.26	
				192	191.961 479	40.78	
				194*	193.965 179		6.0 yr
77	Iridium	Ir	192.217	191	190.960 591	37.3	
				193	192.962 924	62.7	
78	Platinum	Pt	195.078	190*	189.959 930	0.014	6.5×10^{11} yr
				192	191.961 035	0.782	
				194	193.962 664	32.967	
				195	194.964 774	33.832	
				196	195.964 935	25.242	
				198	197.967 876	7.163	
79	Gold	Au	196.966 55	197	196.966 552	100	
80	Mercury	Hg	200.59	196	195.965 815	0.15	
				198	197.966 752	9.97	
				199	198.968 262	16.87	
				200	199.968 309	23.10	
				201	200.970 285	13.18	
				202	201.970 626	29.86	
				204	203.973 476	6.87	
81	Thallium	Tl	204.383 3	203	202.972 329	29.524	
				204*	203.973 849		3.78 yr
				205	204.974 412	70.476	
		(Ra E″)		206*	205.976 095		4.2 min
		(Ac C″)		207*	206.977 408		4.77 min
		(Th C″)		208*	207.982 005		3.053 min
		(Ra C″)		210*	209.990 066		1.30 min

continued

Table A.3

Table of Atomic Masses[a] *continued*

Atomic Number Z	Element	Symbol	Chemical Atomic Mass (u)	Mass Number (*Indicates Radioactive) A	Atomic Mass (u)	Percent Abundance	Half-Life (If Radioactive) $T_{1/2}$
82	Lead	Pb	207.2	202*	201.972 144		5×10^4 yr
				204*	203.973 029	1.4	$\geq 1.4 \times 10^{17}$ yr
				205*	204.974 467		1.5×10^7 yr
				206	205.974 449	24.1	
				207	206.975 881	22.1	
				208	207.976 636	52.4	
		(Ra D)		210*	209.984 173		22.3 yr
		(Ac B)		211*	210.988 732		36.1 min
		(Th B)		212*	211.991 888		10.64 h
		(Ra B)		214*	213.999 798		26.8 min
83	Bismuth	Bi	208.980 38	207*	206.978 455		32.2 yr
				208*	207.979 727		3.7×10^5 yr
				209	208.980 383	100	
		(Ra E)		210*	209.984 105		5.01 days
		(Th C)		211*	210.987 258		2.14 min
				212*	211.991 272		60.6 min
		(Ra C)		214*	213.998 699		19.9 min
				215*	215.001 832		7.4 min
84	Polonium	Po		209*	208.982 416		102 yr
		(Ra F)		210*	209.982 857		138.38 days
		(Ac C')		211*	210.986 637		0.52 s
		(Th C')		212*	211.988 852		0.30 μs
		(Ra C')		214*	213.995 186		164 μs
		(Ac A)		215*	214.999 415		0.001 8 s
		(Th A)		216*	216.001 905		0.145 s
		(Ra A)		218*	218.008 966		3.10 min
85	Astatine	At		215*	214.998 641		≈ 100 μs
				218*	218.008 682		1.6 s
				219*	219.011 297		0.9 min
86	Radon	Rn					
		(An)		219*	219.009 475		3.96 s
		(Tn)		220*	220.011 384		55.6 s
		(Rn)		222*	222.017 570		3.823 days
87	Francium	Fr					
		(Ac K)		223*	223.019 731		22 min
88	Radium	Ra					
		(Ac X)		223*	223.018 497		11.43 days
		(Th X)		224*	224.020 202		3.66 days
		(Ra)		226*	226.025 403		1 600 yr
		(Ms Th$_1$)		228*	228.031 064		5.75 yr
89	Actinium	Ac		227*	227.027 747		21.77 yr
		(Ms Th$_2$)		228*	228.031 015		6.15 h
90	Thorium	Th	232.038 1				
		(Rd Ac)		227*	227.027 699		18.72 days
		(Rd Th)		228*	228.028 731		1.913 yr
				229*	229.031 755		7 300 yr
		(Io)		230*	230.033 127		75.000 yr

continued

Table A.3

Table of Atomic Masses[a] *continued*						
Atomic Number Z	Element	Symbol	Chemical Atomic Mass (u)	Mass Number (*Indicates Radioactive) A	Atomic Mass (u)	Percent Abundance	Half-Life (If Radioactive) $T_{1/2}$
(90)	Thorium	(UY)		231*	231.036 297		25.52 h
		(Th)		232*	232.038 050	100	1.40×10^{10} yr
		(UX$_1$)		234*	234.043 596		24.1 days
91	Protactinium	Pa	231.035 88	231*	231.035 879		32.760 yr
		(Uz)		234*	234.043 302		6.7 h
92	Uranium	U	238.028 9	232*	232.037 146		69 yr
				233*	233.039 628		1.59×10^5 yr
				234*	234.040 946	0.005 5	2.45×10^5 yr
		(Ac U)		235*	235.043 923	0.720 0	7.04×10^8 yr
				236*	236.045 562		2.34×10^7 yr
		(UI)		238*	238.050 783	99.274 5	4.47×10^9 yr
93	Neptunium	Np		235*	235.044 056		396 days
				236*	236.046 560		1.15×10^5 yr
				237*	237.048 167		2.14×10^6 yr
94	Plutonium	Pu		236*	236.046 048		2.87 yr
				238*	238.049 553		87.7 yr
				239*	239.052 156		2.412×10^4 yr
				240*	240.053 808		6 560 yr
				241*	241.056 845		14.4 yr
				242*	242.058 737		3.73×10^6 yr
				244*	244.064 198		8.1×10^7 yr

a   Chemical atomic masses are from T. B. Coplen, "Atomic Weights of the Elements 1999," a technical report to the International Union of Pure and Applied Chemistry, and published in *Pure and Applied Chemistry*, 73(4), 667–683, 2001. Atomic masses of the isotopes are from G. Audi and A. H. Wapstra, "The 1995 Update to the Atomic Mass Evaluation," *Nuclear Physics*, A595, vol. 4, 409–480, December 25, 1995. Percent abundance values are from K. J. R. Rosman and P. D. P. Taylor, "Isotopic Compositions of the Elements 1999", a technical report to the International Union of Pure and Applied Chemistry, and published in *Pure and Applied Chemistry*, 70(1), 217–236, 1998.

Appendix B • Mathematics Review

These appendices in mathematics are intended as a brief review of operations and methods. Early in this course, you should be totally familiar with basic algebraic techniques, analytic geometry, and trigonometry. The appendices on differential and integral calculus are more detailed and are intended for those students who have difficulty applying calculus concepts to physical situations.

B.1 Scientific Notation

Many quantities that scientists deal with often have very large or very small values. For example, the speed of light is about 300 000 000 m/s, and the ink required to make the dot over an i in this textbook has a mass of about 0.000 000 001 kg. Obviously, it is very cumbersome to read, write, and keep track of numbers such as these. We avoid this problem by using a method dealing with powers of the number 10:

$$10^0 = 1$$

$$10^1 = 10$$

$$10^2 = 10 \times 10 = 100$$

$$10^3 = 10 \times 10 \times 10 = 1000$$

$$10^4 = 10 \times 10 \times 10 \times 10 = 10\ 000$$

$$10^5 = 10 \times 10 \times 10 \times 10 \times 10 = 100\ 000$$

and so on. The number of zeros corresponds to the power to which 10 is raised, called the **exponent** of 10. For example, the speed of light, 300 000 000 m/s, can be expressed as 3×10^8 m/s.

In this method, some representative numbers smaller than unity are

$$10^{-1} = \frac{1}{10} = 0.1$$

$$10^{-2} = \frac{1}{10 \times 10} = 0.01$$

$$10^{-3} = \frac{1}{10 \times 10 \times 10} = 0.001$$

$$10^{-4} = \frac{1}{10 \times 10 \times 10 \times 10} = 0.000\ 1$$

$$10^{-5} = \frac{1}{10 \times 10 \times 10 \times 10 \times 10} = 0.000\ 01$$

In these cases, the number of places the decimal point is to the left of the digit 1 equals the value of the (negative) exponent. Numbers expressed as some power of 10 multiplied by another number between 1 and 10 are said to be in **scientific notation.** For example, the scientific notation for 5 943 000 000 is 5.943×10^9 and that for 0.000 083 2 is 8.32×10^{-5}.

When numbers expressed in scientific notation are being multiplied, the following general rule is very useful:

$$10^n \times 10^m = 10^{n+m} \tag{B.1}$$

where n and m can be *any* numbers (not necessarily integers). For example, $10^2 \times 10^5 = 10^7$. The rule also applies if one of the exponents is negative: $10^3 \times 10^{-8} = 10^{-5}$.

When dividing numbers expressed in scientific notation, note that

$$\frac{10^n}{10^m} = 10^n \times 10^{-m} = 10^{n-m} \qquad\qquad \text{(B.2)}$$

Exercises

With help from the above rules, verify the answers to the following:

1. $86\ 400 = 8.64 \times 10^4$
2. $9\ 816\ 762.5 = 9.816\ 762\ 5 \times 10^6$
3. $0.000\ 000\ 039\ 8 = 3.98 \times 10^{-8}$
4. $(4 \times 10^8)(9 \times 10^9) = 3.6 \times 10^{18}$
5. $(3 \times 10^7)(6 \times 10^{-12}) = 1.8 \times 10^{-4}$
6. $\dfrac{75 \times 10^{-11}}{5 \times 10^{-3}} = 1.5 \times 10^{-7}$
7. $\dfrac{(3 \times 10^6)(8 \times 10^{-2})}{(2 \times 10^{17})(6 \times 10^5)} = 2 \times 10^{-18}$

B.2 Algebra

Some Basic Rules

When algebraic operations are performed, the laws of arithmetic apply. Symbols such as x, y, and z are usually used to represent quantities that are not specified, what are called the **unknowns.**

First, consider the equation

$$8x = 32$$

If we wish to solve for x, we can divide (or multiply) each side of the equation by the same factor without destroying the equality. In this case, if we divide both sides by 8, we have

$$\frac{8x}{8} = \frac{32}{8}$$

$$x = 4$$

Next consider the equation

$$x + 2 = 8$$

In this type of expression, we can add or subtract the same quantity from each side. If we subtract 2 from each side, we obtain

$$x + 2 - 2 = 8 - 2$$

$$x = 6$$

In general, if $x + a = b$, then $x = b - a$.

Now consider the equation

$$\frac{x}{5} = 9$$

If we multiply each side by 5, we are left with x on the left by itself and 45 on the right:

$$\left(\frac{x}{5}\right)(5) = 9 \times 5$$

$$x = 45$$

In all cases, *whatever operation is performed on the left side of the equality must also be performed on the right side.*

The following rules for multiplying, dividing, adding, and subtracting fractions should be recalled, where a, b, and c are three numbers:

	Rule	Example
Multiplying	$\left(\dfrac{a}{b}\right)\left(\dfrac{c}{d}\right) = \dfrac{ac}{bd}$	$\left(\dfrac{2}{3}\right)\left(\dfrac{4}{5}\right) = \dfrac{8}{15}$
Dividing	$\dfrac{(a/b)}{(c/d)} = \dfrac{ad}{bc}$	$\dfrac{2/3}{4/5} = \dfrac{(2)(5)}{(4)(3)} = \dfrac{10}{12}$
Adding	$\dfrac{a}{b} \pm \dfrac{c}{d} = \dfrac{ad \pm bc}{bd}$	$\dfrac{2}{3} - \dfrac{4}{5} = \dfrac{(2)(5) - (4)(3)}{(3)(5)} = -\dfrac{2}{15}$

Exercises

In the following exercises, solve for x:

Answers

1. $a = \dfrac{1}{1+x}$ $x = \dfrac{1-a}{a}$

2. $3x - 5 = 13$ $x = 6$

3. $ax - 5 = bx + 2$ $x = \dfrac{7}{a-b}$

4. $\dfrac{5}{2x+6} = \dfrac{3}{4x+8}$ $x = -\dfrac{11}{7}$

Powers

When powers of a given quantity x are multiplied, the following rule applies:

$$x^n x^m = x^{n+m} \tag{B.3}$$

For example, $x^2 x^4 = x^{2+4} = x^6$.

When dividing the powers of a given quantity, the rule is

$$\frac{x^n}{x^m} = x^{n-m} \tag{B.4}$$

For example, $x^8/x^2 = x^{8-2} = x^6$.

A power that is a fraction, such as $\frac{1}{3}$, corresponds to a root as follows:

$$x^{1/n} = \sqrt[n]{x} \tag{B.5}$$

For example, $4^{1/3} = \sqrt[3]{4} = 1.5874$. (A scientific calculator is useful for such calculations.)

Finally, any quantity x^n raised to the mth power is

$$(x^n)^m = x^{nm} \tag{B.6}$$

Table B.1 summarizes the rules of exponents.

Table B.1

Rules of Exponents
$x^0 = 1$
$x^1 = x$
$x^n x^m = x^{n+m}$
$x^n/x^m = x^{n-m}$
$x^{1/n} = \sqrt[n]{x}$
$(x^n)^m = x^{nm}$

Exercises

Verify the following:

1. $3^2 \times 3^3 = 243$
2. $x^5 x^{-8} = x^{-3}$

3. $x^{10}/x^{-5} = x^{15}$
4. $5^{1/3} = 1.709\ 975$ (Use your calculator.)
5. $60^{1/4} = 2.783\ 158$ (Use your calculator.)
6. $(x^4)^3 = x^{12}$

Factoring

Some useful formulas for factoring an equation are

$$ax + ay + az = a(x + y + z)$$ common factor

$$a^2 + 2ab + b^2 = (a + b)^2$$ perfect square

$$a^2 - b^2 = (a + b)(a - b)$$ differences of squares

Quadratic Equations

The general form of a quadratic equation is

$$ax^2 + bx + c = 0 \qquad \text{(B.7)}$$

where x is the unknown quantity and a, b, and c are numerical factors referred to as **coefficients** of the equation. This equation has two roots, given by

$$x = \frac{-b \pm \sqrt{b^2 - 4ac}}{2a} \qquad \text{(B.8)}$$

If $b^2 \geq 4ac$, the roots are real.

Example 1

The equation $x^2 + 5x + 4 = 0$ has the following roots corresponding to the two signs of the square-root term:

$$x = \frac{-5 \pm \sqrt{5^2 - (4)(1)(4)}}{2(1)} = \frac{-5 \pm \sqrt{9}}{2} = \frac{-5 \pm 3}{2}$$

$$x_+ = \frac{-5 + 3}{2} = -1 \qquad x_- = \frac{-5 - 3}{2} = -4$$

where x_+ refers to the root corresponding to the positive sign and x_- refers to the root corresponding to the negative sign.

Exercises

Solve the following quadratic equations:

Answers

1. $x^2 + 2x - 3 = 0$ $x_+ = 1$ $x_- = -3$
2. $2x^2 - 5x + 2 = 0$ $x_+ = 2$ $x_- = \frac{1}{2}$
3. $2x^2 - 4x - 9 = 0$ $x_+ = 1 + \sqrt{22}/2$ $x_- = 1 - \sqrt{22}/2$

Linear Equations

A linear equation has the general form

$$y = mx + b \qquad \text{(B.9)}$$

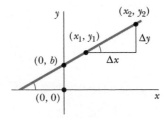

Figure B.1

where m and b are constants. This equation is referred to as being linear because the graph of y versus x is a straight line, as shown in Figure B.1. The constant b, called the **y-intercept,** represents the value of y at which the straight line intersects the y axis. The constant m is equal to the **slope** of the straight line. If any two points on the straight line are specified by the coordinates (x_1, y_1) and (x_2, y_2), as in Figure B.1, then the slope of the straight line can be expressed as

$$\text{Slope} = \frac{y_2 - y_1}{x_2 - x_1} = \frac{\Delta y}{\Delta x} \qquad\qquad \text{(B.10)}$$

Note that m and b can have either positive or negative values. If $m > 0$, the straight line has a *positive* slope, as in Figure B.1. If $m < 0$, the straight line has a *negative* slope. In Figure B.1, both m and b are positive. Three other possible situations are shown in Figure B.2.

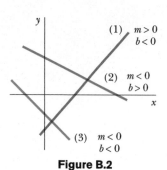

Figure B.2

Exercises

1. Draw graphs of the following straight lines:
    (a) $y = 5x + 3$ (b) $y = -2x + 4$ (c) $y = -3x - 6$

2. Find the slopes of the straight lines described in Exercise 1.

Answers   (a) 5   (b) -2 (c) -3

3. Find the slopes of the straight lines that pass through the following sets of points:
    (a) $(0, -4)$ and $(4, 2)$ (b) $(0, 0)$ and $(2, -5)$ (c) $(-5, 2)$ and $(4, -2)$

Answers   (a) $3/2$ (b) $-5/2$ (c) $-4/9$

Solving Simultaneous Linear Equations

Consider the equation $3x + 5y = 15$, which has two unknowns, x and y. Such an equation does not have a unique solution. For example, note that $(x = 0, y = 3)$, $(x = 5, y = 0)$, and $(x = 2, y = 9/5)$ are all solutions to this equation.

If a problem has two unknowns, a unique solution is possible only if we have *two* equations. In general, if a problem has n unknowns, its solution requires n equations. In order to solve two simultaneous equations involving two unknowns, x and y, we solve one of the equations for x in terms of y and substitute this expression into the other equation.

Example 2

Solve the following two simultaneous equations:

$$(1) \qquad 5x + y = -8$$
$$(2) \qquad 2x - 2y = 4$$

Solution   From Equation (2), $x = y + 2$. Substitution of this into Equation (1) gives

$$5(y + 2) + y = -8$$
$$6y = -18$$
$$y = \boxed{-3}$$
$$x = y + 2 = \boxed{-1}$$

Alternate Solution   Multiply each term in Equation (1) by the factor 2 and add the result to Equation (2):

$$10x + 2y = -16$$
$$\underline{2x - 2y = 4}$$
$$12x = -12$$
$$x = \boxed{-1}$$
$$y = x - 2 = \boxed{-3}$$

Two linear equations containing two unknowns can also be solved by a graphical method. If the straight lines corresponding to the two equations are plotted in a conventional coordinate system, the intersection of the two lines represents the solution. For example, consider the two equations

$$x - y = 2$$
$$x - 2y = -1$$

These are plotted in Figure B.3. The intersection of the two lines has the coordinates $x = 5$, $y = 3$. This represents the solution to the equations. You should check this solution by the analytical technique discussed above.

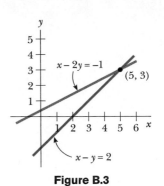

Figure B.3

Exercises

Solve the following pairs of simultaneous equations involving two unknowns:

Answers

1. $x + y = 8$ $x = 5, y = 3$
    $x - y = 2$

2. $98 - T = 10a$ $T = 65, a = 3.3$
    $T - 49 = 5a$

3. $6x + 2y = 6$ $x = 2, y = -3$
    $8x - 4y = 28$

Logarithms

Suppose that a quantity x is expressed as a power of some quantity a:

$$x = a^y \qquad \text{(B.11)}$$

The number a is called the **base** number. The **logarithm** of x with respect to the base a is equal to the exponent to which the base must be raised in order to satisfy the expression $x = a^y$:

$$y = \log_a x \qquad \text{(B.12)}$$

Conversely, the **antilogarithm** of y is the number x:

$$x = \text{antilog}_a y \qquad \text{(B.13)}$$

In practice, the two bases most often used are base 10, called the *common* logarithm base, and base $e = 2.718\ 282$, called Euler's constant or the *natural* logarithm base. When common logarithms are used,

$$y = \log_{10} x \qquad (\text{or } x = 10^y) \qquad \text{(B.14)}$$

When natural logarithms are used,

$$y = \ln x \qquad (\text{or } x = e^y) \qquad \text{(B.15)}$$

For example, $\log_{10} 52 = 1.716$, so that $\text{antilog}_{10} 1.716 = 10^{1.716} = 52$. Likewise, $\ln 52 = 3.951$, so antiln $3.951 = e^{3.951} = 52$.

In general, note that you can convert between base 10 and base e with the equality

$$\ln x = (2.302\ 585) \log_{10} x \qquad \text{(B.16)}$$

Finally, some useful properties of logarithms are

$$
\left.
\begin{aligned}
\log(ab) &= \log a + \log b \\
\log(a/b) &= \log a - \log b \\
\log(a^n) &= n \log a
\end{aligned}
\right\} \text{ any base}
$$

$$\ln e = 1$$
$$\ln e^a = a$$
$$\ln\left(\frac{1}{a}\right) = -\ln a$$

B.3   Geometry

The **distance** d between two points having coordinates (x_1, y_1) and (x_2, y_2) is

$$d = \sqrt{(x_2 - x_1)^2 + (y_2 - y_1)^2} \tag{B.17}$$

Radian measure: The arc length s of a circular arc (Fig. B.4) is proportional to the radius r for a fixed value of θ (in radians):

$$s = r\theta$$
$$\theta = \frac{s}{r} \tag{B.18}$$

Figure B.4

Table B.2 gives the areas and volumes for several geometric shapes used throughout this text:

Table B.2

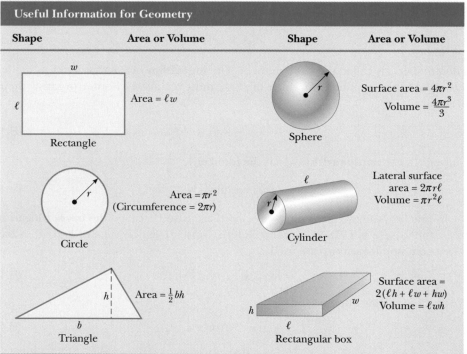

Useful Information for Geometry			
Shape	**Area or Volume**	**Shape**	**Area or Volume**
Rectangle	Area $= \ell w$	Sphere	Surface area $= 4\pi r^2$ Volume $= \frac{4\pi r^3}{3}$
Circle	Area $= \pi r^2$ (Circumference $= 2\pi r$)	Cylinder	Lateral surface area $= 2\pi r \ell$ Volume $= \pi r^2 \ell$
Triangle	Area $= \frac{1}{2} bh$	Rectangular box	Surface area $= 2(\ell h + \ell w + hw)$ Volume $= \ell w h$

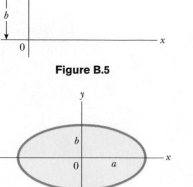

Figure B.5

The equation of a **straight line** (Fig. B.5) is

$$y = mx + b \tag{B.19}$$

where b is the y intercept and m is the slope of the line.

The equation of a **circle** of radius R centered at the origin is

$$x^2 + y^2 = R^2 \tag{B.20}$$

The equation of an **ellipse** having the origin at its center (Fig. B.6) is

$$\frac{x^2}{a^2} + \frac{y^2}{b^2} = 1 \tag{B.21}$$

Figure B.6

where a is the length of the semimajor axis (the longer one) and b is the length of the semiminor axis (the shorter one).

The equation of a **parabola** the vertex of which is at $y = b$ (Fig. B.7) is

$$y = ax^2 + b \tag{B.22}$$

The equation of a **rectangular hyperbola** (Fig. B.8) is

$$xy = \text{constant} \tag{B.23}$$

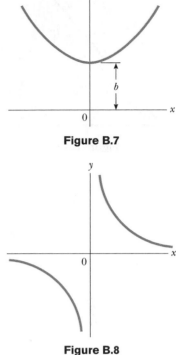

Figure B.7

Figure B.8

B.4 Trigonometry

That portion of mathematics based on the special properties of the right triangle is called trigonometry. By definition, a right triangle is one containing a 90° angle. Consider the right triangle shown in Figure B.9, where side a is opposite the angle θ, side b is adjacent to the angle θ, and side c is the hypotenuse of the triangle. The three basic trigonometric functions defined by such a triangle are the sine (sin), cosine (cos), and tangent (tan) functions. In terms of the angle θ, these functions are defined by

$$\sin \theta \equiv \frac{\text{side opposite } \theta}{\text{hypotenuse}} = \frac{a}{c} \tag{B.24}$$

$$\cos \theta \equiv \frac{\text{side adjacent to } \theta}{\text{hypotenuse}} = \frac{b}{c} \tag{B.25}$$

$$\tan \theta \equiv \frac{\text{side opposite } \theta}{\text{side adjacent to } \theta} = \frac{a}{b} \tag{B.26}$$

The Pythagorean theorem provides the following relationship among the sides of a right triangle:

$$c^2 = a^2 + b^2 \tag{B.27}$$

From the above definitions and the Pythagorean theorem, it follows that

$$\sin^2 \theta + \cos^2 \theta = 1$$

$$\tan \theta = \frac{\sin \theta}{\cos \theta}$$

The cosecant, secant, and cotangent functions are defined by

$$\csc \theta \equiv \frac{1}{\sin \theta} \qquad \sec \theta \equiv \frac{1}{\cos \theta} \qquad \cot \theta \equiv \frac{1}{\tan \theta}$$

The relationships below follow directly from the right triangle shown in Figure B.9:

$$\sin \theta = \cos(90° - \theta)$$

$$\cos \theta = \sin(90° - \theta)$$

$$\cot \theta = \tan(90° - \theta)$$

Some properties of trigonometric functions are

$$\sin(-\theta) = -\sin \theta$$

$$\cos(-\theta) = \cos \theta$$

$$\tan(-\theta) = -\tan \theta$$

a = opposite side
b = adjacent side
c = hypotenuse

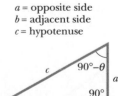

Figure B.9

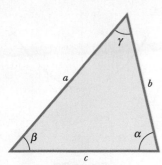

Figure B.10

The following relationships apply to *any* triangle, as shown in Figure B.10:

$$\alpha + \beta + \gamma = 180°$$

Law of cosines
$$a^2 = b^2 + c^2 - 2bc \cos \alpha$$
$$b^2 = a^2 + c^2 - 2ac \cos \beta$$
$$c^2 = a^2 + b^2 - 2ab \cos \gamma$$

Law of sines
$$\frac{a}{\sin \alpha} = \frac{b}{\sin \beta} = \frac{c}{\sin \gamma}$$

Table B.3 lists a number of useful trigonometric identities.

Table B.3

Some Trigonometric Identities	
$\sin^2 \theta + \cos^2 \theta = 1$	$\csc^2 \theta = 1 + \cot^2 \theta$
$\sec^2 \theta = 1 + \tan^2 \theta$	$\sin^2 \dfrac{\theta}{2} = \frac{1}{2}(1 - \cos \theta)$
$\sin 2\theta = 2 \sin \theta \cos \theta$	$\cos^2 \dfrac{\theta}{2} = \frac{1}{2}(1 + \cos \theta)$
$\cos 2\theta = \cos^2 \theta - \sin^2 \theta$	$1 - \cos \theta = 2 \sin^2 \dfrac{\theta}{2}$
$\tan 2\theta = \dfrac{2 \tan \theta}{1 - \tan^2 \theta}$	$\tan \dfrac{\theta}{2} = \sqrt{\dfrac{1 - \cos \theta}{1 + \cos \theta}}$
$\sin(A \pm B) = \sin A \cos B \pm \cos A \sin B$	
$\cos(A \pm B) = \cos A \cos B \mp \sin A \sin B$	
$\sin A \pm \sin B = 2 \sin[\frac{1}{2}(A \pm B)]\cos[\frac{1}{2}(A \mp B)]$	
$\cos A + \cos B = 2 \cos[\frac{1}{2}(A + B)]\cos[\frac{1}{2}(A - B)]$	
$\cos A - \cos B = 2 \sin[\frac{1}{2}(A + B)]\sin[\frac{1}{2}(B - A)]$	

Example 3

Consider the right triangle in Figure B.11, in which $a = 2$, $b = 5$, and c is unknown. From the Pythagorean theorem, we have

$$c^2 = a^2 + b^2 = 2^2 + 5^2 = 4 + 25 = 29$$

$$c = \sqrt{29} = \boxed{5.39}$$

To find the angle θ, note that

$$\tan \theta = \frac{a}{b} = \frac{2}{5} = 0.400$$

From a table of functions or from a calculator, we have

$$\theta = \tan^{-1}(0.400) = \boxed{21.8°}$$

where $\tan^{-1}(0.400)$ is the notation for "angle whose tangent is 0.400," sometimes written as arctan (0.400).

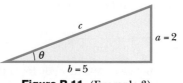

Figure B.11 (Example 3).

Exercises

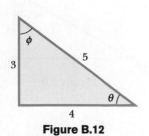

Figure B.12

1. In Figure B.12, identify (a) the side opposite θ (b) the side adjacent to ϕ. Then find (c) $\cos \theta$ (d) $\sin \phi$ (e) $\tan \phi$.

   Answers   (a) 3   (b) 3   (c) $\frac{4}{5}$ (d) $\frac{4}{5}$ (e) $\frac{4}{3}$

2. In a certain right triangle, the two sides that are perpendicular to each other are 5 m and 7 m long. What is the length of the third side?

   Answer   8.60 m

3. A right triangle has a hypotenuse of length 3 m, and one of its angles is 30°. What is the length of (a) the side opposite the 30° angle (b) the side adjacent to the 30° angle?

Answers   (a) 1.5 m   (b) 2.60 m

B.5   Series Expansions

$$(a + b)^n = a^n + \frac{n}{1!} a^{n-1}b + \frac{n(n-1)}{2!} a^{n-2}b^2 + \cdots$$

$$(1 + x)^n = 1 + nx + \frac{n(n-1)}{2!} x^2 + \cdots$$

$$e^x = 1 + x + \frac{x^2}{2!} + \frac{x^3}{3!} + \cdots$$

$$\ln(1 \pm x) = \pm x - \tfrac{1}{2}x^2 \pm \tfrac{1}{3}x^3 - \cdots$$

$$\left. \begin{array}{l} \sin x = x - \dfrac{x^3}{3!} + \dfrac{x^5}{5!} - \cdots \\[2ex] \cos x = 1 - \dfrac{x^2}{2!} + \dfrac{x^4}{4!} - \cdots \\[2ex] \tan x = x + \dfrac{x^3}{3} + \dfrac{2x^5}{15} + \cdots \quad |x| < \pi/2 \end{array} \right\} \; x \text{ in radians}$$

For $x \ll 1$, the following approximations can be used[1]:

$$(1 + x)^n \approx 1 + nx \qquad \sin x \approx x$$

$$e^x \approx 1 + x \qquad \cos x \approx 1$$

$$\ln(1 \pm x) \approx \pm x \qquad \tan x \approx x$$

B.6   Differential Calculus

In various branches of science, it is sometimes necessary to use the basic tools of calculus, invented by Newton, to describe physical phenomena. The use of calculus is fundamental in the treatment of various problems in Newtonian mechanics, electricity, and magnetism. In this section, we simply state some basic properties and "rules of thumb" that should be a useful review to the student.

First, a **function** must be specified that relates one variable to another (such as a coordinate as a function of time). Suppose one of the variables is called y (the dependent variable), the other x (the independent variable). We might have a function relationship such as

$$y(x) = ax^3 + bx^2 + cx + d$$

If a, b, c, and d are specified constants, then y can be calculated for any value of x. We usually deal with continuous functions, that is, those for which y varies "smoothly" with x.

The **derivative** of y with respect to x is defined as the limit, as Δx approaches zero, of the slopes of chords drawn between two points on the y versus x curve. Mathematically, we write this definition as

$$\frac{dy}{dx} = \lim_{\Delta x \to 0} \frac{\Delta y}{\Delta x} = \lim_{\Delta x \to 0} \frac{y(x + \Delta x) - y(x)}{\Delta x} \tag{B.28}$$

where Δy and Δx are defined as $\Delta x = x_2 - x_1$ and $\Delta y = y_2 - y_1$ (Fig. B.13). It is important to note that dy/dx does *not* mean dy divided by dx, but is simply a notation of the limiting process of the derivative as defined by Equation B.28.

---

[1]   The approximations for the functions $\sin x$, $\cos x$, and $\tan x$ are for $x \le 0.1$ rad.

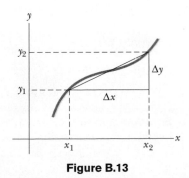

Figure B.13

A useful expression to remember when $y(x) = ax^n$, where a is a *constant* and n is *any* positive or negative number (integer or fraction), is

$$\frac{dy}{dx} = nax^{n-1} \tag{B.29}$$

If $y(x)$ is a polynomial or algebraic function of x, we apply Equation B.29 to *each* term in the polynomial and take $d[\text{constant}]/dx = 0$. In Examples 4 through 7, we evaluate the derivatives of several functions.

Special Properties of the Derivative

A. Derivative of the product of two functions   If a function $f(x)$ is given by the product of two functions, say, $g(x)$ and $h(x)$, then the derivative of $f(x)$ is defined as

$$\frac{d}{dx} f(x) = \frac{d}{dx} [g(x)h(x)] = g\frac{dh}{dx} + h\frac{dg}{dx} \tag{B.30}$$

B. Derivative of the sum of two functions   If a function $f(x)$ is equal to the sum of two functions, then the derivative of the sum is equal to the sum of the derivatives:

$$\frac{d}{dx} f(x) = \frac{d}{dx} [g(x) + h(x)] = \frac{dg}{dx} + \frac{dh}{dx} \tag{B.31}$$

C. Chain rule of differential calculus   If $y = f(x)$ and $x = g(z)$, then dy/dz can be written as the product of two derivatives:

$$\frac{dy}{dz} = \frac{dy}{dx}\frac{dx}{dz} \tag{B.32}$$

D. The second derivative   The second derivative of y with respect to x is defined as the derivative of the function dy/dx (the derivative of the derivative). It is usually written

$$\frac{d^2y}{dx^2} = \frac{d}{dx}\left(\frac{dy}{dx}\right) \tag{B.33}$$

Example 4

Suppose $y(x)$ (that is, y as a function of x) is given by

$$y(x) = ax^3 + bx + c$$

where a and b are constants. Then it follows that

$$y(x + \Delta x) = a(x + \Delta x)^3 + b(x + \Delta x) + c$$

$$y(x + \Delta x) = a(x^3 + 3x^2\Delta x + 3x\Delta x^2 + \Delta x^3) + b(x + \Delta x) + c$$

so

$$\Delta y = y(x + \Delta x) - y(x) = a(3x^2\Delta x + 3x\Delta x^2 + \Delta x^3) + b\Delta x$$

Substituting this into Equation B.28 gives

$$\frac{dy}{dx} = \lim_{\Delta x \to 0}\frac{\Delta y}{\Delta x} = \lim_{\Delta x \to 0}[3ax^2 + 3x\Delta x + \Delta x^2] + b$$

$$\frac{dy}{dx} = \boxed{3ax^2 + b}$$

Example 5

Find the derivative of

$$y(x) = 8x^5 + 4x^3 + 2x + 7$$

Solution   Applying Equation B.29 to each term independently, and remembering that d/dx (constant) = 0, we have

$$\frac{dy}{dx} = 8(5)x^4 + 4(3)x^2 + 2(1)x^0 + 0$$

$$\frac{dy}{dx} = \boxed{40x^4 + 12x^2 + 2}$$

Example 6

Find the derivative of $y(x) = x^3/(x + 1)^2$ with respect to x.

Solution We can rewrite this function as $y(x) = x^3(x + 1)^{-2}$ and apply Equation B.30:

$$\frac{dy}{dx} = (x + 1)^{-2}\frac{d}{dx}(x^3) + x^3\frac{d}{dx}(x + 1)^{-2}$$

$$= (x + 1)^{-2}3x^2 + x^3(-2)(x + 1)^{-3}$$

$$\frac{dy}{dx} = \frac{3x^2}{(x + 1)^2} - \frac{2x^3}{(x + 1)^3}$$

Example 7

A useful formula that follows from Equation B.30 is the derivative of the quotient of two functions. Show that

$$\frac{d}{dx}\left[\frac{g(x)}{h(x)}\right] = \frac{h\dfrac{dg}{dx} - g\dfrac{dh}{dx}}{h^2}$$

$$\frac{d}{dx}\left(\frac{g}{h}\right) = \frac{d}{dx}(gh^{-1}) = g\frac{d}{dx}(h^{-1}) + h^{-1}\frac{d}{dx}(g)$$

$$= -gh^{-2}\frac{dh}{dx} + h^{-1}\frac{dg}{dx}$$

$$= \frac{h\dfrac{dg}{dx} - g\dfrac{dh}{dx}}{h^2}$$

Solution We can write the quotient as gh^{-1} and then apply Equations B.29 and B.30:

Some of the more commonly used derivatives of functions are listed in Table B.4.

B.7 Integral Calculus

We think of integration as the inverse of differentiation. As an example, consider the expression

$$f(x) = \frac{dy}{dx} = 3ax^2 + b \qquad \text{(B.34)}$$

which was the result of differentiating the function

$$y(x) = ax^3 + bx + c$$

in Example 4. We can write Equation B.34 as $dy = f(x)\ dx = (3ax^2 + b)\ dx$ and obtain $y(x)$ by "summing" over all values of x. Mathematically, we write this inverse operation

$$y(x) = \int f(x)\ dx$$

For the function $f(x)$ given by Equation B.34, we have

$$y(x) = \int (3ax^2 + b)\ dx = ax^3 + bx + c$$

where c is a constant of the integration. This type of integral is called an *indefinite integral* because its value depends on the choice of c.

A general **indefinite integral** $I(x)$ is defined as

$$I(x) = \int f(x)\ dx \qquad \text{(B.35)}$$

where $f(x)$ is called the *integrand* and $f(x) = dI(x)/dx$.

For a *general continuous* function $f(x)$, the integral can be described as the area under the curve bounded by $f(x)$ and the x axis, between two specified values of x, say, x_1 and x_2, as in Figure B.14.

The area of the blue element is approximately $f(x_i)\,\Delta x_i$. If we sum all these area elements from x_1 and x_2 and take the limit of this sum as $\Delta x_i \rightarrow 0$, we obtain the *true*

Table B.4

Derivative for Several Functions
$\dfrac{d}{dx}(a) = 0$
$\dfrac{d}{dx}(ax^n) = nax^{n-1}$
$\dfrac{d}{dx}(e^{ax}) = ae^{ax}$
$\dfrac{d}{dx}(\sin ax) = a\cos ax$
$\dfrac{d}{dx}(\cos ax) = -a\sin ax$
$\dfrac{d}{dx}(\tan ax) = a\sec^2 ax$
$\dfrac{d}{dx}(\cot ax) = -a\csc^2 dx$
$\dfrac{d}{dx}(\sec x) = \tan x\sec x$
$\dfrac{d}{dx}(\csc x) = -\cot x\csc x$
$\dfrac{d}{dx}(\ln ax) = \dfrac{1}{x}$

Note: The symbols a and n represent constants.

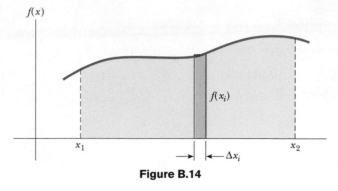

$f(x)$

$f(x_i)$

x_1 $\longrightarrow$ $|\!\!\longleftarrow \Delta x_i$ x_2

Figure B.14

area under the curve bounded by $f(x)$ and x, between the limits x_1 and x_2:

$$\text{Area} = \lim_{\Delta x \to 0} \sum_i f(x_i)\,\Delta x_i = \int_{x_1}^{x_2} f(x)\,dx \qquad (B.36)$$

Integrals of the type defined by Equation B.36 are called **definite integrals.**

One common integral that arises in practical situations has the form

$$\int x^n\,dx = \frac{x^{n+1}}{n+1} + c \qquad (n \neq -1) \qquad (B.37)$$

This result is obvious, being that differentiation of the right-hand side with respect to x gives $f(x) = x^n$ directly. If the limits of the integration are known, this integral becomes a *definite integral* and is written

$$\int_{x_1}^{x_2} x^n\,dx = \frac{x^{n+1}}{n+1}\bigg|_{x_1}^{x_2} = \frac{x_2^{n+1} - x_1^{n+1}}{n+1} \qquad (n \neq -1) \qquad (B.38)$$

Examples

1. $\displaystyle\int_0^a x^2\,dx = \frac{x^3}{3}\bigg]_0^a = \frac{a^3}{3}$

2. $\displaystyle\int_0^b x^{3/2}\,dx = \frac{x^{5/2}}{5/2}\bigg]_0^b = \tfrac{2}{5}b^{5/2}$

3. $\displaystyle\int_3^5 x\,dx = \frac{x^2}{2}\bigg]_3^5 = \frac{5^2 - 3^2}{2} = 8$

Partial Integration

Sometimes it is useful to apply the method of *partial integration* (also called "integrating by parts") to evaluate certain integrals. The method uses the property that

$$\int u\,dv = uv - \int v\,du \qquad (B.39)$$

where u and v are *carefully* chosen so as to reduce a complex integral to a simpler one. In many cases, several reductions have to be made. Consider the function

$$I(x) = \int x^2 e^x\,dx$$

This can be evaluated by integrating by parts twice. First, if we choose $u = x^2$, $v = e^x$, we obtain

$$\int x^2 e^x\,dx = \int x^2\,d(e^x) = x^2 e^x - 2\int e^x x\,dx + c_1$$

Now, in the second term, choose $u = x$, $v = e^x$, which gives

$$\int x^2 e^x \, dx = x^2 e^x - 2x e^x + 2 \int e^x \, dx + c_1$$

or

$$\int x^2 e^x \, dx = x^2 e^x - 2x e^x + 2 e^x + c_2$$

The Perfect Differential

Another useful method to remember is the use of the *perfect differential*, in which we look for a change of variable such that the differential of the function is the differential of the independent variable appearing in the integrand. For example, consider the integral

$$I(x) = \int \cos^2 x \sin x \, dx$$

This becomes easy to evaluate if we rewrite the differential as $d(\cos x) = -\sin x \, dx$. The integral then becomes

$$\int \cos^2 x \sin x \, dx = - \int \cos^2 x \, d(\cos x)$$

If we now change variables, letting $y = \cos x$, we obtain

$$\int \cos^2 x \sin x \, dx = - \int y^2 dy = -\frac{y^3}{3} + c = -\frac{\cos^3 x}{3} + c$$

Table B.5 lists some useful indefinite integrals. Table B.6 gives Gauss's probability integral and other definite integrals. A more complete list can be found in various handbooks, such as *The Handbook of Chemistry and Physics*, CRC Press.

Table B.5

Some Indefinite Integrals (An arbitrary constant should be added to each of these integrals.)

$$\int x^n \, dx = \frac{x^{n+1}}{n+1} \qquad (\text{provided } n \neq -1)$$

$$\int \frac{dx}{\sqrt{a^2 - x^2}} = \sin^{-1}\frac{x}{a} = -\cos^{-1}\frac{x}{a} \qquad (a^2 - x^2 > 0)$$

$$\int \frac{dx}{x} = \int x^{-1} dx = \ln x$$

$$\int \frac{dx}{\sqrt{x^2 \pm a^2}} = \ln(x + \sqrt{x^2 \pm a^2})$$

$$\int \frac{dx}{a + bx} = \frac{1}{b} \ln(a + bx)$$

$$\int \frac{x \, dx}{\sqrt{a^2 - x^2}} = -\sqrt{a^2 - x^2}$$

$$\int \frac{x dx}{a + bx} = \frac{x}{b} - \frac{a}{b^2} \ln(a + bx)$$

$$\int \frac{x \, dx}{\sqrt{x^2 \pm a^2}} = \sqrt{x^2 \pm a^2}$$

$$\int \frac{dx}{x(x + a)} = -\frac{1}{a} \ln \frac{x + a}{x}$$

$$\int \sqrt{a^2 - x^2} \, dx = \frac{1}{2}\left(x\sqrt{a^2 - x^2} + a^2 \sin^{-1}\frac{x}{a} \right)$$

$$\int \frac{dx}{(a + bx)^2} = -\frac{1}{b(a + bx)}$$

$$\int x\sqrt{a^2 - x^2} \, dx = -\frac{1}{3}(a^2 - x^2)^{3/2}$$

$$\int \frac{dx}{a^2 + x^2} = \frac{1}{a} \tan^{-1}\frac{x}{a}$$

$$\int \sqrt{x^2 \pm a^2} \, dx = \frac{1}{2}[x\sqrt{x^2 \pm a^2} \pm a^2 \ln(x + \sqrt{x^2 \pm a^2})]$$

$$\int \frac{dx}{a^2 - x^2} = \frac{1}{2a} \ln \frac{a + x}{a - x} \qquad (a^2 - x^2 > 0)$$

$$\int x(\sqrt{x^2 \pm a^2}) \, dx = \frac{1}{3}(x^2 \pm a^2)^{3/2}$$

$$\int \frac{dx}{x^2 - a^2} = \frac{1}{2a} \ln \frac{x - a}{x + a} \qquad (x^2 - a^2 > 0)$$

$$\int e^{ax} \, dx = \frac{1}{a} e^{ax}$$

$$\int \frac{x \, dx}{a^2 \pm x^2} = \pm \frac{1}{2}\ln(a^2 \pm x^2)$$

$$\int \ln ax \, dx = (x \ln ax) - x$$

continued

Table B.5

Some Indefinite Integrals (An arbitrary constant should be added to each of these integrals.) *continued*

$$\int xe^{ax}\,dx = \frac{e^{ax}}{a^2}(ax - 1)$$

$$\int \frac{dx}{a + be^{cx}} = \frac{x}{a} - \frac{1}{ac}\ln(a + be^{cx})$$

$$\int \sin ax\,dx = -\frac{1}{a}\cos ax$$

$$\int \cos ax\,dx = \frac{1}{a}\sin ax$$

$$\int \tan ax\,dx = -\frac{1}{a}\ln(\cos ax) = \frac{1}{a}\ln(\sec ax)$$

$$\int \cot ax\,dx = \frac{1}{a}\ln(\sin ax)$$

$$\int \sec ax\,dx = \frac{1}{a}\ln(\sec ax + \tan ax) = \frac{1}{a}\ln\left[\tan\left(\frac{ax}{2} + \frac{\pi}{4}\right)\right]$$

$$\int \csc ax\,dx = \frac{1}{a}\ln(\csc ax - \cot ax) = \frac{1}{a}\ln\left(\tan\frac{ax}{2}\right)$$

$$\int \sin^2 ax\,dx = \frac{x}{2} - \frac{\sin 2ax}{4a}$$

$$\int \cos^2 ax\,dx = \frac{x}{2} + \frac{\sin 2ax}{4a}$$

$$\int \frac{dx}{\sin^2 ax} = -\frac{1}{a}\cot ax$$

$$\int \frac{dx}{\cos^2 ax} = \frac{1}{a}\tan ax$$

$$\int \tan^2 ax\,dx = \frac{1}{a}(\tan ax) - x$$

$$\int \cot^2 ax\,dx = -\frac{1}{a}(\cot ax) - x$$

$$\int \sin^{-1} ax\,dx = x(\sin^{-1} ax) + \frac{\sqrt{1 - a^2 x^2}}{a}$$

$$\int \cos^{-1} ax\,dx = x(\cos^{-1} ax) - \frac{\sqrt{1 - a^2 x^2}}{a}$$

$$\int \frac{dx}{(x^2 + a^2)^{3/2}} = \frac{x}{a^2\sqrt{x^2 + a^2}}$$

$$\int \frac{x\,dx}{(x^2 + a^2)^{3/2}} = -\frac{1}{\sqrt{x^2 + a^2}}$$

Table B.6

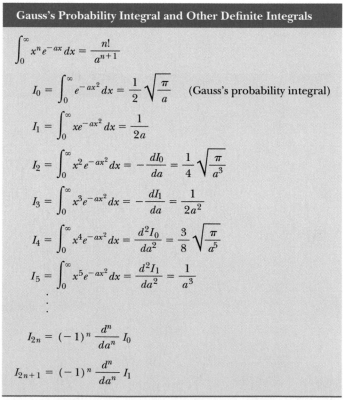

Gauss's Probability Integral and Other Definite Integrals

$$\int_0^\infty x^n e^{-ax}\,dx = \frac{n!}{a^{n+1}}$$

$$I_0 = \int_0^\infty e^{-ax^2}\,dx = \frac{1}{2}\sqrt{\frac{\pi}{a}}\qquad \text{(Gauss's probability integral)}$$

$$I_1 = \int_0^\infty xe^{-ax^2}\,dx = \frac{1}{2a}$$

$$I_2 = \int_0^\infty x^2 e^{-ax^2}\,dx = -\frac{dI_0}{da} = \frac{1}{4}\sqrt{\frac{\pi}{a^3}}$$

$$I_3 = \int_0^\infty x^3 e^{-ax^2}\,dx = -\frac{dI_1}{da} = \frac{1}{2a^2}$$

$$I_4 = \int_0^\infty x^4 e^{-ax^2}\,dx = \frac{d^2 I_0}{da^2} = \frac{3}{8}\sqrt{\frac{\pi}{a^5}}$$

$$I_5 = \int_0^\infty x^5 e^{-ax^2}\,dx = \frac{d^2 I_1}{da^2} = \frac{1}{a^3}$$

$$\vdots$$

$$I_{2n} = (-1)^n \frac{d^n}{da^n} I_0$$

$$I_{2n+1} = (-1)^n \frac{d^n}{da^n} I_1$$

B.8 Propagation of Uncertainty

In laboratory experiments, a common activity is to take measurements that act as raw data. These measurements are of several types—length, time interval, temperature, voltage, etc.—and are taken by a variety of instruments. Regardless of the measurement and the quality of the instrumentation, **there is always uncertainty associated with a physical measurement.** This uncertainty is a combination of that associated with the instrument and that related to the system being measured. An example of the former is the inability to exactly determine the position of a length measurement between the lines on a meter stick. An example of uncertainty related to the system being measured is the variation of temperature within a sample of water so that a single temperature for the sample is difficult to determine.

Uncertainties can be expressed in two ways. **Absolute uncertainty** refers to an uncertainty expressed in the same units as the measurement. Thus, a length might be expressed as (5.5 ± 0.1) cm, as was the length of the computer disk label in Section 1.7. The uncertainty of ± 0.1 cm by itself is not descriptive enough for some purposes, however. This is a large uncertainty if the measurement is 1.0 cm, but it is a small uncertainty if the measurement is 100 m. To give a more descriptive account of the uncertainty, **fractional uncertainty** or **percent uncertainty** is used. In this type of description, the uncertainty is divided by the actual measurement. Thus, the length of the computer disk label could be expressed as

$$\ell = 5.5 \text{ cm} \pm \frac{0.1 \text{ cm}}{5.5 \text{ cm}} = 5.5 \text{ cm} \pm 0.018 \qquad \text{(fractional uncertainty)}$$

or as

$$\ell = 5.5 \text{ cm} \pm 1.8\% \qquad \text{(percent uncertainty)}$$

When combining measurements in a calculation, the uncertainty in the final result is larger than the uncertainty in the individual measurements. This is called **propagation of uncertainty** and is one of the challenges of experimental physics. As a calculation becomes more complicated, there is increased propagation of uncertainty and the uncertainty in the value of the final result can grow to be quite large.

There are simple rules that can provide a reasonable estimate of the uncertainty in a calculated result:

Multiplication and division: When measurements with uncertainties are multiplied or divided, add the *percent uncertainties* to obtain the percent uncertainty in the result.

Example: The Area of a Rectangular Plate

$$A = \ell w = (5.5 \text{ cm} \pm 1.8\%) \times (6.4 \text{ cm} \pm 1.6\%) = 35 \text{ cm}^2 \pm 3.4\%$$
$$= (35 \pm 1) \text{ cm}^2$$

Addition and subtraction: When measurements with uncertainties are added or subtracted, add the *absolute uncertainties* to obtain the absolute uncertainty in the result.

Example: A Change in Temperature

$$\Delta T = T_2 - T_1 = (99.2 \pm 1.5)°\text{C} - (27.6 \pm 1.5)°\text{C} = (71.6 \pm 3.0)°\text{C}$$
$$= 71.6°\text{C} \pm 4.2\%$$

Powers: If a measurement is taken to a power, the percent uncertainty is multiplied by that power to obtain the percent uncertainty in the result.

Example: The Volume of a Sphere

$$V = \tfrac{4}{3}\pi r^3 = \tfrac{4}{3}\pi(6.20 \text{ cm} \pm 2.0\%)^3 = 998 \text{ cm}^3 \pm 6.0\%$$
$$= (998 \pm 60) \text{ cm}^3$$

Notice that uncertainties in a calculation always add. As a result, an experiment involving a subtraction should be avoided if possible. This is especially true if the measurements being subtracted are close together. The result of such a calculation is a small difference in the measurements and uncertainties that add together. It is possible that the uncertainty in the result could be larger than the result itself!

Appendix C • Periodic Table of the Elements

Group I	Group II	Transition elements							
H 1 1.007 9 1s									
Li 3 6.941 $2s^1$	**Be** 4 9.0122 $2s^2$								
Na 11 22.990 $3s^1$	**Mg** 12 24.305 $3s^2$								
K 19 39.098 $4s^1$	**Ca** 20 40.078 $4s^2$	**Sc** 21 44.956 $3d^14s^2$	**Ti** 22 47.867 $3d^24s^2$	**V** 23 50.942 $3d^34s^2$	**Cr** 24 51.996 $3d^54s^1$	**Mn** 25 54.938 $3d^54s^2$	**Fe** 26 55.845 $3d^64s^2$	**Co** 27 58.933 $3d^74s^2$	
Rb 37 85.468 $5s^1$	**Sr** 38 87.62 $5s^2$	**Y** 39 88.906 $4d^15s^2$	**Zr** 40 91.224 $4d^25s^2$	**Nb** 41 92.906 $4d^45s^1$	**Mo** 42 95.94 $4d^55s^1$	**Tc** 43 (98) $4d^55s^2$	**Ru** 44 101.07 $4d^75s^1$	**Rh** 45 102.91 $4d^85s^1$	
Cs 55 132.91 $6s^1$	**Ba** 56 137.33 $6s^2$	57-71*	**Hf** 72 178.49 $5d^26s^2$	**Ta** 73 180.95 $5d^36s^2$	**W** 74 183.84 $5d^46s^2$	**Re** 75 186.21 $5d^56s^2$	**Os** 76 190.23 $5d^66s^2$	**Ir** 77 192.2 $5d^76s^2$	
Fr 87 (223) $7s^1$	**Ra** 88 (226) $7s^2$	89-103**	**Rf** 104 (261) $6d^27s^2$	**Db** 105 (262) $6d^37s^2$	**Sg** 106 (266)	**Bh** 107 (264)	**Hs** 108 (269)	**Mt** 109 (268)	

Symbol — **Ca** 20 — Atomic number
Atomic mass † — 40.078
$4s^2$ — Electron configuration

*Lanthanide series

La 57 138.91 $5d^16s^2$	**Ce** 58 140.12 $5d^14f^16s^2$	**Pr** 59 140.91 $4f^36s^2$	**Nd** 60 144.24 $4f^46s^2$	**Pm** 61 (145) $4f^56s^2$	**Sm** 62 150.36 $4f^66s^2$
Ac 89 (227) $6d^17s^2$	**Th** 90 232.04 $6d^27s^2$	**Pa** 91 231.04 $5f^26d^17s^2$	**U** 92 238.03 $5f^36d^17s^2$	**Np** 93 (237) $5f^46d^17s^2$	**Pu** 94 (244) $5f^66d^07s^2$

**Actinide series

▫ Atomic mass values given are averaged over isotopes in the percentages in which they exist in nature.
† For an unstable element, mass number of the most stable known isotope is given in parentheses.
†† Elements 110, 111, 112, and 114 have not yet been named.
††† For a description of the atomic data, visit *physics.nist.gov/atomic*

					Group III	Group IV	Group V	Group VI	Group VII	Group 0
									H 1 1.007 9 $1s^1$	**He** 2 4.002 6 $1s^2$
					B 5 10.811 $2p^1$	**C** 6 12.011 $2p^2$	**N** 7 14.007 $2p^3$	**O** 8 15.999 $2p^4$	**F** 9 18.998 $2p^5$	**Ne** 10 20.180 $2p^6$
					Al 13 26.982 $3p^1$	**Si** 14 28.086 $3p^2$	**P** 15 30.974 $3p^3$	**S** 16 32.066 $3p^4$	**Cl** 17 35.453 $3p^5$	**Ar** 18 39.948 $3p^6$
Ni 28 58.693 $3d^8 4s^2$	**Cu** 29 63.546 $3d^{10} 4s^1$	**Zn** 30 65.39 $3d^{10} 4s^2$			**Ga** 31 69.723 $4p^1$	**Ge** 32 72.61 $4p^2$	**As** 33 74.922 $4p^3$	**Se** 34 78.96 $4p^4$	**Br** 35 79.904 $4p^5$	**Kr** 36 83.80 $4p^6$
Pd 46 106.42 $4d^{10}$	**Ag** 47 107.87 $4d^{10} 5s^1$	**Cd** 48 112.41 $4d^{10} 5s^2$			**In** 49 114.82 $5p^1$	**Sn** 50 118.71 $5p^2$	**Sb** 51 121.76 $5p^3$	**Te** 52 127.60 $5p^4$	**I** 53 126.90 $5p^5$	**Xe** 54 131.29 $5p^6$
Pt 78 195.08 $5d^9 6s^1$	**Au** 79 196.97 $5d^{10} 6s^1$	**Hg** 80 200.59 $5d^{10} 6s^2$			**Tl** 81 204.38 $6p^1$	**Pb** 82 207.2 $6p^2$	**Bi** 83 208.98 $6p^3$	**Po** 84 (209) $6p^4$	**At** 85 (210) $6p^5$	**Rn** 86 (222) $6p^6$
110†† (271)	111†† (272)	112†† (285)			114†† (289)					

Eu 63 151.96 $4f^7 6s^2$	**Gd** 64 157.25 $5d^1 4f^7 6s^2$	**Tb** 65 158.93 $5d^1 4f^8 6s^2$	**Dy** 66 162.50 $4f^{10} 6s^2$	**Ho** 67 164.93 $4f^{11} 6s^2$	**Er** 68 167.26 $4f^{12} 6s^2$	**Tm** 69 168.93 $4f^{13} 6s^2$	**Yb** 70 173.04 $4f^{14} 6s^2$	**Lu** 71 174.97 $5d^1 4f^{14} 6s^2$
Am 95 (243) $5f^7 6d^0 7s^2$	**Cm** 96 (247) $5f^7 6d^1 7s^2$	**Bk** 97 (247) $5f^8 6d^1 7s^2$	**Cf** 98 (251) $5f^{10} 6d^0 7s^2$	**Es** 99 (252) $5f^{11} 6d^0 7s^2$	**Fm** 100 (257) $5f^{12} 6d^0 7s^2$	**Md** 101 (258) $5f^{13} 6d^0 7s^2$	**No** 102 (259) $6d^0 7s^2$	**Lr** 103 (262) $6d^1 7s^2$

Appendix D • SI Units

Table D.1

SI Units		
	SI Base Unit	
Base Quantity	**Name**	**Symbol**
Length	Meter	m
Mass	Kilogram	kg
Time	Second	s
Electric current	Ampere	A
Temperature	Kelvin	K
Amount of substance	Mole	mol
Luminous intensity	Candela	cd

Table D.2

Some Derived SI Units				
Quantity	**Name**	**Symbol**	**Expression in Terms of Base Units**	**Expression in Terms of Other SI Units**
Plane angle	radian	rad	m/m	
Frequency	hertz	Hz	s^{-1}	
Force	newton	N	$kg \cdot m/s^2$	J/m
Pressure	pascal	Pa	$kg/m \cdot s^2$	N/m^2
Energy; work	joule	J	$kg \cdot m^2/s^2$	$N \cdot m$
Power	watt	W	$kg \cdot m^2/s^3$	J/s
Electric charge	coulomb	C	$A \cdot s$	
Electric potential	volt	V	$kg \cdot m^2/A \cdot s^3$	W/A
Capacitance	farad	F	$A^2 \cdot s^4/kg \cdot m^2$	C/V
Electric resistance	ohm	Ω	$kg \cdot m^2/A^2 \cdot s^3$	V/A
Magnetic flux	weber	Wb	$kg \cdot m^2/A \cdot s^2$	$V \cdot s$
Magnetic field	tesla	T	$kg/A \cdot s^2$	
Inductance	henry	H	$kg \cdot m^2/A^2 \cdot s^2$	$T \cdot m^2/A$

All Nobel Prizes in physics are listed (and marked with a P), as well as relevant Nobel Prizes in Chemistry (C). The key dates for some of the scientific work are supplied; they often antedate the prize considerably.

1901 (P) *Wilhelm Roentgen* for discovering x-rays (1895).

1902 (P) *Hendrik A. Lorentz* for predicting the Zeeman effect and *Pieter Zeeman* for discovering the Zeeman effect, the splitting of spectral lines in magnetic fields.

1903 (P) *Antoine-Henri Becquerel* for discovering radioactivity (1896) and *Pierre* and *Marie Curie* for studying radioactivity.

1904 (P) *Lord Rayleigh* for studying the density of gases and discovering argon.
      (C) *William Ramsay* for discovering the inert gas elements helium, neon, xenon, and krypton, and placing them in the periodic table.

1905 (P) *Philipp Lenard* for studying cathode rays, electrons (1898–1899).

1906 (P) *J. J. Thomson* for studying electrical discharge through gases and discovering the electron (1897).

1907 (P) *Albert A. Michelson* for inventing optical instruments and measuring the speed of light (1880s).

1908 (P) *Gabriel Lippmann* for making the first color photographic plate, using interference methods (1891).
      (C) *Ernest Rutherford* for discovering that atoms can be broken apart by alpha rays and for studying radioactivity.

1909 (P) *Guglielmo Marconi* and *Carl Ferdinand Braun* for developing wireless telegraphy.

1910 (P) *Johannes D. van der Waals* for studying the equation of state for gases and liquids (1881).

1911 (P) *Wilhelm Wien* for discovering Wien's law giving the peak of a blackbody spectrum (1893).
      (C) *Marie Curie* for discovering radium and polonium (1898) and isolating radium.

1912 (P) *Nils Dalén* for inventing automatic gas regulators for lighthouses.

1913 (P) *Heike Kamerlingh Onnes* for the discovery of superconductivity and liquefying helium (1908).

1914 (P) *Max T. F. von Laue* for studying x-rays from their diffraction by crystals, showing that x-rays are electromagnetic waves (1912).
      (C) *Theodore W. Richards* for determining the atomic weights of sixty elements, indicating the existence of isotopes.

1915 (P) *William Henry Bragg* and *William Lawrence Bragg*, his son, for studying the diffraction of x-rays in crystals.

1917 (P) *Charles Barkla* for studying atoms by x-ray scattering (1906).

1918 (P) *Max Planck* for discovering energy quanta (1900).

1919 (P) *Johannes Stark*, for discovering the Stark effect, the splitting of spectral lines in electric fields (1913).

1920 (P) *Charles-Édouard Guillaume* for discovering invar, a nickel–steel alloy with low coefficient of expansion.
      (C) *Walther Nernst* for studying heat changes in chemical reactions and formulating the third law of thermodynamics (1918).

1921 (P) *Albert Einstein* for explaining the photoelectric effect and for his services to theoretical physics (1905).
      (C) *Frederick Soddy* for studying the chemistry of radioactive substances and discovering isotopes (1912).

1922 (P) *Niels Bohr* for his model of the atom and its radiation (1913).

(C) *Francis W. Aston* for using the mass spectrograph to study atomic weights, thus discovering 212 of the 287 naturally occurring isotopes.

1923 (P) *Robert A. Millikan* for measuring the charge on an electron (1911) and for studying the photoelectric effect experimentally (1914).

1924 (P) *Karl M. G. Siegbahn* for his work in x-ray spectroscopy.

1925 (P) *James Franck* and *Gustav Hertz* for discovering the Franck–Hertz effect in electron–atom collisions.

1926 (P) *Jean-Baptiste Perrin* for studying Brownian motion to validate the discontinuous structure of matter and measure the size of atoms.

1927 (P) *Arthur Holly Compton* for discovering the Compton effect on x-rays, their change in wavelength when they collide with matter (1922), and *Charles T. R. Wilson* for inventing the cloud chamber, used to study charged particles (1906).

1928 (P) *Owen W. Richardson* for studying the thermionic effect and electrons emitted by hot metals (1911).

1929 (P) *Louis Victor de Broglie* for discovering the wave nature of electrons (1923).

1930 (P) *Chandrasekhara Venkata Raman* for studying Raman scattering, the scattering of light by atoms and molecules with a change in wavelength (1928).

1932 (P) *Werner Heisenberg* for creating quantum mechanics (1925).

1933 (P) *Erwin Schrödinger* and *Paul A. M. Dirac* for developing wave mechanics (1925) and relativistic quantum mechanics (1927).

(C) *Harold Urey* for discovering heavy hydrogen, deuterium (1931).

1935 (P) *James Chadwick* for discovering the neutron (1932).

(C) *Irène* and *Frédéric Joliot-Curie* for synthesizing new radioactive elements.

1936 (P) *Carl D. Anderson* for discovering the positron in particular and antimatter in general (1932) and *Victor F. Hess* for discovering cosmic rays.

(C) *Peter J. W. Debye* for studying dipole moments and diffraction of x-rays and electrons in gases.

1937 (P) *Clinton Davisson* and *George Thomson* for discovering the diffraction of electrons by crystals, confirming de Broglie's hypothesis (1927).

1938 (P) *Enrico Fermi* for producing the transuranic radioactive elements by neutron irradiation (1934–1937).

1939 (P) *Ernest O. Lawrence* for inventing the cyclotron.

1943 (P) *Otto Stern* for developing molecular-beam studies (1923) and using them to discover the magnetic moment of the proton (1933).

1944 (P) *Isidor I. Rabi* for discovering nuclear magnetic resonance in atomic and molecular beams.

(C) *Otto Hahn* for discovering nuclear fission (1938).

1945 (P) *Wolfgang Pauli* for discovering the exclusion principle (1924).

1946 (P) *Percy W. Bridgman* for studying physics at high pressures.

1947 (P) *Edward V. Appleton* for studying the ionosphere.

1948 (P) *Patrick M. S. Blackett* for studying nuclear physics with cloud-chamber photographs of cosmic-ray interactions.

1949 (P) *Hideki Yukawa* for predicting the existence of mesons (1935).

1950 (P) *Cecil F. Powell* for developing the method of studying cosmic rays with photographic emulsions and discovering new mesons.

1951 (P) *John D. Cockcroft* and *Ernest T. S. Walton* for transmuting nuclei in an accelerator (1932).

(C) *Edwin M. McMillan* for producing neptunium (1940) and *Glenn T. Seaborg* for producing plutonium (1941) and further transuranic elements.

1952 (P) *Felix Bloch* and *Edward Mills Purcell* for discovering nuclear magnetic resonance in liquids and gases (1946).

1953 (P) *Frits Zernike* for inventing the phase-contrast microscope, which uses interference to provide high contrast.

1954 (P) *Max Born* for interpreting the wave function as a probability (1926) and other quantum-mechanical discoveries and *Walther Bothe* for developing the coincidence method to study subatomic particles (1930–1931), producing, in particular, the particle interpreted by Chadwick as the neutron.

1955 (P) *Willis E. Lamb, Jr.,* for discovering the Lamb shift in the hydrogen spectrum (1947) and *Polykarp Kusch* for determining the magnetic moment of the electron (1947).

1956 (P) *John Bardeen, Walter H. Brattain,* and *William Shockley* for inventing the transistor (1956).

1957 (P) *T.-D. Lee* and *C.-N. Yang* for predicting that parity is not conserved in beta decay (1956).

1958 (P) *Pavel A. Čerenkov* for discovering Čerenkov radiation (1935) and *Ilya M. Frank* and *Igor Tamm* for interpreting it (1937).

1959 (P) *Emilio G. Segrè* and *Owen Chamberlain* for discovering the antiproton (1955).

1960 (P) *Donald A. Glaser* for inventing the bubble chamber to study elementary particles (1952).

(C) *Willard Libby* for developing radiocarbon dating (1947).

1961 (P) *Robert Hofstadter* for discovering internal structure in protons and neutrons and *Rudolf L. Mössbauer* for discovering the Mössbauer effect of recoilless gamma-ray emission (1957).

1962 (P) *Lev Davidovich Landau* for studying liquid helium and other condensed matter theoretically.

1963 (P) *Eugene P. Wigner* for applying symmetry principles to elementary-particle theory and *Maria Goeppert Mayer* and *J. Hans D. Jensen* for studying the shell model of nuclei (1947).

1964 (P) *Charles H. Townes, Nikolai G. Basov,* and *Alexandr M. Prokhorov* for developing masers (1951–1952) and lasers.

1965 (P) *Sin-itiro Tomonaga, Julian S. Schwinger,* and *Richard P. Feynman* for developing quantum electrodynamics (1948).

1966 (P) *Alfred Kastler* for his optical methods of studying atomic energy levels.

1967 (P) *Hans Albrecht Bethe* for discovering the routes of energy production in stars (1939).

1968 (P) *Luis W. Alvarez* for discovering resonance states of elementary particles.

1969 (P) *Murray Gell-Mann* for classifying elementary particles (1963).

1970 (P) *Hannes Alfvén* for developing magnetohydrodynamic theory and *Louis Eugène Félix Néel* for discovering antiferromagnetism and ferrimagnetism (1930s).

1971 (P) *Dennis Gabor* for developing holography (1947).

(C) *Gerhard Herzberg* for studying the structure of molecules spectroscopically.

1972 (P) *John Bardeen, Leon N. Cooper,* and *John Robert Schrieffer* for explaining superconductivity (1957).

1973 (P) *Leo Esaki* for discovering tunneling in semiconductors, *Ivar Giaever* for discovering tunneling in superconductors, and *Brian D. Josephson* for predicting the Josephson effect, which involves tunneling of paired electrons (1958–1962).

1974 (P) *Anthony Hewish* for discovering pulsars and *Martin Ryle* for developing radio interferometry.

1975 (P) *Aage N. Bohr, Ben R. Mottelson,* and *James Rainwater* for discovering why some nuclei take asymmetric shapes.

1976 (P) *Burton Richter* and *Samuel C. C. Ting* for discovering the J/psi particle, the first charmed particle (1974).

1977 (P) *John H. Van Vleck, Nevill F. Mott,* and *Philip W. Anderson* for studying solids quantum-mechanically.

(C) *Ilya Prigogine* for extending thermodynamics to show how life could arise in the face of the second law.

1978 (P) *Arno A. Penzias* and *Robert W. Wilson* for discovering the cosmic background radiation (1965) and *Pyotr Kapitsa* for his studies of liquid helium.

1979 (P) *Sheldon L. Glashow, Abdus Salam,* and *Steven Weinberg* for developing the theory that unified the weak and electromagnetic forces (1958–1971).

1980 (P) *Val Fitch* and *James W. Cronin* for discovering CP (charge-parity) violation (1964), which possibly explains the cosmological dominance of matter over antimatter.

1981 (P) *Nicolaas Bloembergen* and *Arthur L. Schawlow* for developing laser spectroscopy and *Kai M. Siegbahn* for developing high-resolution electron spectroscopy (1958).

1982 (P) *Kenneth G. Wilson* for developing a method of constructing theories of phase transitions to analyze critical phenomena.

1983 (P) *William A. Fowler* for theoretical studies of astrophysical nucleosynthesis and *Subramanyan Chandrasekhar* for studying physical processes of importance to stellar structure and evolution, including the prediction of white dwarf stars (1930).

1984 (P) *Carlo Rubbia* for discovering the W and Z particles, verifying the electroweak unification, and *Simon van der Meer*, for developing the method of stochastic cooling of the CERN beam that allowed the discovery (1982–1983).

1985 (P) *Klaus von Klitzing* for the quantized Hall effect, relating to conductivity in the presence of a magnetic field (1980).

1986 (P) *Ernst Ruska* for inventing the electron microscope (1931), and *Gerd Binnig* and *Heinrich Rohrer* for inventing the scanning-tunneling electron microscope (1981).

1987 (P) *J. Georg Bednorz* and *Karl Alex Müller* for the discovery of **high-temperature** superconductivity (1986).

1988 (P) *Leon M. Lederman, Melvin Schwartz,* and *Jack Steinberger* for a collaborative experiment that led to the development of a new tool for studying the weak nuclear force, which affects the radioactive decay of atoms.

1989 (P) *Norman Ramsay* for various techniques in atomic physics; and *Hans Dehmelt* and *Wolfgang Paul* for the development of techniques for trapping single-charge particles.

1990 (P) *Jerome Friedman, Henry Kendall* and *Richard Taylor* for experiments important to the development of the quark model.

1991 (P) *Pierre-Gilles de Gennes* for discovering that methods developed for studying order phenomena in simple systems can be generalized to more complex forms of matter, in particular to liquid crystals and polymers.

1992 (P) *George Charpak* for developing detectors that trace the paths of evanescent subatomic particles produced in particle accelerators.

1993 (P) *Russell Hulse* and *Joseph Taylor* for discovering evidence of gravitational waves.

1994 (P) *Bertram N. Brockhouse* and *Clifford G. Shull* for pioneering work in neutron scattering.

1995 (P) *Martin L. Perl* and *Frederick Reines* for discovering the tau particle and the neutrino, respectively.

1996 (P) *David M. Lee, Douglas C. Osheroff,* and *Robert C. Richardson* for developing a superfluid using helium-3.

1997 (P) *Steven Chu, Claude Cohen-Tannoudji,* and *William D. Phillips* for developing methods to cool and trap atoms with laser light.

1998 (P) *Robert B. Laughlin, Horst L. Störmer,* and *Daniel C. Tsui* for discovering a new form of quantum fluid with fractionally charged excitations.

1999 (P) *Gerardus 'T Hooft* and *Martinus J. G. Veltman* for studies in the quantum structure of electroweak interactions in physics.

2000 (P) *Zhores I. Alferov* and *Herbert Kroemer* for developing semiconductor heterostructures used in high-speed electronics and optoelectronics and *Jack St. Clair Kilby* for participating in the invention of the integrated circuit.

2001 (P) *Eric A. Cornell, Wolfgang Ketterle,* and *Carl E. Wieman* for the achievement of Bose–Einstein condensation in dilute gases of alkali atoms.

2002 (P) *Raymond Davis Jr.* and *Masatoshi Koshiba* for the detection of cosmic neutrinos and *Riccardo Giacconi* for contributions to astrophysics that led to the discovery of cosmic x-ray sources.

Answers to Odd-Numbered Problems

CHAPTER 1

1. 0.141 nm

3. 2.15×10^4 kg/m^3

5. $4\pi\rho(r_2{}^3 - r_1{}^3)/3$

7. (a) 4.00 u $= 6.64 \times 10^{-24}$ g (b) 55.9 u $= 9.28 \times 10^{-23}$ g (c) 207 u $= 3.44 \times 10^{-22}$ g

9. 8.72×10^{11} atom/s

11. (a) 72.6 kg (b) 7.82×10^{26} atoms

13. No.

15. (b) only

17. The units of G are m^3/kg$\cdot$s^2

19. 9.19 nm/s

21. 1.39×10^3 m^2

23. (a) 0.071 4 gal/s (b) 2.70×10^{-4} m^3/s (c) 1.03 h

25. 11.4×10^3 kg/m^3

27. 667 lb/s

29. (a) 190 yr (b) 2.32×10^4 times

31. 151 μm

33. 1.00×10^{10} lb

35. (a) 2.07 mm (b) 8.62×10^{13} times as large

37. 5.0 m

39. 2.86 cm

41. $\sim 10^6$ balls

43. $\sim 10^7$

45. $\sim 10^2$ kg; $\sim 10^3$ kg

47. $\sim 10^2$ tuners

49. (a) (346 ± 13) m^2 (b) (66.0 ± 1.3) m

51. $(1.61 \pm 0.17) \times 10^3$ kg/m^3

53. 31 556 926.0 s

55. 5.2 m^3, 3%

57. 2.57×10^{-10} m

59. $0.579\, t$ ft^3/s $+ 1.19 \times 10^{-9}\, t^2$ ft^3/s^2

61. 3.41 m

63. 0.449%

65. (a) 0.529 cm/s (b) 11.5 cm/s

67. 1×10^{10} gal/yr

69. $\sim 10^{11}$ stars

71. (a) 3.16×10^7 s/yr (b) 6.05×10^{10} yr

CHAPTER 2

1. (a) 2.30 m/s (b) 16.1 m/s (c) 11.5 m/s

3. (a) 5 m/s (b) 1.2 m/s (c) -2.5 m/s (d) -3.3 m/s (e) 0

5. (a) 3.75 m/s (b) 0

7. (a) -2.4 m/s (b) -3.8 m/s (c) 4.0 s

9. (a) 5.0 m/s (b) -2.5 m/s (c) 0 (d) 5.0 m/s

11. 1.34×10^4 m/s^2

13. (a) 52.4 ft/s, 55.0 ft/s, 55.5 ft/s, 57.4 ft/s (b) 0.598 ft/s^2

15. (a) 2.00 m (b) -3.00 m/s (c) -2.00 m/s^2

17. (a) 1.3 m/s^2 (b) 2.0 m/s^2 at 3 s (c) at $t = 6$ s and for $t > 10$ s (d) -1.5 m/s^2 at 8 s

19. 2.74×10^5 m/s^2, which is 2.79×10^4 g

21. -16.0 cm/s^2

23. (a) 4.53 s (b) 14.1 m/s

25. (a) 2.56 m (b) -3.00 m/s

27. (a) 20.0 s (b) no

29. 3.10 m/s

31. (a) -202 m/s^2 (b) 198 m

33. (a) 4.98×10^{-9} s (b) 1.20×10^{15} m/s^2

35. (a) v_c/t_m (c) $v_c t_0/2$ (d) $v_c t_0$ (e) yes, no

37. (a) 3.00 m/s (b) 6.00 s (c) -0.300 m/s^2 (d) 2.05 m/s

39. 31 s

41. $99.3/h

43. (a) 10.0 m/s up (b) 4.68 m/s down

45. (a) 2.17 s (b) -21.2 m/s (c) 2.23 s

47. (a) 29.4 m/s (b) 44.1 m

49. (a) 7.82 m (b) 0.782 s

51. 7.96 s

53. (a) $a_x(t) = a_{xi} + Jt$, $v_x(t) = v_{xi} + a_{xi}t + (1/2)Jt^2$, $x(t) = x_i + v_{xi}t + (1/2)a_{xi}t^2 + (1/6)Jt^3$

55. (a) $a = -(10.0 \times 10^7$ m/s$^3)t + 3.00 \times 10^5$ m/s^2; $x = -(1.67 \times 10^7$ m/s$^3)t^3 + (1.50 \times 10^5$ m/s$^2)t^2$ (b) 3.00×10^{-3} s (c) 450 m/s (d) 0.900 m

59. (a) Acela steadily cruises out of the city center at 45 mi/h. In less than a minute it smoothly speeds up to 150 mi/h; then its speed is nudged up to 170 mi/h. Next it smoothly slows to a very low speed, which it maintains as it rolls into a railroad yard. When it stops, it immediately begins backing up and smoothly speeds up to 50 mi/h in reverse, all in less than seven minutes after it started. (b) 2.2 mi/h/s $= 0.98$ m/s^2 (c) 6.7 mi

61. 48.0 mm

63. (a) 15.0 s (b) 30.0 m/s (c) 225 m

65. (a) 5.43 m/s^2 and 3.83 m/s^2 (b) 10.9 m/s and 11.5 m/s (c) Maggie by 2.62 m

67. $\sim 10^3$ m/s^2

69. (a) 3.00 s   (b) −15.3 m/s   (c) 31.4 m/s down and 34.8 m/s down

71. (c) v_{boy}^2/h, 0   (d) v_{boy}, 0

73. (a) 5.46 s   (b) 73.0 m
(c) $v_{Stan} = 22.6$ m/s, $v_{Kathy} = 26.7$ m/s

75. $0.577v$

CHAPTER 3

1. $(-2.75, -4.76)$ m

3. (a) 2.24 m   (b) 2.24 m at 26.6°

5. $y = 1.15$; $r = 2.31$

7. 70.0 m

9. 310 km at 57° S of W

11. (a) 10.0 m   (b) 15.7 m   (c) 0

13. (a) $\sim 10^5$ m   vertically   upward   (b) $\sim 10^3$ m   vertically upward

15. (a) 5.2 m at 60°   (b) 3.0 m at 330°   (c) 3.0 m at 150°
(d) 5.2 m at 300°

17. approximately 420 ft at −3°

19. 47.2 units at 122°

21. (a) $(-11.1\hat{i} + 6.40\hat{j})$ m   (b) $(1.65\hat{i} + 2.86\hat{j})$ cm
(c) $(-18.0\hat{i} - 12.6\hat{j})$ in.

23. (a) 5.00 blocks at 53.1° N of E   (b) 13.0 blocks

25. 358 m at 2.00° S of E

27. (a)

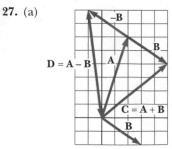

(b) $\mathbf{C} = 5.00\hat{i} + 4.00\hat{j}$ or 6.40 at 38.7°; $\mathbf{D} = -1.00\hat{i} + 8.00\hat{j}$ or 8.06 at 97.2°

29. 196 cm at 345°

31. (a) $2.00\hat{i} - 6.00\hat{j}$ (b) $4.00\hat{i} + 2.00\hat{j}$ (c) 6.32
(d) 4.47   (e) 288°; 26.6°

33. 9.48 m at 166°

35. (a) 185 N at 77.8° from the $+x$ axis
(b) $(-39.3\hat{i} - 181\hat{j})$ N

37. $\mathbf{A} + \mathbf{B} = (2.60\hat{i} + 4.50\hat{j})$ m

39. $|\mathbf{B}| = 7.81$, $\theta_x = 59.2°$, $\theta_y = 39.8°$, $\theta_z = 67.4°$

41. (a) $8.00\hat{i} + 12.0\hat{j} - 4.00\hat{k}$ (b) $2.00\hat{i} + 3.00\hat{j} - 1.00\hat{k}$
(c) $-24.0\hat{i} - 36.0\hat{j} + 12.0\hat{k}$

43. (a) 5.92 m is the magnitude of $(5.00\hat{i} - 1.00\hat{j} - 3.00\hat{k})$ m
(b) 19.0 m is the magnitude of $(4.00\hat{i} - 11.0\hat{j} - 15.0\hat{k})$ m

45. 157 km

47. (a) $-3.00\hat{i} + 2.00\hat{j}$ (b) 3.61 at 146°
(c) $3.00\hat{i} - 6.00\hat{j}$

49. (a) $49.5\hat{i} + 27.1\hat{j}$ (b) 56.4 units at 28.7°

51. 1.15°

53. (a) 2.00, 1.00, 3.00   (b) 3.74   (c) $\theta_x = 57.7°$,
$\theta_y = 74.5°$, $\theta_z = 36.7°$

55. 2.29 km

57. (a) 11.2 m   (b) 12.9 m at 36.4°

59. 240 m at 237°

61. 390 mi/h at 7.37° north of east

63. (a) zero   (b) zero

65. 106°

CHAPTER 4

1. (a) 4.87 km at 209° from east   (b) 23.3 m/s   (c) 13.5 m/s at 209°

3. 2.50 m/s

5. (a) $(2.00\hat{i} + 3.00\hat{j})$ m/s^2
(b) $(3.00t + t^2)\hat{i}$ m + $(1.50t^2 - 2.00t)\hat{j}$ m

7. (a) $(0.800\hat{i} - 0.300\hat{j})$ m/s^2 (b) 339°
(c) $(360\hat{i} - 72.7\hat{j})$ m, −15.2°

9. (a) $x = 0.010\ 0$ m, $y = 2.41 \times 10^{-4}$ m
(b) $\mathbf{v} = (1.84 \times 10^7\hat{i} + 8.78 \times 10^5\hat{j})$ m/s
(c) $v = 1.85 \times 10^7$ m/s
(d) $\theta = 2.73°$

11. (a) $3.34\hat{i}$ m/s   (b) −50.9°

13. (a) 20.0°   (b) 3.05 s

15. 53.1°

17. (a) 22.6 m   (b) 52.3 m   (c) 1.18 s

19. (a) The ball clears by 0.889 m while
(b) descending

21. (a) 18.1 m/s   (b) 1.13 m   (c) 2.79 m

23. 9.91 m/s

25. (a) 30.3 m/s   (b) 2.09 s

27. 377 m/s^2

29. 10.5 m/s, 219 m/s^2 inward

31. (a) 6.00 rev/s   (b) 1.52 km/s^2
(c) 1.28 km/s^2

33. 1.48 m/s^2 inward and 29.9° backward

35. (a) 13.0 m/s^2 (b) 5.70 m/s   (c) 7.50 m/s^2

37. $\theta = \tan^{-1}(1/4\pi) = 4.55°$

39. (a) 57.7 km/h at 60.0° west of vertical
(b) 28.9 km/h downward

41. 2.02×10^3 s; 21.0% longer

43. $t_{Alan} = \dfrac{2L/c}{1 - v^2/c^2}$, $t_{Beth} = \dfrac{2L/c}{\sqrt{1 - v^2/c^2}}$. Beth returns first.

45. 15.3 m

47. (a) 101 m/s   (b) 32 700 ft   (c) 20.6 s
(d) 180 m/s

49. 54.4 m/s^2

51. (a) 41.7 m/s   (b) 3.81 s   (c) $(34.1\hat{i} - 13.4\hat{j})$ m/s;
36.7 m/s

53. (a) 25.0 m/s^2; 9.80 m/s^2

(b)

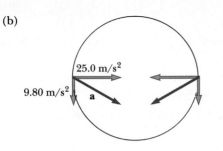

(c) 26.8 m/s^2 inward at 21.4° below the horizontal

55. (a) 26.6°   (b) 0.949

57. (a) 0.600 m   (b) 0.402 m   (c) 1.87 m/s^2 toward center
   (d) 9.80 m/s^2 down

59. (a) 6.80 km   (b) 3.00 km vertically above the impact
   point   (c) 66.2°

61. (a) 46.5 m/s   (b) −77.6°   (c) 6.34 s

63. (a) 20.0 m/s, 5.00 s   (b) $(16.0\hat{\mathbf{i}} − 27.1\hat{\mathbf{j}})$ m/s   (c) 6.53 s
   (d) $24.5\hat{\mathbf{i}}$ m

65. (a) 22.9 m/s   (b) 360 m from the base of the cliff
   (c) $\mathbf{v} = (114\hat{\mathbf{i}} − 44.3\hat{\mathbf{j}})$ m/s

67. (a) 43.2 m   (b) $(9.66\hat{\mathbf{i}} − 25.5\hat{\mathbf{j}})$ m/s

69. (a) 4.00 km/h   (b) 4.00 km/h

71. Safe distances are less than 270 m or greater than
   3.48×10^3 m from the western shore.

CHAPTER 5

1. (a) 1/3   (b) 0.750 m/s^2

3. $(6.00\hat{\mathbf{i}} + 15.0\hat{\mathbf{j}})$ N; 16.2 N

5. (a) $(2.50\hat{\mathbf{i}} + 5.00\hat{\mathbf{j}})$ N   (b) 5.59 N

7. (a) 3.64×10^{-18} N   (b) 8.93×10^{-30} N is 408 billion
   times smaller

9. 2.38 kN

11. (a) 5.00 m/s^2 at 36.9°   (b) 6.08 m/s^2 at 25.3°

13. (a) $\sim 10^{-22}$ m/s^2 (b) $\sim 10^{-23}$ m

15. (a) 15.0 lb up   (b) 5.00 lb up   (c) 0

17. 613 N

9.80 N

21. (a) 49.0 N   (b) 98.0 N   (c) 24.5 N

23. 8.66 N east

25. 3.73 m

27. A is in compression 3.83 kN and B is in tension 3.37 kN

29. 950 N

31. (a) $F_x > 19.6$ N   (b) $F_x \le − 78.4$ N
   (c)

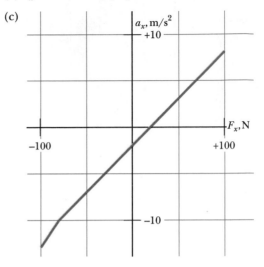

33. (a) 706 N   (b) 814 N   (c) 706 N   (d) 648 N

35. (a) 0.404   (b) 45.8 lb

37. (a) 256 m   (b) 42.7 m

39. (a) 1.10 s   (b) 0.875 s

41. (a) 1.78 m/s^2 (b) 0.368   (c) 9.37 N   (d) 2.67 m/s

43. 37.8 N

45. (a)

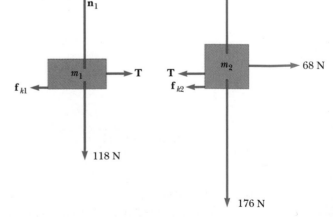

(b) 27.2 N, 1.29 m/s^2

47. $\mu_k = (3/5)\tan\theta$

49. (a) 8.05 N   (b) 53.2 N   (c) 42.0 N

51. (a)

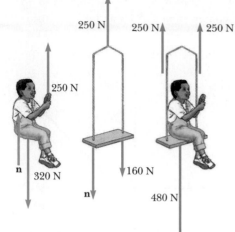

250 N 250 N 250 N

250 N

n 320 N 160 N

n 480 N

(b) 0.408 m/s² (c) 83.3 N

53. (a) $F_A = mg(\sin\theta - \mu_s \cos\theta)$
(b) $F_B = mg(\sin\theta - \mu_s \cos\theta)/(\cos\theta + \mu_s \sin\theta)$
(c) A's job is easier
(d) B's job is easier

55. (a) $Mg/2$, $Mg/2$, $Mg/2$, $3Mg/2$, Mg (b) $Mg/2$

57. (b)

θ	0	15°	30°	45°	60°
P(N)	40.0	46.4	60.1	94.3	260

59. (a) 19.3° (b) 4.21 N

61. $(M + m_1 + m_2)(m_2g/m_1)$

63. (a) $m_2g\left[\dfrac{m_1M}{m_1M + m_2(m_1 + M)}\right]$

(b) $\dfrac{m_2g(M + m_1)}{m_1M + m_2(m_1 + M)}$

(c) $\dfrac{m_1m_2g}{m_1M + m_2(m_1 + M)}$

(d) $\dfrac{Mm_2g}{m_1M + m_2(m_1 + M)}$

65. (c) 3.56 N

67. (a) $T = f/(2\sin\theta)$ (b) 410 N

69. (a) 30.7° (b) 0.843 N

71. 0.060 0 m

73. (a) $T_1 = \dfrac{2mg}{\sin\theta_1}$

$T_2 = \dfrac{mg}{\sin\theta_2} = \dfrac{mg}{\sin[\tan^{-1}(\frac{1}{2}\tan\theta_1)]}$

$T_3 = 2mg/\tan\theta_1$

(b) $\theta_2 = \tan^{-1}\left(\dfrac{\tan\theta_1}{2}\right)$

CHAPTER 6

1. Any speed up to 8.08 m/s

3. (a) 8.32×10^{-8} N toward the nucleus
(b) 9.13×10^{22} m/s² inward

5. (a) static friction (b) 0.085 0

7. $v \le 14.3$ m/s

9. (a) 68.6 N toward the center of the circle and 784 N up
(b) 0.857 m/s²

11. (a) 108 N (b) 56.2 N

13. (a) 4.81 m/s (b) 700 N up

15. No. The jungle lord needs a vine of tensile strength 1.38 kN.

17. 3.13 m/s

19. (a) 2.49×10^4 N up (b) 12.1 m/s

21. (a) 3.60 m/s² (b) zero (c) An observer in the car (a noninertial frame) claims an 18.0-N force toward the left and an 18.0-N force toward the right. An inertial observer (outside the car) claims only an 18.0-N force toward the right.

23. (a) 17.0° (b) 5.12 N

25. (a) 491 N (b) 50.1 kg (c) 2.00 m/s²

27. (a) $v = [2(a - \mu_k g)\ell]^{1/2}$; (b) $v' = (2\mu_k g\ell/v)$, where $v = [2(a - \mu_k g)\ell]^{1/2}$

29. 93.8 N

31. 0.092 7°

33. (a) 32.7 s⁻¹ (b) 9.80 m/s² down (c) 4.90 m/s² down

35. 3.01 N up

37. (a) 1.47 N·s/m (b) 2.04×10^{-3} s (c) 2.94×10^{-2} N

39. (a) $0.034\,7$ s⁻¹ (b) 2.50 m/s (c) $a = -cv$

41. (a) $x = k^{-1}\ln(1 + kv_0t)$ (b) $v = v_0e^{-kx}$

43. $\sim 10^1$ N

45. (a) 13.7 m/s down

(b)

t (s)	x (m)	v (m/s)
0	0	0
0.2	0	−1.96
0.4	−0.392	−3.88
... 1.0	−3.77	−8.71
... 2.0	−14.4	−12.56
... 4.0	−41.0	−13.67

47. (a) 49.5 m/s down and 4.95 m/s down

(b)

t (s)	y (m)	v (m/s)
0	1 000	0
... 1	995	−9.7
... 2	980	−18.6
... 10	674	−47.7
... 10.1	671	−16.7
... 12	659	−4.95
... 145	0	−4.95

49. (a) 2.33×10^{-4} kg/m (b) 57.0 m/s (c) 44.9 m/s. The second trajectory is higher and shorter than the first. In both cases, the ball attains maximum height when it has covered 56% of its horizontal range, and attains minimum speed a little later. The impact speeds are also similar, 30 m/s and 29 m/s.

51. (a) 11.5 kN   (b) 14.1 m/s = 50.9 km/h

53. (a) 0.016 2 kg/m   (b) $\frac{1}{2}D\rho A$ (c) 0.778   (d) 1.5%
(e) For stacked coffee filters falling in air at terminal speed, the graph of resistive force as a function of squared speed demonstrates that the force is proportional to the speed squared, within the experimental uncertainty, estimated as ±2%. This proportionality agrees with that predicted by the theoretical equation $R = \frac{1}{2}D\rho Av^2$. The value of the constant slope of the graph implies that the drag coefficient for coffee filters is $D = 0.78 \pm 2\%$.

55. $g(\cos\phi\tan\theta - \sin\phi)$

57. (b) 732 N down at the equator and 735 N down at the poles

59. (a) 967 lb   (b) −647 lb (pilot must be strapped in)   (c) Speed and radius of path can be adjusted so that $v^2 = gR$.

61. (a) 1.58 m/s²   (b) 455 N   (c) 329 N   (d) 397 N upward and 9.15° inward

63. (a) 5.19 m/s   (b) $T = 555$ N

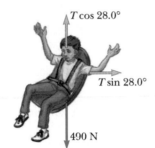

65. (b) 2.54 s; 23.6 rev/min

67. (a) $v_{\min} = \sqrt{\dfrac{Rg(\tan\theta - \mu_s)}{1 + \mu_s\tan\theta}}$, $v_{\max} = \sqrt{\dfrac{Rg(\tan\theta + \mu_s)}{1 - \mu_s\tan\theta}}$
(b) $\mu_s = \tan\theta$ (c) 8.57 m/s ≤ v ≤ 16.6 m/s

69. (a) 0.013 2 m/s   (b) 1.03 m/s   (c) 6.87 m/s

71. 12.8 N

73. $\sum\mathbf{F} = -km\mathbf{v}$

CHAPTER 7

1. (a) 31.9 J   (b) 0   (c) 0   (d) 31.9 J

3. −4.70 kJ

5. 28.9

7. (a) 16.0 J   (b) 36.9°

9. (a) 11.3°   (b) 156°   (c) 82.3°

11. (a) 24.0 J   (b) −3.00 J   (c) 21.0 J

13. (a) 7.50 J   (b) 15.0 J   (c) 7.50 J   (d) 30.0 J

15. (a) 0.938 cm   (b) 1.25 J

17. (a) 0.768 m   (b) 1.68 × 10⁵ J

19. 12.0 J

21. (a) 0.020 4 m   (b) 720 N/m

23. kg/s²

25. (a) 33.8 J   (b) 135 J

27. 878 kN up

29. (a) 4.56 kJ   (b) 6.34 kN   (c) 422 km/s²   (d) 6.34 kN

31. (a) 650 J   (b) 588 J   (c) 0   (d) 0   (e) 62.0 J   (f) 1.76 m/s

33. (a) −168 J   (b) 184 J   (c) 500 J   (d) 148 J   (e) 5.65 m/s

35. 2.04 m

37. 875 W

39. (a) 20.6 kJ   (b) 686 W

41. $46.2

43. (a) 423 mi/gal   (b) 776 mi/gal

45. (a) 0.013 5 gal   (b) 73.8   (c) 8.08 kW

47. 2.92 m/s

49. (a) $(2 + 24t^2 + 72t^4)$ J   (b) $12t$ m/s²; $48t$ N   (c) $(48t + 288t^3)$ W   (d) 1 250 J

51. $k_1 x_{\max}^2/2 + k_2 x_{\max}^3/3$

53. (a) $\sqrt{2W/m}$ (b) W/d

55. (b) 240 W

57. (a) 1.38 × 10⁴ J   (b) 3.02 × 10⁴ W

59. (a) $\mathcal{P} = 2Mgv_T$ (b) $\mathcal{P} = 24Mgv_T$

61. (a) 4.12 m   (b) 3.35 m

63. 1.68 m/s

65. −1.37 × 10⁻²¹ J

67. 0.799 J

69. (b) For a block of weight w pushed over a rough horizontal surface at constant velocity, $b = \mu_k$. For a load pulled vertically upward at constant velocity, $b = 1$.

CHAPTER 8

1. (a) 259 kJ, 0, −259 kJ   (b) 0, −259 kJ, −259 kJ

3. 22.0 kW

5. (a) $v = (3gR)^{1/2}$ (b) 0.098 0 N down

7. (a) 1.47 m/s   (b) 1.35 m/s

9. (a) 2.29 m/s   (b) 1.98 m/s

11. 10.2 m

13. (a) 4.43 m/s   (b) 5.00 m

15. 5.49 m/s

17. (a) 18.5 km, 51.0 km   (b) 10.0 MJ

19. (a) 25.8 m   (b) 27.1 m/s²

21. (a) −196 J   (b) −196 J   (c) −196 J. The force is conservative.

23. (a) 125 J   (b) 50.0 J   (c) 66.7 J   (d) Nonconservative. The results differ.

25. (a) −9.00 J; no; the force is conservative.   (b) 3.39 m/s   (c) 9.00 J

27. 26.5 m/s

29. 6.92 m/s

31. 3.74 m/s

33. (a) -160 J (b) 73.5 J (c) 28.8 N (d) 0.679

35. (a) 1.40 m/s (b) 4.60 cm after release (c) 1.79 m/s

37. (a) 0.381 m (b) 0.143 m (c) 0.371 m

39. (a) $a_x = -\mu_k gx/L$ (b) $v = (\mu_k gL)^{1/2}$

41. (a) 40.0 J (b) -40.0 J (c) 62.5 J

43. (A/r^2) away from the other particle

45. (a) $+$ at Ⓑ, $-$ at Ⓓ, 0 at Ⓐ, Ⓒ, and Ⓔ (b) Ⓒ stable; Ⓐ and Ⓔ unstable

(c)

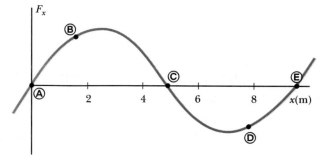

47. (b)

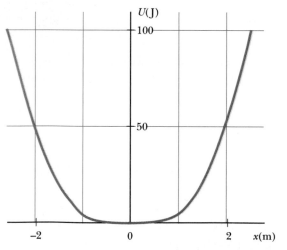

Equilibrium at $x = 0$

(c) 0.823 m/s

49. $\sim 10^3$ W peak or $\sim 10^2$ W sustainable

51. 48.2°

53. (a) 0.225 J (b) $\Delta E_{\text{mech}} = -0.363$ J (c) No; the normal force changes in a complicated way.

55. (a) 23.6 cm (b) 5.90 m/s^2 up the incline; no. (c) Gravitational potential energy is transformed into kinetic energy plus elastic potential energy and then entirely into elastic potential energy.

57. 0.328

59. 1.24 m/s

61. (a) 0.400 m (b) 4.10 m/s (c) The block stays on the track.

63. $(h/5)(4\sin^2\theta + 1)$

65. (a) 6.15 m/s (b) 9.87 m/s

67. (a) 11.1 m/s (b) 19.6 m/s^2 upward (c) 2.23×10^3 N upward (d) 1.01×10^3 J (e) 5.14 m/s (f) 1.35 m (g) 1.39 s

69. (b) 1.44 m (c) 0.400 m (d) No. A very strong wind pulls the string out horizontally. The largest possible equilibrium height is equal to L.

73. (a) 2.5R

CHAPTER 9

1. (a) $(9.00\hat{\mathbf{i}} - 12.0\hat{\mathbf{j}})$ kg·m/s (b) 15.0 kg·m/s at 307°

3. $\sim 10^{-23}$ m/s

5. (b) $p = \sqrt{2mK}$

7. (a) 13.5 N·s (b) 9.00 kN (c) 18.0 kN

9. 260 N normal to the wall

11. (a) $(9.05\hat{\mathbf{i}} + 6.12\hat{\mathbf{j}})$ N·s (b) $(377\hat{\mathbf{i}} + 255\hat{\mathbf{j}})$ N

13. 15.0 N in the direction of the initial velocity of the exiting water stream

15. 65.2 m/s

17. 301 m/s

19. (a) 2.50 m/s (b) 37.5 kJ (c) Each process is the time-reversal of the other. The same momentum conservation equation describes both.

21. (a) $v_{gx} = 1.15$ m/s (b) $v_{px} = -0.346$ m/s

23. (a) 0.284 (b) 115 fJ and 45.4 fJ

25. 91.2 m/s

27. (a) 2.24 m/s to the right (b) No. Coupling order makes no difference.

29. $v_{\text{orange}} = 3.99$ m/s, $v_{\text{yellow}} = 3.01$ m/s

31. $v_{\text{green}} = 7.07$ m/s, $v_{\text{blue}} = 5.89$ m/s

33. 2.50 m/s at $-60.0°$

35. $(3.00\hat{\mathbf{i}} - 1.20\hat{\mathbf{j}})$ m/s

37. (a) $(-9.33\hat{\mathbf{i}} - 8.33\hat{\mathbf{j}})$ Mm/s (b) 439 fJ

39. 0.006 73 nm from the oxygen nucleus along the bisector of the angle

41. $\mathbf{r}_{\text{CM}} = (11.7\hat{\mathbf{i}} + 13.3\hat{\mathbf{j}})$ cm

43. (a) 15.9 g (b) 0.153 m

45. (a) $(1.40\hat{\mathbf{i}} + 2.40\hat{\mathbf{j}})$ m/s (b) $(7.00\hat{\mathbf{i}} + 12.0\hat{\mathbf{j}})$ kg·m/s

47. 0.700 m

49. (a) 39.0 MN (b) 3.20 m/s^2 up

51. (a) 442 metric tons (b) 19.2 metric tons

53. 4.41 kg

55. (a) $1.33\hat{\mathbf{i}}$ m/s (b) $-235\hat{\mathbf{i}}$ N (c) 0.680 s (d) $-160\hat{\mathbf{i}}$ N·s and $+160\hat{\mathbf{i}}$ N·s (e) 1.81 m (f) 0.454 m (g) -427 J (h) $+107$ J (i) Equal friction forces act through different distances on person and cart, to do different amounts of work on them. The total work on both together, -320 J, becomes $+320$ J of extra internal energy in this perfectly inelastic collision.

57. 240 s

59. (a) 0; inelastic (b) $(-0.250\hat{\mathbf{i}} + 0.750\hat{\mathbf{j}} - 2.00\hat{\mathbf{k}})$ m/s; perfectly inelastic (c) either $a = -6.74$ with $\mathbf{v} = -0.419\hat{\mathbf{k}}$ m/s or $a = 2.74$ with $\mathbf{v} = -3.58\hat{\mathbf{k}}$ m/s

61. (a) $v_i = v(m + \rho V)/m$ (b) The cart slows with constant acceleration and eventually comes to rest.

63. (a) $m/M = 0.403$ (b) No changes; no difference.

65. (a) 6.29 m/s (b) 6.16 m/s

67. (a) 100 m/s (b) 374 J

69. (a) $(20.0\hat{\mathbf{i}} + 7.00\hat{\mathbf{j}})$ m/s (b) $4.00\hat{\mathbf{i}}$ m/s^2 (c) $4.00\hat{\mathbf{i}}$ m/s^2 (d) $(50.0\hat{\mathbf{i}} + 35.0\hat{\mathbf{j}})$ m (e) 600 J (f) 674 J (g) 674 J

71. $(3Mgx/L)\hat{\mathbf{j}}$

73. $\dfrac{m_1(R + \ell/2)}{(m_1 + m_2)}$

CHAPTER 10

1. (a) 5.00 rad, 10.0 rad/s, 4.00 rad/s^2 (b) 53.0 rad, 22.0 rad/s, 4.00 rad/s^2

3. (a) 4.00 rad/s^2 (b) 18.0 rad

5. (a) 5.24 s (b) 27.4 rad

7. 50.0 rev

9. (a) 7.27×10^{-5} rad/s (b) 2.57×10^4 s $= 428$ min

11. $\sim 10^7$ rev

13. (a) 8.00 rad/s (b) 8.00 m/s, $a_r = -64.0$ m/s^2, $a_t = 4.00$ m/s^2 (c) 9.00 rad

15. (a) 25.0 rad/s (b) 39.8 rad/s^2 (c) 0.628 s

17. (a) 126 rad/s (b) 3.77 m/s (c) 1.26 km/s^2 (d) 20.1 m

19. (a) $\omega(2h^3/g)^{1/2}$ (b) 0.011 6 m (c) Yes; the deflection is only 0.02% of the original height.

21. (a) 143 kg·m^2 (b) 2.57 kJ

23. $11mL^2/12$

25. 5.80 kg·m^2; the height makes no difference

29. $(23/48)MR^2\omega^2$

31. -3.55 N·m

33. 8.02×10^3 N

35. (a) 24.0 N·m (b) 0.035 6 rad/s^2 (c) 1.07 m/s^2

37. (a) 0.309 m/s^2 (b) 7.67 N and 9.22 N

39. 21.5 N

41. 24.5 km

43. (a) 1.59 m/s (b) 53.1 rad/s

45. (a) 11.4 N, 7.57 m/s^2, 9.53 m/s down (b) 9.53 m/s

49. (a) $2(Rg/3)^{1/2}$ (b) $4(Rg/3)^{1/2}$ (c) $(Rg)^{1/2}$

51. (a) 500 J (b) 250 J (c) 750 J

53. (a) $\frac{2}{3}g\sin\theta$ for the disk, larger than $\frac{1}{2}g\sin\theta$ for the hoop (b) $\frac{1}{3}\tan\theta$

55. 1.21×10^{-4} kg·m^2; height is unnecessary

57. $\frac{1}{3}\ell$

59. (a) 4.00 J (b) 1.60 s (c) yes

61. (a) $(3g/L)^{1/2}$ (b) $3g/2L$ (c) $-\frac{3}{2}g\hat{\mathbf{i}} - \frac{3}{4}g\hat{\mathbf{j}}$ (d) $-\frac{3}{2}Mg\hat{\mathbf{i}} + \frac{1}{4}Mg\hat{\mathbf{j}}$

63. -0.322 rad/s^2

65. (b) $2gM(\sin\theta - \mu\cos\theta)(m + 2M)^{-1}$

67. (a) $\sim -10^{-22}$ s^{-2} (b) $\sim -10^{16}$ N·m (c) $\sim 10^{13}$ m

71. (a) 118 N and 156 N (b) 1.17 kg·m^2

73. (a) $\alpha = -0.176$ rad/s^2 (b) 1.29 rev (c) 9.26 rev

75. (a) 61.2 J (b) 50.8 J

79. (a) $2.70R$ (b) $F_x = -20mg/7$, $F_y = -mg$

81. $\sim 10^1$ m

83. (a) $(3gh/4)^{1/2}$ (b) $(3gh/4)^{1/2}$

85. (c) $(8Fd/3M)^{1/2}$

87. $\mathbf{F}_1$ to right, $\mathbf{F}_2$ no rolling, $\mathbf{F}_3$ and $\mathbf{F}_4$ to left

CHAPTER 11

1. $-7.00\hat{\mathbf{i}} + 16.0\hat{\mathbf{j}} - 10.0\hat{\mathbf{k}}$

3. (a) $-17.0\hat{\mathbf{k}}$ (b) 70.6°

5. 0.343 N·m horizontally north

7. 45.0°

9. $F_3 = F_1 + F_2$; no

11. $(17.5\hat{\mathbf{k}})$ kg·m^2/s

13. $(60.0\hat{\mathbf{k}})$ kg·m^2/s

15. $mvR[\cos(vt/R) + 1]\hat{\mathbf{k}}$

17. (a) zero (b) $[-mv_i^3 \sin^2\theta\cos\theta/2g]\hat{\mathbf{k}}$ (c) $[-2mv_i^3 \sin^2\theta\cos\theta/g]\hat{\mathbf{k}}$ (d) The downward gravitational force exerts a torque in the $-z$ direction.

19. $-m\ell gt\cos\theta\hat{\mathbf{k}}$

23. (a) 0.360 kg·m^2/s (b) 0.540 kg·m^2/s

25. (a) 0.433 kg·m^2/s (b) 1.73 kg·m^2/s

27. (a) 1.57×10^8 kg·m^2/s (b) 6.26×10^3 s $= 1.74$ h

29. 7.14 rev/min

31. (a) 9.20 rad/s (b) 9.20 rad/s

33. (a) 0.360 rad/s counterclockwise (b) 99.9 J

35. (a) $mv\ell$ down (b) $M/(M + m)$

37. (a) $\omega = 2mv_id/(M + 2m)R^2$ (b) No; some mechanical energy changes into internal energy

39. $\sim 10^{-13}$ rad/s

41. 5.45×10^{22} N·m

43. 7.50×10^{-11} s

45. (a) $7md^2/3$ (b) $mgd\,\hat{\mathbf{k}}$ (c) $3g/7d$ counterclockwise (d) $2g/7$ upward (e) mgd (f) $\sqrt{6g/7d}$ (g) $m\sqrt{14gd^3/3}$ (h) $\sqrt{2gd/21}$

47. 0.910 km/s

49. (a) $v_i r_i/r$ (b) $T = (mv_i^2 r_i^2)r^{-3}$ (c) $\frac{1}{2}mv_i^2(r_i^2/r^2 - 1)$ (d) 4.50 m/s, 10.1 N, 0.450 J

51. (a) 3 750 kg·m^2/s (b) 1.88 kJ (c) 3 750 kg·m^2/s (d) 10.0 m/s (e) 7.50 kJ (f) 5.62 kJ

53. An increase of 0.550 s

55. $4[ga(\sqrt{2} - 1)/3]^{1/2}$

CHAPTER 12

1. 10.0 N up; 6.00 N·m counterclockwise

3. $[(m_1 + m_b)d + (m_1\ell/2)]/m_2$

5. (3.85 cm, 6.85 cm)

7. $(-1.50$ m, -1.50 m)

9. 177 kg

11. 8.33%

13. (a) $f_s = 268$ N, $n = 1\,300$ N   (b) 0.324

15. (a) 1.04 kN at 60.0°   (b) $(370\hat{\mathbf{i}} + 900\hat{\mathbf{j}})$ N

17. 2.94 kN on each rear wheel and 4.41 kN on each front wheel

19. (a) 29.9 N   (b) 22.2 N

21. (a) 1.73 rad/s²   (b) 1.56 rad/s
    (c) $(-4.72\hat{\mathbf{i}} + 6.62\hat{\mathbf{j}})$ kN   (d) $38.9\hat{\mathbf{j}}$ kN

23. 2.82 m

25. 88.2 N and 58.8 N

27. 4.90 mm

29. 10×10^{10} N/m²

31. 23.8 μm

33. (a) 3.14×10^4 N   (b) 6.28×10^4 N

35. 1.65×10^8 N/m²

37. 0.860 mm

39. $n_A = 5.98 \times 10^5$ N, $n_B = 4.80 \times 10^5$ N

41. 9.00 ft

43. (a)

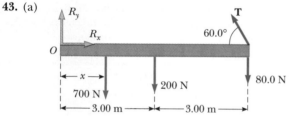

(b) $T = 343$ N; $R_x = 171$ N to the right, $R_y = 683$ N up
    (c) 5.13 m

45. (a) $T = F_g(L + d)/\sin\theta\,(2L + d)$
    (b) $R_x = F_g(L + d)\cot\theta/(2L + d)$; $R_y = F_gL/(2L + d)$

47. $\mathbf{F}_A = (-6.47 \times 10^5\hat{\mathbf{i}} + 1.27 \times 10^5\hat{\mathbf{j}})$ N,
    $\mathbf{F}_B = 6.47 \times 10^5\hat{\mathbf{i}}$ N

49. 5.08 kN; $R_x = 4.77$ kN, $R_y = 8.26$ kN

51. $T = 2.71$ kN, $R_x = 2.65$ kN

53. (a) 20.1 cm to the left of the front edge; $\mu_k = 0.571$
    (b) 0.501 m

55. (a) $M = (m/2)(2\mu_s\sin\theta - \cos\theta)(\cos\theta - \mu_s\sin\theta)^{-1}$
    (b) $R = (m + M)g(1 + \mu_s^2)^{1/2}$;
    $F = g[M^2 + \mu_s^2(m + M)^2]^{1/2}$

57. (a) 133 N   (b) $n_A = 429$ N and $n_B = 257$ N
    (c) $R_x = 133$ N and $R_y = -257$ N

59. 66.7 N

63. 1.09 m

65. (a) 4 500 N   (b) 4.50×10^6 N/m²   (c) The board will break.

67. 5.73 rad/s

69. $n_A = 11.0$ kN, $n_E = 3.67$ kN; $F_{AB} = F_{DE} = 7.35$ kN compression; $F_{AC} = F_{CE} = 6.37$ kN compression; $F_{BC} = F_{CD} =$ 4.24 kN tension; $F_{BD} = 8.49$ kN compression

71. (a) $P_y = (F_g/L)(d - ah/g)$ (b) 0.306 m
    (c) $(-306\hat{\mathbf{i}} + 5.53\hat{\mathbf{j}})$ N

73. Decrease h, increase d

CHAPTER 13

1. $\sim 10^{-7}$ N toward you

3. (a) 2.50×10^{-5} N toward the 500-kg object
    (b) between the objects and 0.245 m from the 500-kg object

5. $(-100\hat{\mathbf{i}} + 59.3\hat{\mathbf{j}})$ pN

7. 7.41×10^{-10} N

9. 0.613 m/s² toward the Earth

11. (a) 3.46×10^8 m   (b) 3.34×10^{-3} m/s² toward the Earth

13. 1.26×10^{32} kg

15. 1.90×10^{27} kg

17. 35.2 AU

19. 8.92×10^7 m

21. After 393 yr, Mercury would be farther from the Sun than Pluto

23. $\mathbf{g} = (Gm/\ell^2)\left(\frac{1}{2} + \sqrt{2}\right)$ toward the opposite corner

25. $\mathbf{g} = 2MGr(r^2 + a^2)^{-3/2}$ toward the center of mass

27. 4.17×10^{10} J

29. (a) 1.84×10^9 kg/m³   (b) 3.27×10^6 m/s²
    (c) -2.08×10^{13} J

31. (a) -1.67×10^{-14} J   (b) at the center

33. 1.66×10^4 m/s

37. (a) 5.30×10^3 s   (b) 7.79 km/s   (c) 6.43×10^9 J

39. 469 MJ

41. 15.6 km/s

43. (b) 1.00×10^7 m   (c) 1.00×10^4 m/s

45. (a) 0.980   (b) 127 yr   (c) -2.13×10^{17} J

49. (b) $2[Gm^3(1/2r - 1/R)]^{1/2}$

51. (b) 1.10×10^{32} kg

53. (a) -7.04×10^4 J   (b) -1.57×10^5 J   (c) 13.2 m/s

55. 7.79×10^{14} kg

57. $\omega = 0.057\,2$ rad/s or 1 rev in 110 s

59. $v_{esc} = (8\pi G\rho/3)^{1/2}R$

61. (a) $m_2(2G/d)^{1/2}(m_1 + m_2)^{-1/2}$ and
    $m_1(2G/d)^{1/2}(m_1 + m_2)^{-1/2}$;
    relative speed $(2G/d)^{1/2}(m_1 + m_2)^{1/2}$
    (b) 1.07×10^{32} J and 2.67×10^{31} J

63. (a) 8.50×10^8 J   (b) 2.71×10^9 J

65. (a) 200 Myr   (b) $\sim 10^{41}$ kg; $\sim 10^{11}$ stars

67. $(GM_E/4R_E)^{1/2}$

71.

t (s)	x (m)	y (m)	v_x (m/s)	v_y (m/s)
0	0	12 740 000	5 000	0
10	50 000	12 740 000	4 999.9	-24.6
20	99 999	12 739 754	4 999.7	-49.1
30	149 996	12 739 263	4 999.4	$-73.7\ldots$

The object does not hit the Earth; its minimum radius is $1.33R_E$ as shown in the diagram below. Its period is 1.09×10^4 s. A circular orbit would require speed 5.60 km/s.

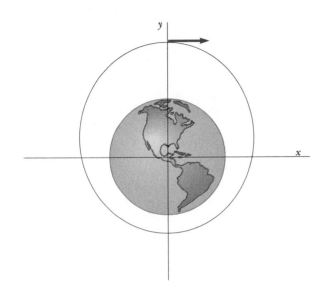

CHAPTER 14

1. 0.111 kg

3. 6.24 MPa

5. 5.27×10^{18} kg

7. 1.62 m

9. 7.74×10^{-3} m^2

11. 271 kN horizontally backward

13. $P_0 + \frac{1}{2}\rho d\sqrt{g^2 + a^2}$

15. 0.722 mm

17. 10.5 m; no; some alcohol and water evaporate

19. 98.6 kPa

21. (a) 1.57 Pa, 1.55×10^{-2} atm, 11.8 mm Hg   (b) The fluid level in the tap should rise.   (c) Blockage of flow of the cerebrospinal fluid

23. 0.258 N

25. (a) 9.80 N   (b) 6.17 N

27. (a) $1.017\,9 \times 10^3$ N down, $1.029\,7 \times 10^3$ N up   (b) 86.2 N

29. (a) 7.00 cm   (b) 2.80 kg

33. 1 430 m^3

35. 1 250 kg/m^3 and 500 kg/m^3

37. 1.28×10^4 m^2

39. (a) 17.7 m/s   (b) 1.73 mm

41. 31.6 m/s

43. 0.247 cm

45. (a) 1 atm + 15.0 MPa   (b) 2.95 m/s   (c) 4.34 kPa

47. 2.51×10^{-3} m^3/s

49. 103 m/s

51. (a) 4.43 m/s
    (b) The siphon can be no higher than 10.3 m.

53. 12.6 m/s

55. 1.91 m

59. 0.604 m

63. 17.3 N and 31.7 N

65. 90.04%

67. 758 Pa

69. 4.43 m/s

71. (a) 1.25 cm   (b) 13.8 m/s

73. (a) 3.307 g   (b) 3.271 g   (c) 3.48×10^{-4} N

75. (c) 1.70 m^2

CHAPTER 15

1. (a) The motion repeats precisely.   (b) 1.82 s
   (c) No, the force is not in the form of Hooke's law.

3. (a) 1.50 Hz, 0.667 s   (b) 4.00 m   (c) π rad
   (d) 2.83 m

5. (b) 18.8 cm/s, 0.333 s   (c) 178 cm /s^2, 0.500 s
   (d) 12.0 cm

7. (a) 2.40 s   (b) 0.417 Hz   (c) 2.62 rad/s

9. 40.9 N/m

11. (a) 40.0 cm/s, 160 cm/s^2 (b) 32.0 cm/s, -96.0 cm/s^2
    (c) 0.232 s

13. 0.628 m/s

15. (a) 0.542 kg   (b) 1.81 s   (c) 1.20 m/s^2

17. 2.23 m/s

19. (a) 28.0 mJ   (b) 1.02 m/s   (c) 12.2 mJ   (d) 15.8 mJ

21. (a) E increases by a factor of 4.   (b) v_{max} is doubled.
    (c) a_{max} is doubled.   (d) Period is unchanged.

23. 2.60 cm and -2.60 cm

25. (b) 0.628 s

27. (a) 35.7 m   (b) 29.1 s

29. $\sim 10^0$ s

31. Assuming simple harmonic motion, (a) 0.820 m/s
    (b) 2.57 rad/s^2 (c) 0.641 N. More precisely,
    (a) 0.817 m/s   (b) 2.54 rad/s^2 (c) 0.634 N

35. 0.944 kg · m^2

39. (a) 5.00×10^{-7} kg · m^2 (b) 3.16×10^{-4} N · m/rad

41. 1.00×10^{-3} s^{-1}

43. (a) 7.00 Hz   (b) 2.00%   (c) 10.6 s

45. (a) 1.00 s   (b) 5.09 cm

47. 318 N

49. 1.74 Hz

51. (a) $2Mg$; $Mg(1 + y/L)$
    (b) $T = (4\pi/3)(2L/g)^{1/2}$; 2.68 s

53. 6.62 cm

55. 9.19×10^{13} Hz

57. (a)

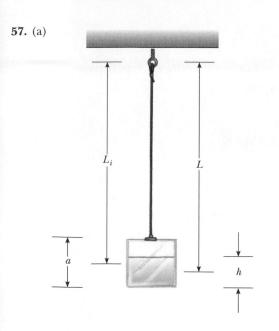

(b) $\dfrac{dT}{dt} = \dfrac{\pi(dM/dt)}{2\rho a^2 g^{1/2}[L_i + (dM/dt)\,t/2\rho a^2]^{1/2}}$

(c) $T = 2\pi g^{-1/2}[L_i + (dM/dt)\,t/2\rho a^2]^{1/2}$

59. $f = (2\pi L)^{-1}(gL + kh^2/M)^{1/2}$

61. (b) 1.23 Hz

63. (a) 3.00 s   (b) 14.3 J   (c) 25.5°

65. If the cyclist goes over them at one certain speed, the washboard bumps can excite a resonance vibration of the bike, so large in amplitude as to make the rider lose control. ~10^1 m

73. For $\theta_{max} = 5.00°$ there is precise agreement. For $\theta_{max} = 100°$ there are large differences, and the period is 23% greater than small-angle period.

75. (b) after 42.1 min

CHAPTER 16

1. $y = 6\,[(x - 4.5t)^2 + 3]^{-1}$

3. (a) left   (b) 5.00 m/s

5. 184 km

7. 0.319 m

9. 2.00 cm, 2.98 m, 0.576 Hz, 1.72 m/s

11. (a) 3.77 m/s   (b) 118 m/s^2

13. (a) 0.250 m   (b) 40.0 rad/s   (c) 0.300 rad/m
(d) 20.9 m   (e) 133 m/s   (f) $+x$

15. (a) $y = (8.00 \text{ cm}) \sin(7.85x + 6\pi t)$
(b) $y = (8.00 \text{ cm}) \sin(7.85x + 6\pi t - 0.785)$

17. (a) -1.51 m/s, 0   (b) 16.0 m, 0.500 s, 32.0 m/s

19. (a) 0.500 Hz, 3.14 rad/s   (b) 3.14 rad/m
(c) $(0.100 \text{ m}) \sin(3.14x/\text{m} - 3.14t/\text{s})$
(d) $(0.100 \text{ m}) \sin(-3.14t/\text{s})$
(e) $(0.100 \text{ m}) \sin(4.71 \text{ rad} - 3.14t/\text{s})$ (f) 0.314 m/s

21. 80.0 N

23. 520 m/s

25. 1.64 m/s^2

27. 13.5 N

29. 185 m/s

31. 0.329 s

33. (a) s and kg·m/s^2 (b) time interval (period) and force (tension)

37. 55.1 Hz

39. (a) 62.5 m/s   (b) 7.85 m   (c) 7.96 Hz   (d) 21.1 W

41. $\sqrt{2}\,\mathscr{P}_0$

43. (a) $A = 40$ (b) $A = 7.00$, $B = 0$, $C = 3.00$. One can take the dot product of the given equation with each one of $\hat{\mathbf{i}}, \hat{\mathbf{j}},$ and $\hat{\mathbf{k}}$.   (c) $A = 0$, $B = 7.00$ mm, $C = 3.00/\text{m}$, $D = 4.00/\text{s}$, $E = 2.00$. Consider the average value of both sides of the given equation to find A. Then consider the maximum value of both sides to find B. One can evaluate the partial derivative of both sides of the given equation with respect to x and separately with respect to t to obtain equations yielding C and D upon chosen substitutions for x and t. Then substitute $x = 0$ and $t = 0$ to obtain E.

47. ~1 min

49. (a) $(3.33\hat{\mathbf{i}})$ m/s   (b) -5.48 cm   (c) 0.667 m, 5.00 Hz
(d) 11.0 m/s

51. 0.456 m/s

53. (a) 39.2 N   (b) 0.892 m   (c) 83.6 m/s

55. (a) 179 m/s   (b) 17.7 kW

57. 0.084 3 rad

61. (a) $(0.707)2(L/g)^{1/2}$ (b) $L/4$

63. 3.86×10^{-4}

65. (b) 31.6 m/s

67. (a) $\dfrac{\mu\omega^3}{2k}A_0^2 e^{-2bx}$ (b) $\dfrac{\mu\omega^3}{2k}A_0^2$ (c) e^{-2bx}

69. (a) $\mu_0 + (\mu_L - \mu_0)x/L$

CHAPTER 17

1. 5.56 km

3. 7.82 m

5. (a) 826 m   (b) 1.47 s

7. 5.67 mm

9. 1.50 mm to 75.0 μm

11. (a) 2.00 μm, 40.0 cm, 54.6 m/s   (b) -0.433 μm
(c) 1.72 mm/s

13. $\Delta P = (0.200 \text{ N/m}^2) \sin(62.8\,x/\text{m} - 2.16 \times 10^4\,t/\text{s})$

15. 5.81 m

19. 66.0 dB

21. (a) 3.75 W/m^2 (b) 0.600 W/m^2

23. (a) 2.34 m and 0.390 m   (b) 0.161 N/m^2 for both notes
(c) 4.25×10^{-7} m   and 7.09×10^{-8} m   (d) The wavelengths and displacement amplitudes would be larger by a factor of 1.09. The answer to (b) is unchanged.

25. (a) 1.32×10^{-4} W/m^2 (b) 81.2 dB

27. (a) 0.691 m   (b) 691 km

29. 65.6 dB

31. (a) 65.0 dB   (b) 67.8 dB   (c) 69.6 dB

33. (a) 30.0 m   (b) 9.49×10^5 m

35. (a) 332 J   (b) 46.4 dB

37. (a) 338 Hz   (b) 483 Hz

39. 26.4 m/s

41. 19.3 m

43. (a) 0.364 m   (b) 0.398 m   (c) 941 Hz   (d) 938 Hz

45. 2.82×10^8 m/s

47. (a) 56.3 s   (b) 56.6 km farther along

49. 22.3° left of center

51. $f \sim$ 300 Hz, $\lambda \sim 10^0$ m, duration $\sim 10^{-1}$ s

55. 6.01 km

57. (a) 55.8 m/s   (b) 2 500 Hz

59. 1 204.2 Hz

61. 1.60

63. 2.34 m

65. (a) 0.948°   (b) 4.40°

67. 1.34×10^4 N

69. (b) 531 Hz

71. (a) 6.45   (b) 0

CHAPTER 18

1. (a) −1.65 cm   (b) −6.02 cm   (c) 1.15 cm

3. (a) $+x, -x$ (b) 0.750 s   (c) 1.00 m

5. (a) 9.24 m   (b) 600 Hz

7. (a) zero   (b) 0.300 m

9. (a) 2   (b) 9.28 m and 1.99 m

11. (a) 156°   (b) 0.058 4 cm

13. 15.7 m, 31.8 Hz, 500 m/s

15. At 0.089 1 m, 0.303 m, 0.518 m, 0.732 m, 0.947 m, 1.16 m from one speaker

17. (a) 4.24 cm   (b) 6.00 cm   (c) 6.00 cm
(d) 0.500 cm, 1.50 cm, 2.50 cm

19. 0.786 Hz, 1.57 Hz, 2.36 Hz, 3.14 Hz

21. (a) 350 Hz   (b) 400 kg

23. 1.27 cm

25. (a) reduced by 1/2   (b) reduced by $1/\sqrt{2}$
(c) increased by $\sqrt{2}$

27. (a) 163 N   (b) 660 Hz

29. $\dfrac{Mg}{4Lf^2 \tan \theta}$

31. (a) 3 loops   (b) 16.7 Hz   (c) 1 loop

33. (a) 3.66 m/s   (b) 0.200 Hz

35. 9.00 kHz

37. (a) 0.357 m   (b) 0.715 m

39. 57.6 Hz

41. n(206 Hz) for $n = 1$ to 9 and n(84.5 Hz) for $n = 2$ to 23

43. 50.0 Hz, 1.70 m

45. (a) 350 m/s   (b) 1.14 m

47. (a) 162 Hz   (b) 1.06 m

49. (a) 1.59 kHz   (b) odd-numbered harmonics
(c) 1.11 kHz

51. 5.64 beats/s

53. (a) 1.99 beats/s   (b) 3.38 m/s

55. The second harmonic of E is close to the third harmonic of A, and the fourth harmonic of $C^{\#}$ is close to the fifth harmonic of A.

57. (a) 34.8 m/s   (b) 0.977 m

59. 3.85 m/s away from the station or 3.77 m/s toward the station

61. 21.5 m

63. (a) 59.9 Hz   (b) 20.0 cm

65. (a) 1/2   (b) $[n/(n + 1)]^2 T$ (c) 9/16

67. $y_1 + y_2 = 11.2 \sin(2.00x - 10.0t + 63.4°)$

69. (a) 78.9 N   (b) 211 Hz

CHAPTER 19

1. (a) −274°C   (b) 1.27 atm   (c) 1.74 atm

3. (a) −320°F   (b) 77.3 K

5. (a) 810°F   (b) 450 K

7. (a) 1 337 K, 2 993 K   (b) 1 596°C = 1 596 K

9. 3.27 cm

11. 55.0°C

13. (a) 0.176 mm   (b) 8.78 μm   (c) 0.093 0 cm³

15. (a) −179°C (attainable)
(b) −376°C (below 0 K, unattainable)

17. 0.548 gal

19. (a) 99.8 mL
(b) about 6% of the volume change of the acetone

21. (a) 99.4 cm³   (b) 0.943 cm

23. 1.14°C

25. 5 336 images

27. (a) 400 kPa   (b) 449 kPa

29. 1.50×10^{29} molecules

31. 1.61 MPa = 15.9 atm

33. 472 K

35. (a) 41.6 mol   (b) 1.20 kg, nearly in agreement with the tabulated density

37. (a) 1.17 g   (b) 11.5 mN   (c) 1.01 kN
(d) The molecules must be moving very fast.

39. 4.39 kg

41. 3.55 L

43. $m_1 - m_2 = \dfrac{P_0 VM}{R}\left(\dfrac{1}{T_1} - \dfrac{1}{T_2}\right)$

45. (a) 94.97 cm   (b) 95.03 cm

47. 3.55 cm

49. It falls by 0.094 3 Hz

51. (a) Expansion makes density drop.   (b) $5 \times 10^{-5}/°\text{C}$

53. (a) $h = nRT/(mg + P_0A)$ (b) 0.661 m

55. We assume that $\alpha \Delta T$ is much less than 1.

57. (a) 0.340%   (b) 0.480%

59. 0.750

61. 2.74 m

63. (b) 1.33 kg/m^3

67. No. Steel is not strong enough.

69. (a) $L_f = L_i e^{\alpha \Delta T}$ (b) $2.00 \times 10^{-4}\%$; 59.4%

71. (a) 6.17×10^{-3} kg/m   (b) 632 N   (c) 580 N; 192 Hz

73. 4.54 m

CHAPTER 20

1. $(10.0 + 0.117)°\text{C}$

3. 0.234 kJ/kg·°C

5. 1.78×10^4 kg

7. 29.6°C

9. (a) 0.435 cal/g·°C   (b) beryllium

11. 23.6°C

13. 50.7 ks

15. 1.22×10^5 J

17. 0.294 g

19. 0.414 kg

21. (a) 0°C   (b) 114 g

23. -1.18 MJ

25. -466 J

27. (a) $-4P_iV_i$ (b) It is proportional to the square of the volume, according to $T = (P_i/nRV_i) V^2$

29. $Q = -720$ J

31.

	Q	W	ΔE_{int}
BC	$-$	0	$-$
CA	$-$	$+$	$-$
AB	$+$	$-$	$+$

33. 3.60 kJ

35. (a) 7.50 kJ   (b) 900 K

37. -3.10 kJ; 37.6 kJ

39. (a) 0.041 0 m^3 (b) $+5.48$ kJ   (c) -5.48 kJ

41. 2.22×10^{-2} W/m·°C

43. 51.2°C

45. 67.9°C

47. 3.77×10^{26} J/s

49. 3.49×10^3 K

51. 277 K = 4°C

53. 2.27 km

55. (a) 16.8 L   (b) 0.351 L/s

57. $c = \mathcal{P}/\rho R \Delta T$

59. -1.87 kJ

61. 5.87×10^4 °C

63. 5.31 h

65. 1.44 kg

67. 38.6 m^3/d

71. 9.32 kW

73. (a) 3.16×10^{22} W   (b) 5.78×10^3 K, 0.327% less than 5 800 K   (c) 3.17×10^{22} W, 0.408% larger

CHAPTER 21

1. 0.943 N; 1.57 Pa

3. 3.65×10^4 N

5. 3.32 mol

7. (a) 3.54×10^{23} atoms   (b) 6.07×10^{-21} J   (c) 1.35 km/s

9. (a) 8.76×10^{-21} J for both   (b) 1.62 km/s for helium and 514 m/s for argon

13. (a) 3.46 kJ   (b) 2.45 kJ   (c) -1.01 kJ

15. (a) 209 J   (b) zero   (c) 317 K

17. 1.18 atm

19. Between 10^{-2} and 10^{-3} °C

21. (a) 316 K   (b) 200 J

23. (a) $C = \dfrac{n_1C_1 + n_2C_2}{n_1 + n_2}$ (b) $C = \dfrac{\displaystyle\sum_{i=1}^{m} n_iC_i}{\displaystyle\sum_{i=1}^{m} n_i}$

25. (a) 1.39 atm   (b) 366 K, 253 K   (c) 0, -4.66 kJ, -4.66 kJ

27. 227 K

29. (a)

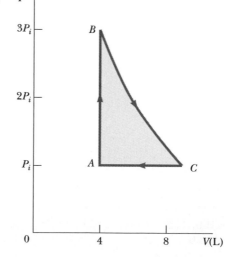

(b) 8.77 L   (c) 900 K   (d) 300 K   (e) -336 J

31. (a) 28.0 kJ   (b) 46.1 kJ   (c) Isothermal process, $P_f = 10.0$ atm; adiabatic process, $P_f = 25.1$ atm

33. (a) 9.95 cal/K, 13.9 cal/K   (b) 13.9 cal/K, 17.9 cal/K

35. 2.33×10^{-21} J

37. (a) 6.80 m/s   (b) 7.41 m/s   (c) 7.00 m/s

41. (a) 2.37×10^4 K   (b) 1.06×10^3 K

43. (b) 0.278

45. (a) 3.21×10^{12} molecules   (b) 779 km
   (c) 6.42×10^{-4} s^{-1}

49. (a) 9.36×10^{-8} m   (b) 9.36×10^{-8} atm   (c) 302 atm

51. (a) 100 kPa, 66.5 L, 400 K, 5.82 kJ, 7.48 kJ, -1.66 kJ

   (b) 133 kPa, 49.9 L, 400 K, 5.82 kJ, 5.82 kJ, 0

   (c) 120 kPa, 41.6 L, 300 K, 0, -910 J, $+910$ J

   (d) 120 kPa, 43.3 L, 312 K, 722 J, 0, $+722$ J

55. 510 K and 290 K

57. 0.623

59. (a) Pressure increases as volume decreases
   (d) 0.500 atm^{-1}, 0.300 atm^{-1}

61. (a) 0.514 m^3 (b) 2.06 m^3 (c) 2.38×10^3 K
   (d) -480 kJ   (e) 2.28 MJ

63. 1.09×10^{-3}; 2.69×10^{-2}; 0.529; 1.00; 0.199; 1.01×10^{-41};
   1.25×10^{-1082}

67. (a) 0.203 mol   (b) $T_B = T_C = 900$ K, $V_C = 15.0$ L

(c, d)	P, atm	V, L	T, K	E_{int}, kJ
A	1.00	5.00	300	0.760
B	3.00	5.00	900	2.28
C	1.00	15.0	900	2.28
A	1.00	5.00	300	0.760

(e) Lock the piston in place and put the cylinder into an oven at 900 K. Keep the gas in the oven while gradually letting the gas expand to lift a load on the piston as far as it can. Move the cylinder from the oven back to the 300-K room and let the gas cool and contract.

(f, g)	Q, kJ	W, kJ	ΔE_{int}, kJ
AB	1.52	0	1.52
BC	1.67	-1.67	0
CD	-2.53	$+1.01$	-1.52
ABCA	0.656	-0.656	0

69. 1.60×10^4 K

CHAPTER 22

1. (a) 6.94%   (b) 335 J

3. (a) 10.7 kJ   (b) 0.533 s

5. (a) 29.4 L/h   (b) 185 hp   (c) 527 N·m
   (d) 1.91×10^5 W

7. (a) 24.0 J   (b) 144 J

9. (a) 2.93   (b) coefficient of performance for a refrigerator
   (c) $300 is twice as large as $150

11. (a) 67.2%   (b) 58.8 kW

13. (a) 741 J   (b) 459 J

15. (a) 4.20 W   (b) 31.2 g

17. (a) 564 K   (b) 212 kW   (c) 47.5%

19. (b) $1 - T_c/T_h$ (c) $(T_c + T_h)/2$ (d) $(T_h T_c)^{1/2}$

21. (a) 214 J, 64.3 J
   (b) -35.7 J, -35.7 J. The net effect is the transport of energy by heat from the cold to the hot reservoir without expenditure of external work.   (c) 333 J, 233 J

(d) 83.3 J, 83.3 J, 0. The net effect is converting energy, taken in by heat, entirely into energy output by work in a cyclic process.
(e) -0.111 J/K. The entropy of the Universe has decreased.

23. 9.00

27. 72.2 J

29. 1.86

31. (a) 244 kPa   (b) 192 J

33. 146 kW, 70.8 kW

35. -610 J/K

37. 195 J/K

39. 236 J/K

41. 1.02 kJ/K

43. $\sim 10^0$ W/K from metabolism; much more if you are using high-power electric appliances or an automobile, or if your taxes are paying for a war.

45. 5.76 J/K; temperature is constant if the gas is ideal

47. 18.4 J/K

49. (a) 1   (b) 6

51. (a)

Result	Number of Ways to Draw
All R	1
2 R, 1 C	3
1R, 2 G	3
All G	1

(b)

Result	Number of Ways to Draw
All R	1
4R, 1G	5
3R, 2G	10
2R, 3G	10
1R, 4G	5
All G	1

53. (a) 5.00 kW   (b) 763 W

55. (a) 0.476 J/K   (b) 417 J   (c) $W_{net} = T_1 \Delta S_U = 167$ J

57. (a) $2nRT_i \ln 2$ (b) 0.273

59. 5.97×10^4 kg/s

61. (a) 3.19 cal/K   (b) 98.19°F, 2.59 cal/K

63. (a) 8.48 kW   (b) 1.52 kW   (c) 1.09×10^4 J/K
   (d) COP drops by 20.0%

65. (a) $10.5nRT_i$ (b) $8.50nRT_i$ (c) 0.190   (d) 0.833

67. (a) $nC_P \ln 3$
   (b) Both ask for the change in entropy between the same two states of the same system. Entropy is a function of state. The change in entropy does not depend on path, but only on original and final states.

71. (a) 20.0°C   (c) $\Delta S = +4.88$ J/K   (d) Yes

CHAPTER 23

1. (a) $+160$ zC, 1.01 u   (b) $+160$ zC, 23.0 u
   (c) -160 zC, 35.5 u   (d) $+320$ zC, 40.1 u
   (e) -480 zC, 14.0 u   (f) $+640$ zC, 14.0 u
   (g) $+1.12$ aC, 14.0 u   (h) -160 zC, 18.0 u

3. The force is $\sim 10^{26}$ N.

5. (a) 1.59 nN away from the other
(b) 1.24×10^{36} times larger
(c) 8.61×10^{-11} C/kg

7. 0.872 N at 330°

9. (a) 2.16×10^{-5} N toward the other   (b) 8.99×10^{-7} N away from the other

11. (a) 82.2 nN   (b) 2.19 Mm/s

13. (a) 55.8 pN/C down   (b) 102 nN/C up

15. 1.82 m to the left of the negative charge

17. $-9Q$ and $+27Q$

19. (a) $(-0.599\hat{\mathbf{i}} - 2.70\hat{\mathbf{j}})$ kN/C   (b) $(-3.00\hat{\mathbf{i}} - 13.5\hat{\mathbf{j}})$ μN

21. (a) $5.91 k_e q/a^2$ at 58.8°   (b) $5.91 k_e q^2/a^2$ at 58.8°

23. (a) $[k_e Qx/(R^2 + x^2)^{3/2}]\hat{\mathbf{i}}$ (b) As long as the charge is symmetrically placed, the number of charges does not matter. A continuous ring corresponds to n becoming larger without limit.

25. 1.59×10^6 N/C toward the rod

27. (a) $6.64\hat{\mathbf{i}}$ MN/C   (b) $24.1\hat{\mathbf{i}}$ MN/C   (c) $6.40\hat{\mathbf{i}}$ MN/C   (d) $0.664\hat{\mathbf{i}}$ MN/C, taking the axis of the ring as the x axis

31. (a) 93.6 MN/C; the near-field approximation is 104 MN/C, about 11% high   (b) 0.516 MN/C; the point-charge approximation is 0.519 MN/C, about 0.6% high

33. $-21.6\hat{\mathbf{i}}$ MN/C

37. (a) 86.4 pC for each
(b) 324 pC, 459 pC, 459 pC, 432 pC
(c) 57.6 pC, 106 pC, 154 pC, 96.0 pC

39.

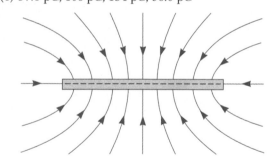

41. (a)

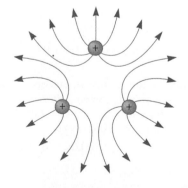

The field is zero at the center of the triangle.
(b) $1.73 k_e q\hat{\mathbf{j}}/a^2$

43. (a) 61.3 Gm/s²   (b) 19.5 μs   (c) 11.7 m   (d) 1.20 fJ

45. K/ed in the direction of motion

47. (a) 111 ns   (b) 5.68 mm   (c) $(450\hat{\mathbf{i}} + 102\hat{\mathbf{j}})$ km/s

49. (a) 36.9°, 53.1°   (b) 167 ns, 221 ns

51. (a) 21.8 μm   (b) 2.43 cm

53. (a) mv^2/qR (b) $mv^2/2^{1/2}qR$ oriented at 135° to the x axis

55. (a) 10.9 nC   (b) 5.44 mN

57. 40.9 N at 263°

59. $Q = 2L\sqrt{\dfrac{k(L - L_i)}{k_e}}$

63. $-707\hat{\mathbf{j}}$ mN

65. (a) $\theta_1 = \theta_2$

67. (a) 0.307 s   (b) Yes. Ignoring gravity makes a difference of 2.28%.

69. (a) $\mathbf{F} = 1.90(k_e q^2/s^2)(\hat{\mathbf{i}} + \hat{\mathbf{j}} + \hat{\mathbf{k}})$ (b) $\mathbf{F} = 3.29(k_e q^2/s^2)$ in the direction away from the diagonally opposite vertex

CHAPTER 24

1. (a) 858 N·m²/C   (b) 0   (c) 657 N·m²/C

3. 4.14 MN/C

5. (a) aA (b) bA (c) 0

7. 1.87 kN·m²/C

9. (a) -6.89 MN·m²/C   (b) The number of lines entering exceeds the number leaving by 2.91 times or more.

11. $-Q/\epsilon_0$ for S_1; 0 for S_2; $-2Q/\epsilon_0$ for S_3; 0 for S_4

13. $E_0 \pi r^2$

15. (a) $+Q/2\epsilon_0$ (b) $-Q/2\epsilon_0$

17. -18.8 kN·m²/C

19. 0 if $R \le d$; $\dfrac{2\lambda}{\epsilon_0}\sqrt{R^2 - d^2}$ if $R > d$

21. (a) 3.20 MN·m²/C   (b) 19.2 MN·m²/C   (c) The answer to (a) could change, but the answer to (b) would stay the same.

23. 2.33×10^{21} N/C

25. -2.48 μC/m²

27. 5.94×10^5 m/s

29. $\mathbf{E} = \rho r/2\epsilon_0$ away from the axis

31. (a) 0   (b) 7.19 MN/C away from the center

33. (a) ~1 mN   (b) ~100 nC   (c) ~10 kN/C   (d) ~10 kN·m²/C

35. (a) 51.4 kN/C outward   (b) 646 N·m²/C

37. 508 kN/C up

39. (a) 0   (b) 5 400 N/C outward   (c) 540 N/C outward

41. $\mathbf{E} = Q/2\epsilon_0 A$ vertically upward in each case if $Q > 0$

43. (a) $+708$ nC/m² and -708 nC/m²   (b) $+177$ nC and -177 nC

45. 2.00 N

47. (a) $-\lambda$, $+3\lambda$ (b) $3\lambda/2\pi\epsilon_0 r$ radially outward

49. (a) 80.0 nC/m² on each face   (b) $9.04\hat{\mathbf{k}}$ kN/C   (c) $-9.04\hat{\mathbf{k}}$ kN/C

51. $\mathbf{E} = 0$ inside the sphere and within the material of the shell. $\mathbf{E} = k_e Q/r^2$ radially inward between the sphere and the shell. $\mathbf{E} = 2k_e Q/r^2$ radially outward outside the shell. Charge $-Q$ resides on the outer surface of the sphere.

$+Q$ is on the inner surface of the shell. $+2Q$ is on the outer surface of the shell.

53. (b) $Q/2\epsilon_0$ (c) Q/ϵ_0

55. (a) $+2Q$ (b) radially outward   (c) $2k_eQ/r^2$ (d) 0 (e) 0
(f) $3Q$ (g) $3k_eQ/r^2$ radially   outward   (h) $3Qr^3/a^3$
(i) $3k_eQr/a^3$ radially   outward   (j) $-3Q$ (k) $+2Q$
(l) See below.

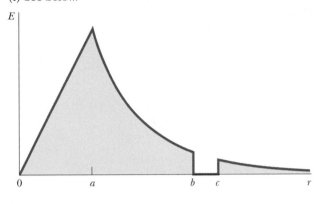

57. (a) $\rho r/3\epsilon_0$; $Q/4\pi\epsilon_0 r^2$; 0; $Q/4\pi\epsilon_0 r^2$, all radially outward
(b) $-Q/4\pi b^2$ and $+Q/4\pi c^2$

59. $\theta = \tan^{-1}[qQ/(2\pi\epsilon_0 dmv^2)]$

61. For $r < a$, $\mathbf{E} = \lambda/2\pi\epsilon_0 r$ radially outward. For $a < r < b$,
$\mathbf{E} = [\lambda+\rho\pi(r^2-a^2)]/2\pi\epsilon_0 r$ radially outward. For $r > b$,
$\mathbf{E} = [\lambda+\rho\pi(b^2-a^2)]/2\pi\epsilon_0 r$ radially outward.

63. (a) σ/ϵ_0 away from both plates   (b) 0   (c) σ/ϵ_0 away from both plates

65. $\sigma/2\epsilon_0$ radially outward

69. $\mathbf{E} = a/2\epsilon_0$ radially outward

73. (b) $\mathbf{g} = GM_E r/R_E^3$ radially inward

CHAPTER 25

1. 1.35 MJ

3. (a) 152 km/s   (b) 6.49 Mm/s

5. (a) $-600\ \mu$J   (b) -50.0 V

7. 38.9 V; the origin

9. $+260$ V

11. (a) $2QE/k$ (b) QE/k (c) $2\pi\sqrt{m/k}$ (d) $2(QE - \mu_k mg)/k$

13. (a) 0.400 m/s   (b) the same

15. (a) 1.44×10^{-7} V   (b) -7.19×10^{-8} V
(c) -1.44×10^{-7} V, $+7.19 \times 10^{-8}$ V

17. (a) 6.00 m   (b) $-2.00\ \mu$C

19. -11.0 MV

21. 8.95 J

25. (a) no point at a finite distance from the charges
(b) $2k_eq/a$

27. (a) $v_1 = \sqrt{\dfrac{2m_2 k_e q_1 q_2}{m_1(m_1 + m_2)}\left(\dfrac{1}{r_1 + r_2} - \dfrac{1}{d}\right)}$

$v_2 = \sqrt{\dfrac{2m_1 k_e q_1 q_2}{m_2(m_1 + m_2)}\left(\dfrac{1}{r_1 + r_2} - \dfrac{1}{d}\right)}$

(b) faster than calculated in (a)

---

29. $5k_eq^2/9d$

31. 0.720 m, 1.44 m, 2.88 m. No. The radii of the equipotentials are inversely proportional to the potential.

33. 7.26 Mm/s

35. $\left[\left(1 + \sqrt{\dfrac{1}{8}}\right)\dfrac{k_eq^2}{mL}\right]^{1/2}$

37. (a) 10.0 V, -11.0 V, -32.0 V
(b) 7.00 N/C in the $+x$ direction

39. $\mathbf{E} = (-5 + 6xy)\hat{\mathbf{i}} + (3x^2 - 2z^2)\hat{\mathbf{j}} - 4yz\hat{\mathbf{k}}$; 7.07 N/C

41. $E_y = \dfrac{k_eQ}{y\sqrt{\ell^2 + y^2}}$

43. (a) C/m²   (b) $k_e\alpha[L - d\ln(1 + L/d)]$

45. -1.51 MV

47. $k_e\lambda(\pi + 2\ln 3)$

49. (a) 0, 1.67 MV   (b) 5.84 MN/C away, 1.17 MV
(c) 11.9 MN/C away, 1.67 MV

51. (a) 450 kV   (b) 7.51 μC

53. 253 MeV

55. (a) -27.2 eV   (b) -6.80 eV   (c) 0

59. $k_eQ^2/2R$

63. $V_2 - V_1 = (-\lambda/2\pi\epsilon_0)\ln(r_2/r_1)$

69. (b) $E_r = (2k_e p\cos\theta)/r^3$; $E_\theta = (k_e p\sin\theta)/r^3$; yes; no
(c) $V = k_e py(x^2 + y^2)^{-3/2}$;
$\mathbf{E} - 3k_e pxy(x^2 + y^2)^{-5/2}\hat{\mathbf{i}} + k_e p(2y^2 - x^2)(x^2 + y^2)^{-5/2}\hat{\mathbf{j}}$

71. $V = \pi k_e C\left[R\sqrt{x^2 + R^2} + x^2\ln\left(\dfrac{x}{R + \sqrt{x^2 + R^2}}\right)\right]$

73. (a) 8 876 V   (b) 112 V

CHAPTER 26

1. (a) 48.0 μC   (b) 6.00 μC

3. (a) 1.33 μC/m²   (b) 13.3 pF

5. (a) 5.00 μC on the larger and 2.00 μC on the smaller sphere   (b) 89.9 kV

7. (a) 11.1 kV/m toward the negative plate.
(b) 98.3 nC/m²   (c) 3.74 pF   (d) 74.7 pC

9. 4.42 μm

11. (a) 2.68 nF   (b) 3.02 kV

13. (a) 15.6 pF   (b) 256 kV

15. 708 μF

17. (a) 3.53 μF   (b) 6.35 V and 2.65 V   (c) 31.8 μC on each

19. 6.00 pF and 3.00 pF

21. (a) 5.96 μF   (b) 89.5 μC on 20 μF, 63.2 μC on 6 μF, 26.3 μC on 15 μF and on 3 μF

23. 120 μC; 80.0 μC and 40.0 μC

25. 10

27. 6.04 μF

29. 12.9 μF

31. (a) 216 μJ   (b) 54.0 μJ

33. (a) Circuit diagram:

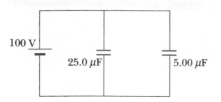

Stored energy = 0.150 J
(b) Potential difference = 268 V
Circuit diagram:

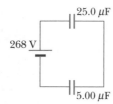

35. (a) 1.50 μC   (b) 1.83 kV

39. 9.79 kg

43. (a) 81.3 pF   (b) 2.40 kV

45. 1.04 m

47. (a) 369 pC   (b) 118 pF, 3.12 V   (c) -45.5 nJ

49. 22.5 V

51. (b) -8.78×10^6 N/C·m; $-5.53 \times 10^{-2} \hat{\mathbf{i}}$ N

55. (a) 11.2 pF   (b) 134 pC   (c) 16.7 pF   (d) 66.9 pC

57. (a) $-2Q/3$ on upper plate, $-Q/3$ on lower plate
(b) $2Qd/3\epsilon_0 A$

59. 0.188 m^2

61. (a) $C = \dfrac{\epsilon_0 A}{d} \left(\dfrac{\kappa_1}{2} + \dfrac{\kappa_2 \kappa_3}{\kappa_2 + \kappa_3} \right)$ (b) 1.76 pF

63. (b) $1/C$ approaches $\dfrac{1}{4\pi\epsilon_0 a} + \dfrac{1}{4\pi\epsilon_0 b}$

65. (a) $Q_0^2 d(\ell - x)/(2\ell^3 \epsilon_0)$ (b) $Q_0^2 d/(2\ell^3 \epsilon_0)$ to the right
(c) $Q_0^2/(2\ell^4 \epsilon_0)$ (d) $Q_0^2/(2\ell^4 \epsilon_0)$

67. 4.29 μF

69. (a) The additional energy comes from work done by the electric field in the wires as it forces more charge onto the already-charged plates.   (b) $Q/Q_0 = \kappa$

71. 750 μC on C_1 and 250 μC on C_2

73. 19.0 kV

75. $\frac{4}{3}C$

CHAPTER 27

1. 7.50×10^{15} electrons

3. (a) $0.632\ I_0\tau$ (b) $0.999\ 95\ I_0\tau$ (c) $I_0\tau$

5. $q\omega/2\pi$

7. 0.265 C

9. (a) 2.55 A/m^2 (b) 5.31×10^{10} m^{-3} (c) 1.20×10^{10} s

11. 0.130 mm/s

13. 500 mA

15. 6.43 A

17. (a) 1.82 m   (b) 280 μm

19. (a) $\sim 10^{18}\ \Omega$ (b) $\sim 10^{-7}\ \Omega$ (c) ~ 100 aA, ~ 1 GA

21. $R/9$

23. $6.00 \times 10^{-15}/\Omega \cdot$m

25. 0.181 V/m

27. 21.2 nm

29. 1.44×10^{3}°C

31. (a) 31.5 n$\Omega \cdot$m   (b) 6.35 MA/m^2 (c) 49.9 mA
(d) 659 μm/s   (e) 0.400 V

33. 0.125

35. 67.6°C

37. 7.50 W

39. 28.9 Ω

41. 36.1%

43. (a) 5.97 V/m   (b) 74.6 W   (c) 66.1 W

45. 0.833 W

47. \$0.232

49. 26.9 cents/d

51. (a) 184 W   (b) 461°C

53. $\sim$\$1

55. (a) $Q/4C$ (b) $Q/4$ and $3Q/4$ (c) $Q^2/32C$ and $3Q^2/32C$ (d) $3Q^2/8C$

59. Experimental resistivity = 1.47 $\mu\Omega \cdot$m $\pm$ 4%, in agreement with 1.50 $\mu\Omega \cdot$m

61. (a) $(8.00\hat{\mathbf{i}})$ V/m   (b) 0.637 Ω (c) 6.28 A
(d) $(200\hat{\mathbf{i}})$ MA/m^2

63. 2 020°C

65. (a) 667 A   (b) 50.0 km

67.

Material	$\alpha' = \alpha/(1 - 20\alpha)$
Silver	4.1×10^{-3}/°C
Copper	4.2×10^{-3}/°C
Gold	3.6×10^{-3}/°C
Aluminum	4.2×10^{-3}/°C
Tungsten	4.9×10^{-3}/°C
Iron	5.6×10^{-3}/°C
Platinum	4.25×10^{-3}/°C
Lead	4.2×10^{-3}/°C
Nichrome	0.4×10^{-3}/°C
Carbon	-0.5×10^{-3}/°C
Germanium	-24×10^{-3}/°C
Silicon	-30×10^{-3}/°C

69. No. The fuses should pass no more than 3.87 A.

73. (b) 1.79 PΩ

75. (a) $\dfrac{\epsilon_0 \ell}{2d} (\ell + 2x + \kappa\ell - 2\kappa x)$

(b) $\dfrac{\epsilon_0 \ell v\, \Delta V (\kappa - 1)}{d}$ clockwise

CHAPTER 28

1. (a) 6.73 Ω (b) 1.97 Ω

3. (a) 4.59 Ω (b) 8.16%

5. 12.0 Ω

7. Circuit diagram:

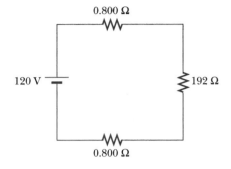

0.800 Ω

120 V

192 Ω

0.800 Ω

power 73.8 W

9. (a) 227 mA   (b) 5.68 V

11. (a) 75.0 V   (b) 25.0 W, 6.25 W, and 6.25 W; 37.5 W

13. 1.00 kΩ

15. 14.2 W to 2 Ω, 28.4 W to 4 Ω, 1.33 W to 3 Ω, 4.00 W to 1 Ω

17. (a) $\Delta t_p = 2\Delta t/3$ (b) $\Delta t_s = 3\Delta t$

19. (a) $\Delta V_4 > \Delta V_3 > \Delta V_1 > \Delta V_2$
    (b) $\Delta V_1 = \mathcal{E}/3$, $\Delta V_2 = 2\mathcal{E}/9$, $\Delta V_3 = 4\mathcal{E}/9$, $\Delta V_4 = 2\mathcal{E}/3$
    (c) $I_1 > I_4 > I_2 = I_3$ (d) $I_1 = I$, $I_2 = I_3 = I/3$, $I_4 = 2I/3$
    (e) I_4 increases while I_1, I_2, and I_3 decrease
    (f) $I_1 = 3I/4$, $I_2 = I_3 = 0$, $I_4 = 3I/4$

21. 846 mA down in the 8-Ω resistor; 462 mA down in the middle branch; 1.31 A up in the right-hand branch

23. (a) -222 J and 1.88 kJ   (b) 687 J, 128 J, 25.6 J, 616 J, 205 J
    (c) 1.66 kJ of chemical energy is transformed into internal energy

25. 50.0 mA from a to e

27. starter 171 A; battery 0.283 A

29. (a) 909 mA   (b) -1.82 V $= V_b - V_a$

31. (a) 5.00 s   (b) 150 μC   (c) 4.06 μA

33. $U_0/4$

37. (a) 6.00 V   (b) 8.29 μs

39. (a) 12.0 s   (b) $I(t) = (3.00\ \mu\text{A})e^{-t/12.0\text{ s}}$;
    $q(t) = (36.0\ \mu\text{C})(1 - e^{-t/12.0\text{ s}})$

41. 0.302 Ω

43. 16.6 kΩ

45.

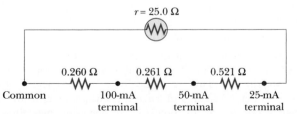

$r = 25.0\ \Omega$

0.260 Ω 0.261 Ω 0.521 Ω

Common   100-mA   50-mA   25-mA
             terminal   terminal   terminal

47. 145 Ω, 0.756 mA

49. (a) 12.5 A, 6.25 A, 8.33 A   (b) No; together they would require 27.1 A.

51. (a) $\sim 10^{-14}$ A   (b) $V_h/2 + (\sim 10^{-10}$ V$)$ and
    $V_h/2 - (\sim 10^{-10}$ V$)$, where V_h is the potential of the live wire, $\sim 10^2$ V

53. (a) either 3.84 Ω or 0.375 Ω (b) impossible

55. (a) $\mathcal{E}^2/3R$ (b) $3\mathcal{E}^2/R$ (c) in the parallel connection

57. (a) $R \rightarrow \infty$ (b) $R \rightarrow 0$ (c) $R = r$

59. 6.00 Ω; 3.00 Ω

61. (a) 4.40 Ω (b) 32.0 W, 9.60 W, 70.4 W   (c) 48.0 W

63. (a) $R \le 1\,050\ \Omega$ (b) $R \ge 10.0\ \Omega$

65. (a) 9.93 μC   (b) 33.7 nA   (c) 334 nW   (d) 337 nW

67. (a) 40.0 W   (b) 80.0 V, 40.0 V, 40.0 V

69. (a) 0.991   (b) 0.648   (c) Insulation should be added to the ceiling.

71. (a) 0 in 3 kΩ and 333 μA in 12 kΩ and 15 kΩ (b) 50.0 μC
    (c) $(278\ \mu\text{A})\ e^{-t/180\text{ ms}}$ (d) 290 ms

73. (a) $\ln(\mathcal{E}/\Delta V) = (0.011\,8)t + 0.088\,2$ (b) 84.7 s, 8.47 μF

75. $q_1 = (240\ \mu\text{C})(1 - e^{-1\,000t/6})$; $q_2 = (360\ \mu\text{C})(1 - e^{-1\,000t/6})$

CHAPTER 29

1. (a) up   (b) out of the plane of the paper   (c) no deflection   (d) into the plane of the paper

3. negative z direction

5. $(-20.9\hat{\mathbf{j}})$ mT

7. 48.9° or 131°

9. 2.34 aN

11. 0.245 T east

13. (a) 4.73 N   (b) 5.46 N   (c) 4.73 N

15. 1.07 m/s

17. $2\pi r I B \sin\theta$ up

19. 2.98 μN west

21. 18.4 mA·m^2

23. 9.98 N·m clockwise as seen looking down from above

27. (a) 118 μN·m   (b) $-118\ \mu\text{J} \le U \le 118\ \mu\text{J}$

29. (a) 49.6 aN south   (b) 1.29 km

31. 115 keV

33. $r_\alpha = r_d = \sqrt{2}r_p$

35. 4.98×10^8 rad/s

37. 7.88 pT

39. $m = 2.99$ u, either $_1^3\text{H}^+$ or $_2^3\text{He}^+$

41. (a) 8.28 cm   (b) 8.23 cm; ratio is independent of both ΔV and B

43. (a) 4.31×10^7 rad/s   (b) 51.7 Mm/s

45. (a) 7.66×10^7 rad/s   (b) 26.8 Mm/s   (c) 3.76 MeV
    (d) 3.13×10^3 rev   (e) 257 μs

47. 70.1 mT

49. 1.28×10^{29} m^{-3}, 1.52

51. 43.3 μT

53. (a) The electric current experiences a magnetic force.

55. (a) -8.00×10^{-21} kg·m/s   (b) 8.90°

57. (a) $(3.52\hat{\mathbf{i}} - 1.60\hat{\mathbf{j}})$ aN   (b) 24.4°

59. $(2\pi/d)(2m_e \Delta V/e)^{1/2}$

61. 0.588 T

63. 0.713 A counterclockwise as seen from above

65. 438 kHz

67. 3.70×10^{-24} N·m

69. (a) 0.501 m   (b) 45.0°

71. (a) 1.33 m/s   (b) Positive ions moving toward you in magnetic field to the right feel upward magnetic force, and migrate upward in the blood vessel. Negative ions moving toward you feel downward magnetic force and accumulate at the bottom of this section of vessel. Thus both species can participate in the generation of the emf.

CHAPTER 30

1. 12.5 T

3. (a) 28.3 μT into the paper   (b) 24.7 μT into the paper

5. $\dfrac{\mu_0 I}{4\pi x}$ into the paper

7. 26.2 μT into the paper

9. (a) $2I_1$ out of the page   (b) $6I_1$ into the page

11. (a) along the line ($y = -0.420$ m, $z = 0$)
   (b) $(-34.7\hat{\mathbf{j}})$ mN   (c) $(17.3\hat{\mathbf{j}})$ kN/C

13. (a) $4.5\,\dfrac{\mu_0 I}{\pi L}$ (b) stronger

15. $(-13.0\hat{\mathbf{j}})\ \mu$T

17. $(-27.0\hat{\mathbf{i}})\ \mu$N

19. (a) 12.0 cm to the left of wire 1   (b) 2.40 A, downward

21. 20.0 μT toward the bottom of the page

23. 200 μT toward the top of the page; 133 μT toward the bottom of the page

25. (a) 6.34 mN/m inward   (b) greater

27. (a) 0   (b) $\dfrac{\mu_0 I}{2\pi R}$ tangent to the wall in a

counterclockwise sense   (c) $\dfrac{\mu_0 I^2}{(2\pi R)^2}$ inward

29. (a) $\frac{1}{3}\mu_0 b r_1^2$ (b) $\dfrac{\mu_0 b R^3}{3r_2}$

31. 31.8 mA

33. 226 μN away from the center of the loop, 0

35. (a) 3.13 mWb   (b) 0

37. (a) 11.3 GV·m/s   (b) 0.100 A

39. (a) 9.27×10^{-24} A·m^2 (b) down

41. 0.191 T

43. 2.62 MA/m

45. (b) 6.45×10^4 K·A/T·m

47. (a) 8.63×10^{45} electrons   (b) 4.01×10^{20} kg

49. $\dfrac{\mu_0 I}{2\pi w} \ln\left(1 + \dfrac{w}{b}\right)\hat{\mathbf{k}}$

51. 12 layers, 120 m

53. 143 pT away along the axis

59. (a) 2.46 N up   (b) 107 m/s^2 up

61. (a) 274 μT   (b) $(-274\hat{\mathbf{j}})\ \mu$T   (c) $(1.15\hat{\mathbf{i}})$ mN
   (d) $(0.384\hat{\mathbf{i}})$ m/s^2 (e) acceleration is constant
   (f) $(0.999\hat{\mathbf{i}})$ m/s

63. 81.7 A

65. $\dfrac{\mu_0 I_1 I_2 L}{\pi R}$ to the right

69. $\dfrac{\mu_0 I}{4\pi}(1 - e^{-2\pi})$ out of the plane of the paper

71. $\frac{1}{3}\rho\mu_0 \omega R^2$

73. (a) $\dfrac{\mu_0 I(2r^2 - a^2)}{\pi r(4r^2 - a^2)}$ to the left   (b) $\dfrac{\mu_0 I(2r^2 + a^2)}{\pi r(4r^2 + a^2)}$ toward the top of the page

CHAPTER 31

1. 500 mV

3. 9.82 mV

5. 160 A

7. (a) 1.60 A counterclockwise   (b) 20.1 μT   (c) up

9. (a) $(\mu_0 IL/2\pi)\ln(1 + w/h)$ (b) $-4.80\ \mu$V; current is counterclockwise

11. 283 μA upward

13. (68.2 mV) $e^{-1.6t}$, tending to produce counterclockwise current

15. 272 m

17. (0.422 V) cos ωt

19. (a) eastward   (b) 458 μV

21. (a) 3.00 N to the right   (b) 6.00 W

23. 360 T

25. (a) 233 Hz   (b) 1.98 mV

27. 2.83 mV

29. (a) $F = N^2 B^2 w^2 v/R$ to the left   (b) 0   (c) $F = N^2 B^2 w^2 v/R$ to the left

31. 145 μA

33. 1.80 mN/C upward and to the left, perpendicular to r_1

35. (a) 7.54 kV   (b) The plane of the coil is parallel to **B**.

37. (28.6 mV) sin($4\pi t$)

39. (a) 110 V   (b) 8.53 W   (c) 1.22 kW

41. (a) (8.00 mWb) cos($377t$)   (b) (3.02 V) sin($377t$)
   (c) (3.02 A) sin($377t$)   (d) (9.10 W) sin^2($377t$)
   (e) (24.1 mN·m) sin^2($377t$)

43. (b) Larger R makes current smaller, so the loop must travel faster to maintain equality of magnetic force and weight. (c) The magnetic force is proportional to the product of field and current, while the current is itself proportional to field. If B becomes two times smaller, the speed must become four times larger to compensate.

45. $(-2.87\hat{\mathbf{j}} + 5.75\hat{\mathbf{k}})$ Gm/s^2

47. (a) Doubling N doubles the amplitude. (b) Doubling ω doubles the amplitude and halves the period. (c) Doubling ω and halving N leaves the amplitude the same and cuts the period in half.

49. 62.3 mA down through 6.00 Ω, 860 mA down through 5.00 Ω, 923 mA up through 3.00 Ω

51. $\sim 10^{-4}$ V, by reversing a 20-turn coil of diameter 3 cm in 0.1 s in a field of 10^{-3} T

53. (a) 254 km/s (b) 215 V

55. 1.20 μC

57. (a) 0.900 A (b) 0.108 N (c) b (d) no

59. (a) $a\pi r^2$ (b) $-b\pi r^2$ (c) $-b\pi r^2/R$ (d) $b^2\pi^2 r^4/R$

61. (a) 36.0 V (b) 600 mWb/s (c) 35.9 V (d) 4.32 N·m

65. 6.00 A

67. (a) $(1.19\ \text{V})\cos(120\pi t)$ (b) 88.5 mW

71. $(-87.1\ \text{mV})\cos(200\pi t + \phi)$

CHAPTER 32

1. 19.5 mV

3. 100 V

5. $(18.8\ \text{V})\cos(377t)$

7. -0.421 A/s

9. (a) 188 μT (b) 33.3 nT·m^2 (c) 0.375 mH (d) B and Φ_B are proportional to current; L is independent of current

11. 0.750 m

13. $\mathcal{E}_0/k^2 L$

15. (a) 0.139 s (b) 0.461 s

17. (a) 2.00 ms (b) 0.176 A (c) 1.50 A (d) 3.22 ms

19. (a) 0.800 (b) 0

21. (a) 6.67 A/s (b) 0.332 A/s

23. $(500\ \text{mA})(1 - e^{-10t/\text{s}})$, $1.50\ \text{A} - (0.25\ \text{A})\,e^{-10t/\text{s}}$

25. 0 for $t < 0$; $(10\ \text{A})(1 - e^{-10\,000t})$ for $0 < t < 200$ μs; $(63.9\ \text{A})\,e^{-10\,000t}$ for $t > 200$ μs

27. (a) 5.66 ms (b) 1.22 A (c) 58.1 ms

29. 0.064 8 J

31. 2.44 μJ

33. 44.2 nJ/m^3 for the **E**-field and 995 μJ/m^3 for the **B**-field

35. (a) 0.500 J (b) 17.0 W (c) 11.0 W

37. 2.27 mT

39. 1.73 mH

41. 80.0 mH

43. (a) 18.0 mH (b) 34.3 mH (c) -9.00 mV

45. $(L_1 L_2 - M^2)/(L_1 + L_2 - 2M)$

47. 20.0 V

49. 608 pF

51. (a) 135 Hz (b) 119 μC (c) -114 mA

53. (a) 6.03 J (b) 0.529 J (c) 6.56 J

55. (a) 4.47 krad/s (b) 4.36 krad/s (c) 2.53%

57. $L = 199$ mH; $C = 127$ nF

59. (b) $\mu_0 J_s^2/2$ away from the other sheet (c) $\mu_0 J_s$ and zero (d) $\mu_0 J_s^2/2$

61. (a) -20.0 mV (b) $-(10.0\ \text{MV/s}^2)\,t^2$ (c) 63.2 μs

63. $(Q/2N)(3L/C)^{1/2}$

65. (a) $L \approx (\pi/2)N^2\mu_0 R$ (b) ~ 100 nH (c) ~ 1 ns

71. (a) 72.0 V; b
(b)

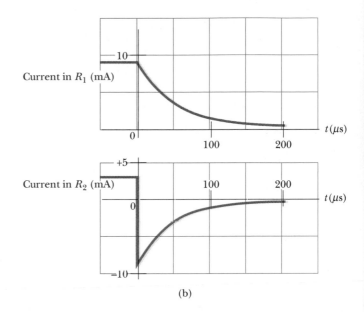

(c) 75.2 μs

73. 300 Ω

75. (a) It creates a magnetic field. (b) The long narrow rectangular area between the conductors encloses all of the magnetic flux.

77. (a) 62.5 GJ (b) 2 000 N

79. (a) 2.93 mT up (b) 3.42 Pa (c) clockwise as seen from above (d) up (e) 1.30 mN

CHAPTER 33

1. $\Delta v(t) = (283\ \text{V})\sin(628t)$

3. 2.95 A, 70.7 V

5. 14.6 Hz

7. 3.38 W

9. (a) 42.4 mH (b) 942 rad/s

11. 5.60 A

13. 0.450 Wb

15. (a) 141 mA (b) 235 mA

17. 100 mA

19. (a) 194 V (b) current leads by 49.9°

21. (a) 78.5 Ω (b) 1.59 kΩ (c) 1.52 kΩ (d) 138 mA (e) $-84.3°$

23. (a) 17.4°   (b) voltage leads the current

25. 1.88 V

27.

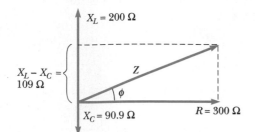

29. (a) either 123 nF or 124 nF   (b) 51.5 kV

31. 8.00 W

33. (a) 16.0 Ω   (b) − 12.0 Ω

35. $\sqrt{\dfrac{800\,\rho\mathscr{P}d}{\pi(\Delta V)^2}}$

37. 1.82 pF

39. (a) 633 fF   (b) 8.46 mm   (c) 25.1 Ω

41. 242 mJ

43. 0.591 and 0.987; the circuit in Problem 23

45. 687 V

47. 87.5 Ω

49. (a) 29.0 kW   (b) 5.80 × 10⁻³   (c) If the generator were limited to 4 500 V, no more than 17.5 kW could be delivered to the load, never 5 000 kW.

51. (b) 0; 1   (c) $f_h = (10.88RC)^{-1}$

53. (a) 613 μF   (b) 0.756

55. (a) 580 μH and 54.6 μF   (b) 1   (c) 894 Hz   (d) ΔV_{out} leads ΔV_{in} by 60.0° at 200 Hz. ΔV_{out} and ΔV_{in} are in phase at 894 Hz. ΔV_{out} lags ΔV_{in} by 60.0° at 4 000 Hz.   (e) 1.56 W, 6.25 W, 1.56 W   (f) 0.408

57. 56.7 W

59. 99.6 mH

61. (a) 225 mA   (b) 450 mA

63. (a) 1.25 A   (b) Current lags voltage by 46.7°.

65. (a) 200 mA; voltage leads by 36.8°   (b) 40.0 V; $\phi = 0°$ (c) 20.0 V; $\phi = -90.0°$ (d) 50.0 V; $\phi = +90.0°$

67. (b) 31.6

71.

f (Hz)	X_L (Ω)	X_C (Ω)	Z (Ω)
300	283	12 600	12 300
600	565	6 280	5 720
800	754	4 710	3 960
1 000	942	3 770	2 830
1 500	1 410	2 510	1 100
2 000	1 880	1 880	40.0
3 000	2 830	1 260	1 570
4 000	3 770	942	2 830
6 000	5 650	628	5 020
10 000	9 420	377	9 040

(b)

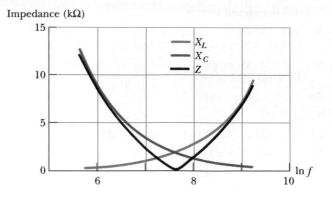

73. (a) 1.84 kHz
     (b)

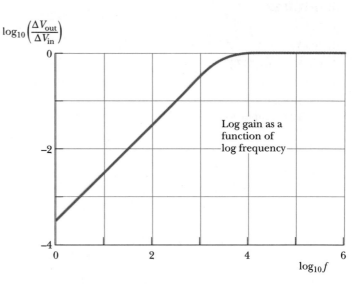

CHAPTER 34

1. (a) $(3.15\hat{\mathbf{j}})$ kN/C   (b) $(525\hat{\mathbf{k}})$ nT   (c) $(-483\hat{\mathbf{j}})$ aN

3. 2.25×10^8 m/s

5. (a) 6.00 MHz   (b) $(-73.3\hat{\mathbf{k}})$ nT
     (c) $\mathbf{B} = [(-73.3\hat{\mathbf{k}})\text{ nT}]\cos(0.126x - 3.77 \times 10^7 t)$

7. (a) 0.333 μT   (b) 0.628 μm   (c) 477 THz

9. 75.0 MHz

11. 3.33 μJ/m^3

13. 307 μW/m^2

15. 3.33×10^3 m^2

17. (a) 332 kW/m^2 radially inward   (b) 1.88 kV/m and 222 μT

19. (a) $\mathbf{E} \cdot \mathbf{B} = 0$ (b) $(11.5\hat{\mathbf{i}} - 28.6\hat{\mathbf{j}})$ W/m^2

21. 29.5 nT

23. (a) 2.33 mT   (b) 650 MW/m^2 (c) 510 W

25. (a) 540 V/m   (b) 2.58 μJ/m^3 (c) 773 W/m^2
     (d) 77.3% of the intensity in Example 34.5

27. 83.3 nPa

29. (a) 1.90 kN/C   (b) 50.0 pJ   (c) 1.67×10^{-19} kg·m/s

31. (a) 11.3 kJ   (b) 1.13×10^{-4} kg·m/s

33. (a) 134 m   (b) 46.9 m

35. (a) away along the perpendicular bisector of the line segment joining the antennas   (b) along the extensions of the line segment joining the antennas

37. (a) $\mathbf{E} = \frac{1}{2}\mu_0 c J_{max}[\cos(kx - \omega t)]\hat{\mathbf{j}}$

(b) $\mathbf{S} = \frac{1}{4}\mu_0 c J_{max}^2[\cos^2(kx - \omega t)]\hat{\mathbf{i}}$

(c) $I = \dfrac{\mu_0 c J_{max}^2}{8}$ (d) 3.48 A/m

39. 545 THz

41. (a) 6.00 pm   (b) 7.50 cm

43. 60.0 km

45. 1.00 Mm = 621 mi; not very practical

47. (a) 3.77×10^{26} W   (b) 1.01 kV/m and 3.35 μT

49. (a) $2\pi^2 r^2 f B_{max} \cos \theta$, where θ is the angle between the magnetic field and the normal to the loop   (b) The loop should be in the vertical plane containing the line of sight to the transmitter.

51. (a) 6.67×10^{-16} T   (b) 5.31×10^{-17} W/m^2
(c) 1.67×10^{-14} W   (d) 5.56×10^{-23} N

53. 95.1 mV/m

55. (a) B_{max} = 583 nT, k = 419 rad/m, ω = 126 Grad/s;
B vibrates in xz plane   (b) $\mathbf{S}_{av} = (40.6\hat{\mathbf{i}})$ W/m^2
(c) 271 nPa   (d) $(406\hat{\mathbf{i}})$ nm/s^2

57. (a) 22.6 h   (b) 30.6 s

59. (a) 8.32×10^7 W/m^2 (b) 1.05 kW

61. (a) 1.50 cm   (b) 25.0 μJ   (c) 7.37 mJ/m^3
(d) 40.8 kV/m, 136 μT   (e) 83.3 μN

63. 637 nPa

65. $\epsilon_0 E^2 A/2m$

67. (a) 16.1 cm   (b) 0.163 m^2 (c) 470 W/m^2 (d) 76.8 W
(e) 595 N/C   (f) 1.98 μT   (g) The cats are nonmagnetic and carry no macroscopic charge or current. Oscillating charges within molecules make them emit infrared radiation.   (h) 119 W

69. 4.77 Gm

CHAPTER 35

1. 299.5 Mm/s

3. 114 rad/s

5. (c) 0.055 7°

9. 23.3°

11. 15.4°; 2.56 m

13. 19.5° above the horizon

15. (a) 1.52   (b) 417 nm   (c) 474 THz   (d) 198 Mm/s

17. 158 Mm/s

19. 30.0° and 19.5° at entry; 19.5° and 30.0° at exit

21. 3.88 mm

23. 30.4° and 22.3°

25. $\sim10^{-11}$ s; between 10^3 and 10^4 wavelengths

29. 0.171°

31. 86.8°

33. 27.9°

35. 4.61°

37. (a) 33.4°   (b) 53.4°   (c) There is no critical angle.

39. 1.000 08

41. 1.08 cm $< d <$ 1.17 cm

43. Skylight incident from above travels down the plastic. If the index of refraction of the plastic is greater than 1.41, the rays close in direction to the vertical are totally reflected from the side walls of the slab and from both facets at the bottom of the plastic, where it is not immersed in gasoline. This light returns up inside the plastic and makes it look bright. Where the plastic is immersed in gasoline, total internal reflection is frustrated and the downward-propagating light passes from the plastic out into the gasoline. Little light is reflected up, and the gauge looks dark.

45. Scattered light leaving the photograph in all forward horizontal directions in air is gathered by refraction into a fan in the water of half-angle 48.6°. At larger angles you see things on the other side of the globe, reflected by total internal reflection at the back surface of the cylinder.

47. 77.5°

49. 2.27 m

51. (a) 0.172 mm/s   (b) 0.345 mm/s   (c) northward at 50.0° below the horizontal   (d) northward at 50.0° below the horizontal

53. 62.2%

55. 82 reflections

57. (b) 68.5%

59. 27.5°

61. (a) It always happens.   (b) 30.3°   (c) It cannot happen.

63. 2.36 cm

67. 1.93

69. (a) $n = [1 + (4t/d)^2]^{1/2}$ (b) 2.10 cm   (c) violet

71. (a) 1.20   (b) 3.40 ns

CHAPTER 36

1. $\sim10^{-9}$ s younger

3. 35.0 in.

5. 10.0 ft, 30.0 ft, 40.0 ft

7. (a) 13.3 cm, -0.333, real and inverted   (b) 20.0 cm, -1.00, real and inverted   (c) no image is formed

9. (a) -12.0 cm; 0.400   (b) -15.0 cm; 0.250   (c) upright

11. (a) q = 45.0 cm; $M = -0.500$ (b) $q = -60.0$ cm; M = 3.00   (c) Image (a) is real, inverted, and diminished. Image (b) is virtual, upright, and enlarged. The ray diagrams are like Figures 36.15a and 36.15b, respectively.

13. At 0.708 cm in front of the reflecting surface. Image is virtual, upright, and diminished.

15. 7.90 mm

17. (a) a concave mirror with radius of curvature 2.08 m
(b) 1.25 m from the object

19. (a) 25.6 m   (b) 0.058 7 rad   (c) 2.51 m   (d) 0.023 9 rad
(e) 62.8 m from your eyes

21. 38.2 cm below the top surface of the ice

23. 8.57 cm

25. (a) 45.0 cm   (b) −90.0 cm   (c) −6.00 cm

27. 1.50 cm/s

29. (a) 16.4 cm   (b) 16.4 cm

31. (a) 650 cm from the lens on the opposite side from the object; real, inverted, enlarged   (b) 600 cm from the lens on the same side as the object; virtual, upright, enlarged

33. 2.84 cm

37. (a) −12.3 cm, to the left of the lens   (b) 0.615
(c)

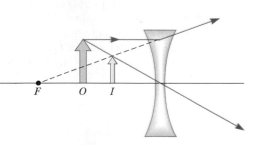

39. (a) 7.10 cm   (b) 0.074 0 mm   (c) 23.3 MW/m^2

41. (a) $p = \dfrac{d}{2} \pm \sqrt{\dfrac{d^2}{4} - fd}$ (b) Both images are real and inverted. One is enlarged, the other diminished.

43. 1.24 cm

45. 21.3 cm

47. −4.00 diopters, a diverging lens

49. −3.70 diopters

51. −575

53. (a) −800   (b) image is inverted

55. (a) virtual   (b) infinity   (c) 15.0 cm, −5.00 cm

57. −40.0 cm

59. (a) 23.1 cm   (b) 0.147 cm

61. (a) 67.5 cm   (b) The lenses can be displaced in two ways. The first lens can be displaced 1.28 cm farther away from the object, and the second lens 17.7 cm toward the object. Alternatively, the first lens can be displaced 0.927 cm toward the object and the second lens 4.44 cm toward the object.

63. $q = 5.71$ cm; real

65. 0.107 m to the right of the vertex of the hemispherical face

67. 8.00 cm

Ray diagram:

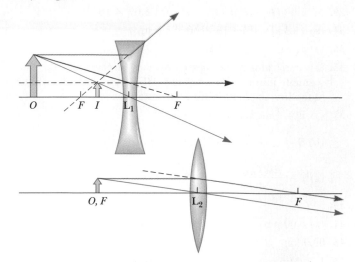

69. 1.50 m in front of the mirror; 1.40 cm (inverted)

71. (a) 30.0 cm and 120 cm   (b) 24.0 cm   (c) real, inverted, diminished with $M = -0.250$

73. −75.0

75. (a) 44.6 diopters   (b) 3.03 diopters

77. (a) 20.0 cm to the right of the second lens, −6.00
(b) inverted   (c) 6.67 cm to the right of the second lens, −2.00, inverted

CHAPTER 37

1. 1.58 cm

3. (a) 55.7 m   (b) 124 m

5. 1.54 mm

7. (a) 2.62 mm   (b) 2.62 mm

9. 11.3 m

11. (a) 10.0 m   (b) 516 m   (c) Only the runway centerline is a maximum for the interference patterns for both frequencies. If the frequencies were related by a ratio of small integers k/ℓ, the plane could by mistake fly along the kth side maximum of one signal where it coincides with the ℓth side maximum of the other.

13. (a) 13.2 rad   (b) 6.28 rad   (c) 0.012 7 degree
(d) 0.059 7 degree

15. (a) 1.93 μm   (b) 3.00λ (c) maximum

17. 48.0 μm

19. (a) 7.95 rad   (b) 0.453

21. (a) and (b) 19.7 kN/C at 35.0°   (c) 9.36 kN/C at 169°

23. 10.0 sin(100πt + 0.927)

25. 26.2 sin(ωt + 36.6°)

27. $\pi/2$

29. 360°/N

31. (a) green   (b) violet

33. 0.500 cm

35. no reflection maxima in the visible spectrum

37. 290 nm

39. 4.35 μm

41. 39.6 μm

43. $1 + N\lambda/2L$

45. 1.25 m

47. (a) $\sim 10^{-3}$ degree   (b) $\sim 10^{11}$ Hz, microwave

49. $20.0 \times 10^{-6}\,°\text{C}^{-1}$

51. 3.58°

53. 1.62 km

55. 421 nm

59. (a) $2(4h^2 + d^2)^{1/2} - 2d$ (b) $(4h^2 + d^2)^{1/2} - d$

61. $y' = (n - 1)tL/d$

63. (a) 70.6 m   (b) 136 m

65. 1.73 cm

67. (a) 4.86 cm from the top   (b) 78.9 nm and 128 nm
(c) 2.63×10^{-6} rad

69. 0.505 mm

CHAPTER 38

1. 4.22 mm

3. 0.230 mm

5. three maxima, at 0° and near 46° on both sides

7. 51.8 μm wide and 949 μm high

9. 0.016 2

11. 1.00 mrad

13. 3.09 m

15. violet; between 186 m and 271 m

17. 13.1 m

19. Neither. It can resolve objects no closer than several centimeters apart.

21. 0.244 rad = 14.0°

23. 7.35°

25. 5.91° in first order, 13.2° in second order, 26.5° in third order

27. (a) 478.7 nm, 647.6 nm, and 696.6 nm   (b) 20.51°, 28.30°, and 30.66°

29. (a) 12 000, 24 000, 36 000   (b) 11.1 pm

31. (a) 2 800 grooves   (b) 4.72 μm

33. (a) 5 orders   (b) 10 orders in the short-wavelength region

35. 93.4 pm

37. 14.4°

39. 5.51 m, 2.76 m, 1.84 m

41. (a) 54.7°   (b) 63.4°   (c) 71.6°

43. 1.11

45. 60.5°

47. 36.9° above the horizon

49. (a) 6   (b) 7.50°

51. 632.8 nm

53. (a) 25.6°   (b) 19.0°

55. 545 nm

57. (a) 3.53×10^3 grooves/cm   (c) Eleven maxima

59. 4.58 μm $< d <$ 5.23 μm

61. 15.4

63. (a) 41.8°   (b) 0.593   (c) 0.262 m

67. (b) 3.77 nm/cm

69. (b) 15.3 μm

71. $\phi = 1.391\,557\,4$ after seventeen steps or fewer

73. $a = 99.5\ \mu\text{m} \pm 1\%$

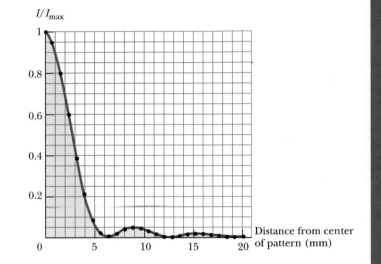

CHAPTER 39

5. $0.866c$

7. (a) 64.9/min   (b) 10.6/min

9. 1.54 ns

11. $0.800c$

13. (a) 39.2 μs   (b) accurate to one digit

15. (a) 20.0 m   (b) 19.0 m   (c) $0.312c$

17. (a) 21.0 yr   (b) 14.7 ly   (c) 10.5 ly   (d) 35.7 yr

19. (c) 2.00 kHz   (d) $\pm 0.075\,0$ m/s $\approx$ 0.2 mi/h

21. $0.220c = 6.59 \times 10^7$ m/s

23. (a) 17.4 m   (b) 3.30°

25. (a) 2.50×10^8 m/s   (b) 4.97 m   (c) -1.33×10^{-8} s

27. $0.960c$

29. (a) 2.73×10^{-24} kg·m/s   (b) 1.58×10^{-22} kg·m/s
(c) 5.64×10^{-22} kg·m/s

31. 4.50×10^{-14}

33. $0.285c$

35. (a) 5.37×10^{-11} J   (b) 1.33×10^{-9} J

37. 1.63×10^3 MeV/c

39. (a) 938 MeV   (b) 3.00 GeV   (c) 2.07 GeV

41. 8.84×10^{-28} kg and 2.51×10^{-28} kg

45. (a) 3.91×10^4 (b) $u = 0.999\,999\,999\,7c$ (c) 7.67 cm

47. 4.08 MeV and 29.6 MeV

49. $\sim 10^{-15}$

51. 0.842 kg

53. 4.19×10^9 kg/s

55. (a) 26.6 Mm (b) 3.87 km/s (c) -8.34×10^{-11}
(d) 5.29×10^{-10} (e) $+4.46 \times 10^{-10}$

57. (a) a few hundred seconds (b) $\sim 10^8$ km

59. (a) $0.800c$ (b) 7.50 ks (c) 1.44 Tm, $-0.385c$ (d) 4.88 ks

61. 0.712%

63. (a) $0.946c$ (b) 0.160 ly (c) 0.114 yr (d) 7.50×10^{22} J

65. (a) 76.0 min (b) 52.1 min

67. yes, with 18.8 m to spare

69. (b) For u small compared to c, the relativistic expression
agrees with the classical expression. As u approaches c, the
acceleration approaches zero, so that the object can never
reach or surpass the speed of light.
(c) Perform $\int (1 - u^2/c^2)^{-3/2} du = (qE/m) \int dt$ to obtain
$u = qEct(m^2c^2 + q^2E^2t^2)^{-1/2}$ and then
$\int dx = \int qEct(m^2c^2 + q^2E^2t^2)^{-1/2} dt$ to obtain
$x = (c/qE)[(m^2c^2 + q^2E^2t^2)^{1/2} - mc]$

75. 1.82×10^{-3} eV

Credits

Photographs

This page constitutes an extension of the copyright page. We have made every effort to trace the ownership of all copyrighted material and to secure permission from copyright holders. In the event of any question arising as to the use of any material, we will be pleased to make the necessary corrections in future printings. Thanks are due to the following authors, publishers, and agents for permission to use the material indicated.

Chapter 1. **xxiv:** Courtesy of NASA **2:** elektraVision/Index Stock Imagery **6:** top left, Courtesy of National Institute of Standards and Technology, U.S. Dept. of Commerce; top right, Courtesy of National Institute of Standards and Technology, U.S. Dept. of Commerce **13:** Phil Boorman/Getty Images **19:** Sylvain Grandadam/Photo Researchers, Inc.

Chapter 2. **23:** George Lepp/Getty Images **26:** Ken White/Allsport/Getty Images **46:** North Wind Picture Archive **52:** bottom left, Courtesy U.S. Air Force; bottom right, Photri, Inc. **53:** George Semple **55:** Courtesy Amtrak Nec Media Relations

Chapter 3. **58:** Mark Wagner/Getty Images

Chapter 4. **77:** © Arndt/Premium Stock/PictureQuest **79:** Mark C. Burnett/Photo Researchers, Inc. **84:** The Telegraph Colour Library/Getty Images **86:** Mike Powell/Allsport/Getty Images **88:** Central Scientific Company **103:** bottom left, McKinney/Getty Images **104:** top left, Jed Jacobsohn/Allsport/Getty Images; top right, Bill Lee/Dembinsky Photo Associates; bottom left, Sam Sargent/Liaison International; bottom right, Courtesy of NASA **106:** Courtesy of NASA

Chapter 5. **111:** © Steve Raymer/CORBIS **114:** Giraudon/Art Resource **119:** Courtesy of NASA **120:** John Gillmoure/corbisstockmarket.com **122:** © John Elk III/Stock, Boston Inc./PictureQuest **139:** Roger Violet, Mill Valley, CA, University Science Books, 1992

Chapter 6. **150:** © Paul Hardy/CORBIS **151:** Mike Powell/Allsport/Getty Images **152:** © Tom Carroll/Index Stock Imagery/PictureQuest **157:** Robin Smith/Getty Images **165:** Jump Run Productions/Getty Images **166:** Charles D. Winters **174:** Frank Cezus/Getty Images **178:** Color Box/Getty Images

Chapter 7. **181:** Billy Hustace/Getty Images **183:** all, Charles D. Winters **184:** Gerard Vandystandt/Photo Researchers, Inc. **198:** all except top right, George Semple **198:** top right, Digital Vision/Getty Images **213:** Ron Chapple/Getty Images

Chapter 8. **217:** Harold E. Edgerton/Courtesy of Palm Press, Inc. **242:** Gamma **250:** Engraving from Scientific American, July 1888

Chapter 9. **251:** Mark Cooper/corbisstockmarket.com **257:** Courtesy of Saab **259:** top, Harold & Esther Edgerton Foundation 2002, courtesy of Palm Press, Inc; bottom, © Tim Wright/CORBIS **263:** No credit available **264:** Courtesy of Central Scientific Company **276:** Richard Megna/Fundamental Photographs **278:** Courtesy of NASA **279:** Courtesy of NASA **281:** Bill Stormont/corbisstockmarket.com **286:** Eye Ubiquitous/CORBIS

Chapter 10. **292:** Courtesy Tourism Malaysia **299:** George Semple **316:** Henry Leap and Jim Lehman **323:** Bruce Ayers/Getty Images **327:** John Lawrence/Getty Images **329:** Jerry Wachter/Photo Researchers, Inc.

Chapter 11. **336:** Otto Gruele/Getty Images **346:** both, © 1998 David Madison **354:** Gerard Lacz/NHPA

Chapter 12. **362:** John W. Jewett, Jr. **366:** Charles D. Winters

Chapter 13. **389:** University of Arizona/JPL/NASA **394:** Courtesy of NASA **410:** Courtesy H. Ford, et al., & NASA **417:** Courtesy of NASA

Chapter 14. **420:** Austin MacRae **422:** Earl Young/Getty Images **424:** right, David Frazier **427:** © Hulton-Deutsch Collection/CORBIS **430:** Geraldine Prentice/Getty Images **431:** Andy Sachs/Getty Images **431:** Werner Wolff/stockphoto.com **432:** George Semple **434:** Bettmann/CORBIS **435:** Courtesy of Central Scientific Company **438:** Galen Rowell/Peter Arnold, Inc. **439:** bottom left, Pamela Zilly/Getty Images **439:** top right, Henry Leap and Jim Lehman **439:** bottom right, Henry Leap and Jim Lehman **444:** George Semple **445:** Stan Osolinski/Dembinsky Photo Associates **447:** The Granger Collection **448:** Courtesy of Jeanne Maier

Chapter 15. **450:** Don Bonsey/Getty Images **452:** both, www.comstock.com **465:** top left, Courtesy of Ford Motor Company; bottom left, © Link/Visuals Unlimited **474:** both, UPI-Bettmann/CORBIS **478:** Telegraph Colour Library/Getty Images **479:** George Semple

Chapter 16. **486:** Kathy Ferguson Johnson/PhotoEdit/PictureQuest **509:** Gregg Adams/Getty Images

Chapter 17. **512:** Getty Images **518:** Courtesy Kenneth Burger Museum Archives/Kent State University **524:** Courtesy of the Educational Development Center, Newton, MA **527:** © 1973 Kim Vandiver and Harold E. Edgerton/Courtesy of Palm Press, Inc. **528:** www.comstock.com

Bohr Library. **1110:** David Parker/Science Photo Library/Photo Researchers, Inc. **1113:** Courtesy of Henry Leap and Jim Lehman **1114:** left, Dennis O'Clair/Getty Images; right, Hank Morgan/Photo Researchers, Inc. **1117:** Courtesy of U.S. Air Force, Langley Air Force Base **1120:** Roy Atkeson Photo Library **1122:** Courtesy Edwin Lo

Chapter 36. **1126:** Don Hammond/CORBIS **1128:** George Semple **1130:** Courtesy of Henry Leap/Jim Lehman **1131:** Ken Kay/Fundamental Photographs **1133:** top, Henry Leap/Jim Lehman **1133:** Courtesy of Thompson Consumer Electronics **1135:** David Rogers **1136:** NASA **1138:** © 1990 Paul Silverman/Fundamental Photographs **1144:** Henry Leap/Jim Lehman **1149:** Henry Leap/Jim Lehman **1155:** From Lennart Nilsson, in collaboration with Jan Lindberg, *Behold Man: A Photographic Journey of Discovery Inside the Body,* Boston, Little, Brown & Co. 1974. **1160:** George Semple **1161:** © Tony Freeman/PhotoEdit **1163:** © Tony Freeman/PhotoEdit **1164:** Orion® Sky View Pro™ 6 EQ Reflector, Orion Telescopes & Binoculars. Copyright © 2003 OrionTelescopes & Binoculars. All rights reserved. "Orion" is the trademark and service mark of Optronic Technologies, Inc. 800-676-1343, www.telescope.com **1166:** © 2003 by Sidney Harris. All rights reserved. **1166:** Richard Megna/Fundamental Photographs **1167:** George Semple **1167:** M.C. Escher/Cordon Art-Baarn Holland. All Rights Reserved. **1169:** THE FAR SIDE © 1985 FARWORKS, INC. Used by permission. All rights reserved. **1174:** © Michael Levin/Opti-Gone Associates

Chapter 37. **1176:** RO-MA/Index Stock Imagery **1177:** © Kolar, Richard/Animals Animals/Earth Scenes **1178:** Courtesy of Sabina Zigman/Benjamin Cardozo High School, and by permission of *The Physics Teacher,* vol. 37, January 1999, p. 55. **1179:** Photograph from M. Cagnet, M. Francon, and J.C. Thierr, *Atlas of Optical Phenomena,* Berlin, Springer-Verlag, 1962. **1179:** Richard Megna/Fundamental Photographs **1184:** Photograph from M. Cagnet, M. Francon, and J.C. Thierr, *Atlas of Optical Phenomena,* Berlin, Springer-Verlag, 1962. **1191:** left, Dr. Jeremy Burgess/Science Photo Library/Photo Researchers, Inc. **1191:** right, Peter Aprahamian/Science Photo Library/Photo Researchers, Inc. **1191:** Courtesy Bausch and Lomb Optical Company **1192:** From Physical Science Study Committee, College Physics, Lexington, MA, Heath, 1968. **1193:** Kristen Brochmann/Fundamental Photographs **1194:** Richard Megna/Fundamental Photographs **1196:** LIGO Hanford Observatory **1201:** Courtesy of Central Scientific Supply

Chapter 38. **1205:** Denis Scott/CORBIS **1207:** right, P.M. Rinard, *Am. J. Phys.* 44:70, 1976 **1207:** From M. Cagnet, M. Francon, and J.C. Thierr, *Atlas of Optical Phenomena,* Berlin, Springer-Verlag, 1962, plate 18. **1212:** From M. Cagnet, M. Francon, and J.C. Thierr, *Atlas of Optical Phenomena,* Berlin, Springer-Verlag, 1962, plate 18. **1213:** Photograph courtesy of Central Scientific Company **1215:** From M. Cagnet, M. Francon, and J.C. Thierr, *Atlas of Optical Phenomena,* Berlin, Springer-Verlag, 1962, plate 16. **1218:** left, U.S. Naval Observatory/James W. Christy; right, Photo courtesy of Gemini Observatory **1220:** Courtesy Silicon Light Machines

1221: Kristen Brochmann/Fundamental Photographs **1223:** Photo by Ronald R. Erickson; hologram by Nicklaus Philips **1224:** bottom left, Used with permission of Eastman Kodak Company; bottom right, I. Andersson, Oxford Molecular Biophysics Laboratory/Science Photo Library/Photo Researchers, Inc. **1227:** Henry Leap/Jim Lehman **1230:** left, Henry Leap/Jim Lehman **1230:** bottom: a) Sepp Seitz 1981; b) Peter Aprahamian/Science Photo Library/Photo Researchers, Inc. **1231:** Photograph by Gary Friedman. Copyright © 2003, Los Angeles Times. Reprinted with permission. **1235:** SuperStock **1238:** top, Susan Allen Sigma/Getty Images **1238:** bottom, left: Riccardo Giovanni and Martha Haynes, Cornell University **1238:** center, right: Diane Schiumo 1988, Fundamental Photographs **1241:** © 2003 by Sidney Harris. All rights reserved.

Chapter 39. **1242:** Fermilab Photo, Courtesy of Fermi National Accelerator Laboratory **1244:** Emily Serway **1251:** AIP Niels Bohr Library **1275:** Courtesy NASA **1279:** Trent Steffler/David R. Frazier Photolibrary **1281:** Photo courtesy of Garmin Ltd. **1283:** © 2003 by Sidney Harris. All rights reserved.

Tables and Illustrations

This page constitutes an extension of the copyright page. We have made every effort to trace the ownership of all copyrighted material and to secure permission from copyright holders. In the event of any question arising as to the use of any material, we will be pleased to make the necessary corrections in future printings. Thanks are due to the following authors, publishers, and agents for permission to use the material indicated.

Chapter 2. **56:** By permission of John Hart and Creators Syndicate, Inc.

Chapter 13. **415:** By permission of John Hart and Creators Syndicate, Inc.

Chapter 14. **449:** Calvin & Hobbes © 1992 Watterson. Reprinted with permission of Universal Press Syndicate. All rights reserved.

Chapter 21. **666:** By permission of John Hart and Creators Syndicate, Inc.

Chapter 30. **966:** Calvin and Hobbes © Watterson. Reprinted with permission of Universal Press Syndicate. All rights reserved.

Chapter 36. **1166:** © 2003 Sidney Harris **1169:** The Far Side® by Gary Larson © 1985 FarWorks, Inc. All Rights Reserved. Used with permission.

Chapter 38. **1241:** © 2003 by Sidney Harris

Chapter 39. **1283:** © 2003 by Sidney Harris

Index

Locator notes: **boldface** indicates a definition; *italics* indicates a figure; *t* indicates a table

Isothermal expansion, *620*–622
Isothermal processes, **620**
 in Carnot cycles, 675–*676*
 one-time, 671
Isotherms, *620*
Isotopes, 8, A.4*t*–A.13*t*
Isotropic materials, 588
Isovolumetric processes, **620**

Jackets, in optical fibers, 1114
Jacob's ladder, *851*
James testers, 146
Jewett, Frank Baldwin, *912*
Joule, James, 605, *606*, 607, 632
Joule (J), **185**, 606
Joule heating, 846
Jumpers, 868–*869*
Junction rule, **869**–873
Junctions, **864**
Jupiter, 399*t*. *See also* Planetary motion
 atmosphere of, 408
 escape speed from, 408*t*
 magnetic field of, 954
 moon of, *389*, 1096
 and speed of light, 1096

Kamerlingh-Onnes, Heike, 844
Kaons (K⁰), 256
Keating, R. E., 1255
Keck Observatory, 1165
Kelvin, William Thomson, Lord, 4, 585, *669*
Kelvin (K), 4, **585**
Kelvin–Planck form of the second law of thermodynamics, **670**
Kelvin temperature scale, **585**–586, 610
Kepler, Johannes, 390, *396*
Kepler's laws, **396**–401. *See also* Astronomy; Gravitation; Planetary motion
Keratometers, 1169
Kilocalorie (kcal), 212
Kilogram (kg), 4–*6*, **5**, 116, 118*t*
Kilowatt-hour (kWh), 204
Kinematic equations
 for motion of charged particles in electric fields, 726–727, 767
 for motion with constant angular acceleration, 296–297*t*
 and numerical modeling, 168
 for one-dimensional motion with constant acceleration, 36–**37**, 38*t*, 46, 297*t*
 for simple harmonic motion, 455, 457
 for two-dimensional motion with constant acceleration, 80–83
Kinematics, 24. *See also* Dynamics
 in one dimension, 23–57
 rotational, 296–297
 in two dimensions, 77–110

Kinetic energy (K), 193–196, **194**. *See also* Conservation of energy; Energy; Potential energy
 and charges in electric fields, 766
 and collisions, 260–261
 and equipartition of energy, 650–654
 and kinetic theory of gases, 641–646
 and planetary motion, 405–407
 relativistic, 1268–1270
 rotational (K_R), **300**–302, 313
 total (K), 313, 318, 462
 and work-kinetic energy theorem, **194**
Kinetic theory of gases, 640–666, **641**. *See also* Statistical mechanics
 and adiabatic processes for an ideal gas, *617*, 619, 649–*650*
 and the Boltzmann distribution law, 654–655
 and distribution of molecular speeds, 655–657
 and entropy, 690
 and equipartition of energy, 650–654
 and mean free paths, 658–659
 and molar specific heat of an ideal gas, 646–649
 and molecular model of an ideal gas, 641–646
Kirchhoff, Gustav, *870*
Kirchhoff's rules, **869**–873
 and RL circuits, 1007
Krypton-86
 and standard meter, 4
Kuiper belt, 399

Ladders, 369–*370*
Lagrange, Joseph Louis, 417
Lagrange points, 417
Laminar flow, *431*
Land, Edwin H., 1226
Laser Interferometer Gravitational-Wave Observatory (LIGO), 1195–*1196*
Laser printers, *784*
Latent heat (L), 606, **611**–615
 of fusion or solidification (L_f), 611–612*t*, 686
 of vaporization or condensation (L_v), 611–612*t*
Lateral magnification (M), **1128**, 1132, 1145
 of microscopes, 1161–1162
Laue patterns, *1224*–1225
Law of atmospheres, 663
Law of cosines, 64, A.22
Law of inertia. *See* First law of motion
Law of reflection, *1099*
 from Fermat's principle, 1115
 from Huygens's principle, *1108*–1109
Law of sines, 64, A.22
Law of thermal conduction, **624**
Law of universal gravitation, **390**–393
Lawrence, Ernest O., 913

Laws of motion, 111–149
 applications of, 122–131
 and circular motion, 150–180
 first, **114**–115
 and rotational motion, 307-314*t*, 340–342
 second, 116–118, **117**
 third, **120**–122
Laws of physics, 1–3. *See also* Ampère–Maxwell law; Ampère's law; Angular impulse–angular momentum theorem; Archimedes's principle; Bernoulli's equation; Biot–Savart law; Boltzmann distribution law; Boyle's law; Bragg's law; Brewster's law; Carnot's theorem; Charles's and Gay–Lussac's law; Conservation of energy; Conservation of momentum; Continuity equation for fluids; Coulomb's law; Curie's law; Dalton's law of partial pressures; Dulong– Petit law; Equations of state; Equipartition of energy theorem; Faraday's law; Fermat's principle; Galilean transformation equations; Gas laws; Gauss's law; Hooke's law; Huygens's principle; Impulse– momentum theorem; Inverse-square laws; Kepler's laws; Kinematic equations; Kinetic theory of gases; Kirchhoff's rules; Law of atmospheres; Law of reflection; Law of thermal conduction; Law of universal gravitation; Laws of motion; Laws of thermodynamics; Lennard–Jones law; Lens makers' equation; Lenz's law; Lorentz force law; Malus's law; Maxwell's equations; Mirror equation; Ohm's law; Parallel-axis theorem; Pascal's law; Principle of equivalence; Snell's law of refraction; Stefan's law; Superposition principle; Thin lens equation; Torricelli's law; Wave equations; Work–kinetic energy theorem
Laws of thermodynamics
 first, **618**–623
 second, 668–**670**, **671**–672
 zeroth, 581–**582**
LC circuits, *1015*–1020
Length (x, y, z, r, l, d, or h)
 path (r), **548**–549
 standards of, 4–5*t*
 units of, A.1*t*
Length contraction, **1258**–*1259*
Lennard–Jones law
 force for, 215
 potential for, 237–*238*, 464
 and simple harmonic motion, 463–*464*
 and thermal expansion, 587

Mass (*m*) *(Continued)*
units of, 4–6, **5**, 116, 118*t*, A.1*t*
vs. weight, 116
Mass number (*A*), **8**, A.4*t*–A.13*t*
Mass spectrometers, *911*–912
Materials science. *See also* Deformable
systems; Friction; Gases; Liquids;
Optics; Rigid Objects; Solids
and crystalline *vs.* amorphous
materials, 1229
and electrical properties of solids, 709,
835–845, 838, 1031
and magnetic properties of solids,
947–952, 1031
and mechanical properties of
materials, 373–376
and optical properties of materials,
1104–1107, 1230, *1230*
and thermal properties of materials,
197, 583, 586–591, 620–622,
623–627
*Mathematical Principles of Natural
Philosophy* [Newton], 390
Mathematics, A.14–A.29. *See also*
Addition; Algebra; Approximating;
Calculus; Determinants; Division;
Equations; Fourier series;
Geometry; Logarithms;
Measurement; Multiplication;
Numerical modeling; Rounding;
Series expansions; Significant
figures; Subtraction; Trigonometric
functions; Units; Vectors
Matrix algebra, 870
Matter
fundamental particles of, 912
structure of, 7–9, *8*
Matter transfer, **197**. *See also* Convection
and energy transfer, 197–*198*, 627–628
and waves, 487
Maxima of intensity, 1180, 1187–*1188*,
1206, 1219
Maximum angular position (θ_max)
[pendulums], 468
Maximum angular separation (θ_max)
[apertures], 1215
Maximum height (*h*) of a projectile,
86–91
Maxwell, James Clerk, *1067*
and electromagnetic waves, 1067–1068,
1093, 1095
and electromagnetism, 705, 896, 942,
944
and Maxwell's equations, 988,
1067–1068
and molecular speed distributions, 655
Maxwell–Boltzmann speed distribution
function (*N_v*), *655–657*, **656**
Maxwell's equations, **988–989**
and electromagnetic waves, 1067–1069
and special relativity, 1245, 1247
Mean free path (ℓ), **658**–659, 842

Mean free time, **658**
Mean solar day, 5
Mean value theorem, 257
Measurement, 2–22. *See also*
Experiments; Instrumentation
of density, *443*
and disturbing the system, 582
of electric current, *879*
of forces, 113–*114*
of the gravitational constant, 393–394
of magnetic fields, 914
of moments of inertia, 470
of potential difference, 879–880
of pressure, *421*, *426*–427
of speed of light, *1096–1097*
of temperature, 582–584
uncertainty in, A.28–A.29
of wavelength of light, 1181
Measurements
of electric current, 879
Mechanical devices. *See also* Heat engines
air conditioners, 671
balances, 393–394, 895, 987–*988*, 1077
machines, 148
photocopiers, *784*
Mechanical energy (*E*_mech), **221**
changes in, for nonconservative forces,
229–234
conservation of, 220–228, **221**
heat equivalent of, 606–*607*
and planetary motion, 406
Mechanical engineering. *See also*
Aeronautics; Airplanes;
Automobiles; Bridges;
Locomotives; Satellites; Spacecraft
and heat engines, *667–683*, **669**, 700
and machines, 148
Mechanical equivalent of heat, 606–**607**
Mechanical waves, **197**, *450–577*, **487**
and energy transfer, 197–*198*, 487,
500–503, 516–522
motion of, 486–511
sound, 512–542
speed of, 513–514
Mechanics, 1–449. *See also* Classical
mechanics; Dynamics; Energy; Fluid
mechanics; Force; Kinematics;
Momentum; Motion; Quantum
mechanics; Statistical mechanics
history of, 1, 112
Media for wave propagation, 487
effects of changes in, 499–501, 560
and ether, 1247–1250
Medicine. *See also* Biophysics; Health
and blood flowmeters, 915–916, 924
and contact lenses, 1169
and cyclotrons, 913
and defibrillators, *810*, 825
and ears, *512*, *519–522*, 564
and eyeglasses, *1157–1158*
and eyes, 1157–1159, 1169, 1174
and fiber optics, 1114

Medicine *(Continued)*
and MRI, 845
and spinal taps, 442
and steam burns, 613
and sunglasses, *1081*, 1229
and ultrasound, 536
Meissner effect, *952*, 1031
Melting. *See* Fusion
Melting points, 612*t*
Mercury [element]
in barometers, 426
superconductivity of, 844
in thermometers, *583*–584
Mercury [planet], 399*t*. *See also*
Planetary motion
escape speed from, 408*t*
Metal detectors, 1051
Metals
and bimetallic strips, *589*, *601*
charge carriers in, 915
thermal conduction of, 623–625, 624*t*
Meter (m), **4**
Michelson, Albert A., 1194, 1248–1250
Michelson interferometers, *1194*–1196,
1249
Michelson–Morley experiment,
1248–1250
Microscopes
compound, **1160**–1162
electron, 102
interference, 1202
Microstates, **683**–684, 690–693
Microwave ovens, 816, 1085
Microwaves, **1080**–*1081*
cosmic background, 1088
Migrating planets, 399
Millikan, Robert, 708, 781–782
Minima of intensity, **1206**
Minor axis, *396*
Mirages, 1121
Mirror equation, **1132**–1133
Mirrors, *1127–1138*. *See also* Reflection
concave, *1131*–1133
convex, *1134*
flat, *1127*–1130
Lloyd's, *1188*
parabolic, *1164*
ray diagrams for, 1134–1136
spherical, *1131–1138*
Models, **7**–9
of atomic nucleus, 791
computer, 169–170
of electric current, 833–835
of electrical conduction, 841–843
of entropy, 690–693
of hydrogen atom, 352–353, 759
of ideal gases, 641–646
numerical, 167–170
particle, 24, 182, 270
of phase changes, 613
of solar system, 396
of solids, 463–*464*

Some Physical Constants[a]

Quantity	Symbol	Value[b]
Atomic mass unit	u	$1.660\ 538\ 73\ (13) \times 10^{-27}$ kg $931.494\ 013\ (37)$ MeV/c^2
Avogadro's number	N_A	$6.022\ 141\ 99\ (47) \times 10^{23}$ particles/mol
Bohr magneton	$\mu_B = \dfrac{e\hbar}{2m_e}$	$9.274\ 008\ 99\ (37) \times 10^{-24}$ J/T
Bohr radius	$a_0 = \dfrac{\hbar^2}{m_e e^2 k_e}$	$5.291\ 772\ 083\ (19) \times 10^{-11}$ m
Boltzmann's constant	$k_B = \dfrac{R}{N_A}$	$1.380\ 650\ 3\ (24) \times 10^{-23}$ J/K
Compton wavelength	$\lambda_C = \dfrac{h}{m_e c}$	$2.426\ 310\ 215\ (18) \times 10^{-12}$ m
Coulomb constant	$k_e = \dfrac{1}{4\pi\epsilon_0}$	$8.987\ 551\ 788\ \ldots \times 10^9$ N·m^2/C^2 (exact)
Deuteron mass	m_d	$3.343\ 583\ 09\ (26) \times 10^{-27}$ kg $2.013\ 553\ 212\ 71\ (35)$ u
Electron mass	m_e	$9.109\ 381\ 88\ (72) \times 10^{-31}$ kg $5.485\ 799\ 110\ (12) \times 10^{-4}$ u $0.510\ 998\ 902\ (21)$ MeV/c^2
Electron volt	eV	$1.602\ 176\ 462\ (63) \times 10^{-19}$ J
Elementary charge	e	$1.602\ 176\ 462\ (63) \times 10^{-19}$ C
Gas constant	R	$8.314\ 472\ (15)$ J/K·mol
Gravitational constant	G	$6.673\ (10) \times 10^{-11}$ N·m^2/kg^2
Josephson frequency–voltage ratio	$\dfrac{2e}{h}$	$4.835\ 978\ 98\ (19) \times 10^{14}$ Hz/V
Magnetic flux quantum	$\Phi_0 = \dfrac{h}{2e}$	$2.067\ 833\ 636\ (81) \times 10^{-15}$ T·m^2
Neutron mass	m_n	$1.674\ 927\ 16\ (13) \times 10^{-27}$ kg $1.008\ 664\ 915\ 78\ (55)$ u $939.565\ 330\ (38)$ MeV/c^2
Nuclear magneton	$\mu_n = \dfrac{e\hbar}{2m_p}$	$5.050\ 783\ 17\ (20) \times 10^{-27}$ J/T
Permeability of free space	μ_0	$4\pi \times 10^{-7}$ T·m/A (exact)
Permittivity of free space	$\epsilon_0 = \dfrac{1}{\mu_0 c^2}$	$8.854\ 187\ 817 \ldots \times 10^{-12}$ C^2/N·m^2 (exact)
Planck's constant	h	$6.626\ 068\ 76\ (52) \times 10^{-34}$ J·s
	$\hbar = \dfrac{h}{2\pi}$	$1.054\ 571\ 596\ (82) \times 10^{-34}$ J·s
Proton mass	m_p	$1.672\ 621\ 58\ (13) \times 10^{-27}$ kg $1.007\ 276\ 466\ 88\ (13)$ u $938.271\ 998\ (38)$ MeV/c^2
Rydberg constant	R_H	$1.097\ 373\ 156\ 854\ 9\ (83) \times 10^7$ m^{-1}
Speed of light in vacuum	c	$2.997\ 924\ 58 \times 10^8$ m/s (exact)

[a] These constants are the values recommended in 1998 by CODATA, based on a least-squares adjustment of data from different measurements. For a more complete list, see P. J. Mohr and B. N. Taylor, *Rev. Mod. Phys.* 72:351, 2000.

[b] The numbers in parentheses for the values above represent the uncertainties of the last two digits.

Solar System Data

Body	Mass (kg)	Mean Radius (m)	Period (s)	Distance from the Sun (m)
Mercury	3.18×10^{23}	2.43×10^{6}	7.60×10^{6}	5.79×10^{10}
Venus	4.88×10^{24}	6.06×10^{6}	1.94×10^{7}	1.08×10^{11}
Earth	5.98×10^{24}	6.37×10^{6}	3.156×10^{7}	1.496×10^{11}
Mars	6.42×10^{23}	3.37×10^{6}	5.94×10^{7}	2.28×10^{11}
Jupiter	1.90×10^{27}	6.99×10^{7}	3.74×10^{8}	7.78×10^{11}
Saturn	5.68×10^{26}	5.85×10^{7}	9.35×10^{8}	1.43×10^{12}
Uranus	8.68×10^{25}	2.33×10^{7}	2.64×10^{9}	2.87×10^{12}
Neptune	1.03×10^{26}	2.21×10^{7}	5.22×10^{9}	4.50×10^{12}
Pluto	$\approx 1.4 \times 10^{22}$	$\approx 1.5 \times 10^{6}$	7.82×10^{9}	5.91×10^{12}
Moon	7.36×10^{22}	1.74×10^{6}	—	—
Sun	1.991×10^{30}	6.96×10^{8}	—	—

Physical Data Often Used[a]

Average Earth–Moon distance	3.84×10^{8} m
Average Earth–Sun distance	1.496×10^{11} m
Average radius of the Earth	6.37×10^{6} m
Density of air (20°C and 1 atm)	1.20 kg/m^3
Density of water (20°C and 1 atm)	1.00×10^{3} kg/m^3
Free-fall acceleration	9.80 m/s^2
Mass of the Earth	5.98×10^{24} kg
Mass of the Moon	7.36×10^{22} kg
Mass of the Sun	1.99×10^{30} kg
Standard atmospheric pressure	1.013×10^{5} Pa

[a] These are the values of the constants as used in the text.

Some Prefixes for Powers of Ten

Power	Prefix	Abbreviation	Power	Prefix	Abbreviation
10^{-24}	yocto	y	10^{1}	deka	da
10^{-21}	zepto	z	10^{2}	hecto	h
10^{-18}	atto	a	10^{3}	kilo	k
10^{-15}	femto	f	10^{6}	mega	M
10^{-12}	pico	p	10^{9}	giga	G
10^{-9}	nano	n	10^{12}	tera	T
10^{-6}	micro	μ	10^{15}	peta	P
10^{-3}	milli	m	10^{18}	exa	E
10^{-2}	centi	c	10^{21}	zetta	Z
10^{-1}	deci	d	10^{24}	yotta	Y

Standard Abbreviations and Symbols for Units

Symbol	Unit	Symbol	Unit
A	ampere	K	kelvin
u	atomic mass unit	kg	kilogram
atm	atmosphere	kmol	kilomole
Btu	British thermal unit	L	liter
C	coulomb	lb	pound
°C	degree Celsius	ly	lightyear
cal	calorie	m	meter
d	day	min	minute
eV	electron volt	mol	mole
°F	degree Fahrenheit	N	newton
F	farad	Pa	pascal
ft	foot	rad	radian
G	gauss	rev	revolution
g	gram	s	second
H	henry	T	tesla
h	hour	V	volt
hp	horsepower	W	watt
Hz	hertz	Wb	weber
in.	inch	yr	year
J	joule	Ω	ohm

Mathematical Symbols Used in the Text and Their Meaning

Symbol	Meaning
$=$	is equal to
$\equiv$	is defined as
$\neq$	is not equal to
$\propto$	is proportional to
$\sim$	is on the order of
$>$	is greater than
$<$	is less than
$\gg (\ll)$	is much greater (less) than
$\approx$	is approximately equal to
Δx	the change in x
$\sum\limits_{i=1}^{N} x_i$	the sum of all quantities x_i from $i = 1$ to $i = N$
$|x|$	the magnitude of x (always a nonnegative quantity)
$\Delta x \rightarrow 0$	Δx approaches zero
$\dfrac{dx}{dt}$	the derivative of x with respect to t
$\dfrac{\partial x}{\partial t}$	the partial derivative of x with respect to t
$\int$	integral

Conversions[a]

Length

1 in. = 2.54 cm (exact)

1 m = 39.37 in. = 3.281 ft

1 ft = 0.304 8 m

12 in. = 1 ft

3 ft = 1 yd

1 yd = 0.914 4 m

1 km = 0.621 mi

1 mi = 1.609 km

1 mi = 5 280 ft

$1 \ \mu\text{m} = 10^{-6} \ \text{m} = 10^3 \ \text{nm}$

$1 \ \text{lightyear} = 9.461 \times 10^{15} \ \text{m}$

Area

$1 \ \text{m}^2 = 10^4 \ \text{cm}^2 = 10.76 \ \text{ft}^2$

$1 \ \text{ft}^2 = 0.092 \ 9 \ \text{m}^2 = 144 \ \text{in.}^2$

$1 \ \text{in.}^2 = 6.452 \ \text{cm}^2$

Volume

$1 \ \text{m}^3 = 10^6 \ \text{cm}^3 = 6.102 \times 10^4 \ \text{in.}^3$

$1 \ \text{ft}^3 = 1 \ 728 \ \text{in.}^3 = 2.83 \times 10^{-2} \ \text{m}^3$

$1 \ \text{L} = 1 \ 000 \ \text{cm}^3 = 1.057 \ 6 \ \text{qt} = 0.035 \ 3 \ \text{ft}^3$

$1 \ \text{ft}^3 = 7.481 \ \text{gal} = 28.32 \ \text{L} = 2.832 \times 10^{-2} \ \text{m}^3$

$1 \ \text{gal} = 3.786 \ \text{L} = 231 \ \text{in.}^3$

Mass

1 000 kg = 1 t (metric ton)

1 slug = 14.59 kg

$1 \ \text{u} = 1.66 \times 10^{-27} \ \text{kg} = 931.5 \ \text{MeV}/c^2$

Some Approximations Useful for Estimation Problems

$1 \ \text{m} \approx 1 \ \text{yd}$

$1 \ \text{kg} \approx 2 \ \text{lb}$

$1 \ \text{N} \approx \frac{1}{4} \ \text{lb}$

$1 \ \text{L} \approx \frac{1}{4} \ \text{gal}$

Force

1 N = 0.224 8 lb

1 lb = 4.448 N

Velocity

1 mi/h = 1.47 ft/s = 0.447 m/s = 1.61 km/h

1 m/s = 100 cm/s = 3.281 ft/s

1 mi/min = 60 mi/h = 88 ft/s

Acceleration

$1 \ \text{m/s}^2 = 3.28 \ \text{ft/s}^2 = 100 \ \text{cm/s}^2$

$1 \ \text{ft/s}^2 = 0.304 \ 8 \ \text{m/s}^2 = 30.48 \ \text{cm/s}^2$

Pressure

$1 \ \text{bar} = 10^5 \ \text{N/m}^2 = 14.50 \ \text{lb/in.}^2$

1 atm = 760 mm Hg = 76.0 cm Hg

$1 \ \text{atm} = 14.7 \ \text{lb/in.}^2 = 1.013 \times 10^5 \ \text{N/m}^2$

$1 \ \text{Pa} = 1 \ \text{N/m}^2 = 1.45 \times 10^{-4} \ \text{lb/in.}^2$

Time

$1 \ \text{yr} = 365 \ \text{days} = 3.16 \times 10^7 \ \text{s}$

$1 \ \text{day} = 24 \ \text{h} = 1.44 \times 10^3 \ \text{min} = 8.64 \times 10^4 \ \text{s}$

Energy

$1 \ \text{J} = 0.738 \ \text{ft} \cdot \text{lb}$

1 cal = 4.186 J

$1 \ \text{Btu} = 252 \ \text{cal} = 1.054 \times 10^3 \ \text{J}$

$1 \ \text{eV} = 1.6 \times 10^{-19} \ \text{J}$

$1 \ \text{kWh} = 3.60 \times 10^6 \ \text{J}$

Power

1 hp = 550 ft·lb/s = 0.746 kW

1 W = 1 J/s = 0.738 ft·lb/s

1 Btu/h = 0.293 W

$1 \ \text{m/s} \approx 2 \ \text{mi/h}$

$1 \ \text{yr} \approx \pi \times 10^7 \ \text{s}$

$60 \ \text{mi/h} \approx 100 \ \text{ft/s}$

$1 \ \text{km} \approx \frac{1}{2} \ \text{mi}$

[a] See Table A.1 of Appendix A for a more complete list.

The Greek Alphabet

Alpha	A	α	Iota	I	ι	Rho	P	ρ
Beta	B	β	Kappa	K	κ	Sigma	Σ	σ
Gamma	Γ	γ	Lambda	Λ	λ	Tau	T	τ
Delta	Δ	δ	Mu	M	μ	Upsilon	Y	υ
Epsilon	E	ϵ	Nu	N	ν	Phi	Φ	ϕ
Zeta	Z	ζ	Xi	Ξ	ξ	Chi	X	χ
Eta	H	η	Omicron	O	o	Psi	Ψ	ψ
Theta	Θ	θ	Pi	Π	π	Omega	Ω	ω